DISCIPLESHIP
Adult Workbook

DISCIPLESHIP
Adult Workbook

Developing the Christlife

Pathway P·R·E·S·S
CLEVELAND, TENNESSEE 37311

ISBN: 87148-265-7

Copyright © 1989
PATHWAY PRESS
Cleveland, Tennessee 37311

Printed in the United States of America

TABLE OF CONTENTS

INTRODUCTION

THE DIMENSIONS OF DISCIPLESHIP

The mission of the church is to "go into all the world" (Mark 16:15, *NKJV*) and "make disciples" (Matthew 28:19, *NKJV*). The church is made up of people--individuals who have responded to the invitation of Christ to follow Him. The command to "make disciples" is for disciples to make other disciples. A person must *be* a disciple before he can help others to develop the traits of discipleship.

Jesus Christ spent the major portion of His earthly ministry training His disciples. Through this training they were prepared to obey His command to "go" and "make disciples." This discipleship study is patterned after the example of Christ and is aimed at preparing you to develop the Christlife and to fulfill the Great Commission.

In condensed form, the goals of the discipleship studies are

To HELP you understand the meaning of biblical stewardship

To GUIDE you in a systematic study of the Bible and how to relate its teachings to everyday life

To SUPPORT you in developing study habits that reinforce discipleship maturity

To LEAD you in interacting with others on the course a disciple should walk and the characteristics he should exhibit

To PROVIDE the opportunity to assist others in learning, serving and growing in Christlikeness.

These goals will be achieved based on how you respond to the challenge. This discipleship program is not easy; it is demanding. It will require the commitment of time every day to study, pray and meditate. Christ never said discipleship would be easy. In fact, He emphasized it would be demanding.

If you follow the program as it is outlined, at the end of the studies you will be a different person. The following things will be different in your life:

1. *You will have a greater appreciation for your position in Christ and the mission of the church.*

2. *You will have a greater appreciation for your personal spiritual gifts and the potential you have to impact the world.*

3. *You will have a greater appreciation of your brothers and sisters in the Lord and how you can perform Kingdom ministry with them.*

Your life at the end of the course will be greatly changed because you will have learned to walk with Christ in a new dimension of love and understanding that can only be experienced through Bible study, life application of Bible truths and the sharing with others of Bible promises.

The Editors
Floyd D. Carey and Hoyt E. Stone

THE FORMAT OF THE STUDY

"Discipleship--Developing the Christlife," is a yearlong emphasis consisting of home studies with a weekly meeting directed by a group leader. Usually the group will consist of 12 people. The size will vary depending upon the local situation. Versatility has been built into the program (19 weeks) to allow weeks off for Christmas, Easter, other holidays and the vacation season. There are eight units, 33 chapters and 165 studies. You should strive to spend at least 45 minutes a day in study, prayer and meditation.

At the beginning of each chapter there is an introduction to the five studies for that week. There are four steps you will take in the studying process each day.

The first step is **READ AND RESEARCH.** Read the listed Bible passages and then study the commentary written about these verses. Next, move to step two, **REFLECT AND MEDITATE.** Activities are listed for you to engage in that will stimulate a deeper understanding of the scriptural message set forth. Step three is **REACT AND RESPOND.** What did the message say to you? What are you going to do about it in your life? Of what value is it? The fourth step is **REJOICE AND WORSHIP.** This is a time for praise and prayer. It is a time to thank God for His provisions and to worship Him for His abundant blessings.

Each week you are to read an assigned number of pages in *The Living Book--A Disciple's Guide to Understanding the Bible.* This volume provides an overview of the Bible. At the end of the study, you will know the plan of God from Genesis to Revelation and the main characters and events in the Bible. Also, you will be acquainted with all the major topics such as sin, salvation, regeneration, heaven and hell.

In addition to receiving a Discipleship Certificate at the conclusion of the discipleship course, you will receive a Church Training Course Bible Diploma. This will be secured by the group leader from the state youth and Christian education director.

The scriptures in the workbook are from the *New Kings James Version.* This version does not use the Elizabethan language and is very close to the King James. It was chosen to create additional excitement about studying and to use language that a disciple uses in his workplace, at home and in his relationship with others. We recommend that you secure a copy of the *New King James Version* of the Bible. A copy can be purchased from Pathway Press, P.O. Box 2250, Cleveland, TN 37320-2250.

DEVELOPING DISCIPLESHIP TRUST

Each week the group will meet for a time of interaction. Subjects and guidelines are outlined in the *Leader's Guide.* The purpose of the weekly meeting is threefold:

1. To DISCUSS the material that has been studied during the previous week

2. To RELATE the principles set forth to the life of a disciple in today's world

3. To SHARE thanksgiving and praise for what God is doing in your life through the discipleship program.

This weekly interaction will be an enriching time and will provide continuity for the program. It will be a time for affirmation and reinforcement of each other through comments, sharing views, and discussing life needs and goals.

The following space is provided for you to list the names of the individuals in your group. Learn each person by name and pray for each one daily.

_____

_____

_____

_____

_____

_____

_____

_____

_____

_____

_____

DISCIPLESHIP TRAINING CHECKLIST

1. Learn the names of the people in your group.
2. Make a personal commitment to completing the discipleship program.
3. Prepare a daily schedule for studying, reading and praying.
4. Review *The Living Book--A Disciple's Guide to Understanding the Bible*. Mark chapters to be completed each week.
5. Look through the *Discipleship* workbook. Note unit themes, chapters and studies.
10. Check the *Discipleship Guide* and see how the devotionals can be used in your daily study routine.
7. Record the weeks off from study for holidays, vacations and special events.
8. List some personal goals you want to achieve during the study.
9. Ask your family to support you with prayer and encouragement during the study.
Pray for divine insight, strength and wisdom to become a Christlike disciple.

READY FOR ACTION

Now you are ready to begin the adventure of discipleship training. The path of developing the Christlife is before you. How challenging! How exciting! Now make a pledge of action and begin with the goal of being a dedicated discipleship in clear view.

PERSONAL DISCIPLESHIP PLEDGE

I understand that Christ has called me to be a disciple and to ''make disciples.'' I respond to this call today in faith and pledge, through the power of the Holy Spirit, to complete the discipleship training by reading The Living Book, *by studying the* Developing the Christlife *workbook, by relating what I learn to daily life and by giving God the glory in all that I do.*

Signed _____

CHAPTER 1

Who Is God?

INTRODUCTION

When God created the heavens and the earth, He never intended for His creation to be estranged and cut off from His living presence. God's desire is to walk and talk with man as a heavenly Father, showing forth the loving-kindness of His nature.

But when man sinned, he disrupted that blissful relationship and became a slave to the wretchedness of his own sinful lusts. Therefore, it was necessary for God to provide for restoration through redemption so that His plan for man would not be frustrated.

The only provision that could truly redeem man from his fallen state was for God himself to become man, pay the ransom price and satisfy the judgment of the righteous law. This was done when Jesus came to earth, born of a virgin, the son of David, the son of Abraham, the son of Adam.

After living sinlessly among mankind and ministering to them, Christ effectively provided for man's salvation by dying on the cross and taking upon Himself all the sins of the world. When He came forth from the grave, the resurrection from the death of hell proved that God was satisfied with Christ's atoning work of redemption and that He had answered His prayer, "'Father, forgive them, for they do not know what they do'" (Luke 23:34).

However, when God made man in His own image, He gave him a will. In order for man to truly be redeemed in God's image, he must be able to retain that will. Therefore, even in salvation God allows every individual to choose whether or not to accept the gift that has already been purchased.

Jesus said to His disciples while on earth, "If anyone desires to come after Me, let him deny himself, and take up his cross daily, and follow Me" (Luke 9:23). Through the Spirit, He said to John on the Isle of Patmos, "And let him who thirsts come. And whoever desires, let him take the water of life freely" (Revelation 22:17).

For those who choose to come to God, the plan of salvation is complete. One simply believes on Christ, confesses all sins, accepts forgiveness and follows Him. But for those who refuse God's plan of salvation, then every sin must be faced at the judgment seat of God.

This week we will be studying together "Who Is God?" The five lessons will be as follows:
1. God Is Creator
2. God Is Heavenly Father
3. God Is Lovingly Good
4. God Is Sole Redeemer
5. God Is Righteous Judge

DISCIPLESHIP GOAL

To be a true disciple, one must truly know the Master. Our goal this week is to come to a fuller understanding of who God is so that we can faithfully follow Him.

READING ASSIGNMENT
The Living Book, pp. 15 - 24

Discipleship

GOD IS CREATOR

READ AND RESEARCH (Genesis 1, 2)

The Creation story in the first two chapters of Genesis comprises one of the most remarkable writings ever penned by man. It is so simple a child can understand its basic lesson. Yet it is so profound that no person can truly comprehend its depths.

That basic lesson is found in the very first verse: "In the beginning God created the heaven's and the earth." The Creator gives us one quick glimpse, almost like the batting of an eye, at that majestic process, and then in two short chapters it is over. The Creator God moves onward to the more important reasons for giving to us the Word of God.

To the 20th-century mind of man this is unthinkable. With his desire for scientific inquiry, he must know more. This desire for more knowledge is not evil in itself. Man truly has made remarkable discoveries concerning the earth and life on it, in the ocean depths and in the heavens above.

However, as man studies nature and the universe about him, the truly enlightened mind will always know that it all began when God spoke. "By the word of the Lord the heavens were made, and all the host of them by the breath of His mouth" (Psalm 33:6).

Because of the blindness created by sin in the world, much of mankind cannot accept the simple truth of God as the Creator. There must be more explanation. There must be more we can see, more we can understand, more we can document.

Consequently, for centuries man has tried to come up with his own explanations as to how we all came to be. These were usually very quickly disregarded until a scientist by the name of Charles Darwin gave us his theory of evolution.

The Christian should not fear this foolish type of speculation. Time and time again the precepts of evolution have been completely disproved. These are the theories of men and women blinded to the truth. In many instances the exponents have actually stooped to fraud to try to prove their theories.

Yet the fact remains: not one single example of evolution (that is, an example of one species evolving into a higher species) has been brought forth to substantiate their so-called scientific studies. This leaves them frustrated and bickering among themselves. They still can give no answer to such basic questions as "Why am I here?" "Where did I come from?" and "Where am I going?" As Paul said, "Professing to be wise, they became fools" (Romans 1:22).

The Christian who has experienced the personal presence of the Spirit of God within his soul is not left in such a quandary. That same Spirit who brings forgiveness, who brings unspeakable joy and peace that surpasses understanding also brings understanding through the Word.

Even though the story of Creation is brief, that is not the last time God assured us He is Creator. God receives pleasure in our worship of Him. Therefore, He said through the psalmist, "Oh, sing to the Lord a new song! Sing to the Lord, all the earth. . . . For the Lord is great and greatly to be praised: He is to be feared above all gods. For all the gods of the peoples are idols, but the Lord made the heavens" (Psalm 96:1, 4, 5).

The prophet Isaiah lived in a day of great skepticism and idolatry. Men would bow to a graven image rather than to Jehovah God. But the prophet wrote, "Thus says God the Lord, who created the heavens and stretched them out, who spread forth the earth and that which comes from it, who gives breath to the people on it, and spirit to those who walk on it: 'I, the Lord, have called You in righteousness, and will hold Your hand; I will keep You'" (Isaiah 42:5, 6).

This belief in God as Creator causes many to scoff. To insist that it is true actually causes some people to become angry. This is simply as it was when Isaiah said, "Thus says the Lord, your Redeemer, and He who formed you from the womb: 'I am the Lord, who makes all things, who stretches out the heavens allalone, who spreads abroad the earth by Myself; who frustrates the signs of the babblers, and drives diviners mad; who turns wise men backward, and makes their knowledge foolishness; who confirms the word of His servant, and performs the counsel of His messengers''' (Isaiah 44:24-26).

God is Creator. We believe as John wrote, ''All things were made through Him, and without Him nothing was made that was made. In him was life, and the life was the light of men'' (John 1:3, 4).

REFLECT AND MEDITATE

Read Psalm 139 and especially meditate on verses 13-16. Consider how you as an individual have been created by God for a purpose.

REACT AND RESPOND

How can you show forth the glory of God in your physical life as a created individual?

REJOICE AND WORSHIP

Give praise to God for your physical being. If in good health, express verbally your thanksgiving. Even in bad health, rejoice for life and the hope of a resurrected body.

Study 2

GOD IS HEAVENLY FATHER

READ AND RESEARCH (Romans 8:14-17; John 17)

Even though God is Creator of all things, He desires to have a very close personal relationship with every human being. This is a difficult concept for us to understand. When something is so big it is larger than our minds can comprehend, it is difficult to understand how there can be a personal relationship.

But we must not simply think of God as *big*. This is a relative term whose meaning is determined by comparing one object with another. But God cannot be so measured. There is nothing He can be compared to. He is no more *big* (that is, larger than certain things) than He is *little* (that is, smaller than certain things).

Rather, God is everywhere. Furthermore, wherever God is, He is there in the totality of His being. He is not simply partly here and partly there, much like you or I would be if we stood in a doorway with one foot in one room and the other foot in another room. God is both here and there in the fullness of His divine person.

This uniqueness of His total presence is what enables God to be Father in the truest sense. He is able to give Himself completely and unreservedly to each individual man, woman or child. He can communicate with each person in a multitude simultaneously and can fully concentrate on each conversation. He listens fully to you even as He listens fully to me.

Three times in the New Testament, God is referred to as ''Abba, Father.'' When Jesus prayed in the Garden of Gethsemane until drops of perspiration became as blood, He prayed, '''Abba, Father''' (Mark 14:36). Twice the apostle Paul said that through the Holy Spirit we now pray, '''Abba, Father''' (Romans 8:15; Galatians 4:6).

This is a remarkable word that God has chosen for His children to use when speaking to Him in the most intimate manner. It's a familiar term, much like we would say ''Daddy'' or ''Dad'' or ''Papa.'' But *Abba* is even more expressive of a simple childlike simplicity because of how the word is formed.

The first syllable, *ah*, is the primary vowel sound of almost every alphabet of man. It is our *a*, the Greek *alpha* and the Hebrew *aleph*. The second syllable *bah* is the primary consonant of practically every alphabet. It is our *b*, the Greek *beta* and the Hebrew *beth*.

These are the easiest of all sounds to make and the most likely sounds a baby will make when it is first born. As it begins to cry its first breath of life, the sound will most likely be a long-drawn-out, ''a-h-h-h-h-h!'' When it stops for breath, the baby will most likely close its lips together to create a *b* consonantal closing. Therefore, as the baby cries, stops and cries again, it probably will sound like ''ah-h-h-h-b-ah-h-h-h!''

How wonderful it is that God has said you and I can call Him '''Abba, Father'''! When we have no more strength or knowledge than a newborn baby, and all we can do is utter the most elementary sounds that come from the lips of mankind, God has said that through His Spirit He will accept that childlike cry of ''Abba'' as being His own name of fatherhood.

But God is much more than simply *named* father. He *is* the Father. As a Father He gives good gifts to His children (Matthew 7:11; Luke 11:13). As a Father He chastens us when we err (Proverbs 3:11, 12; Hebrews 12:5-11). As a Father He receives us unto Himself.

Our relationship with God is much more than simply that of servanthood. '''Come out from among them and be separate, says the Lord. Do not touch what is unclean, and I will receive you. I will be a Father to you, and you shall be My sons and daughters, says the Lord Almighty''' (2 Corinthians 6:17, 18). This is a Father-son, Father-daughter relationship.

We must not feel that God forces us to simply comply with His arbitrary rules of heaven. God is Father and knows what is best for His children. His words are living words that tell us how to live life to its fullest potential. As Father His desire is that we be able to enjoy His fellowship and the fellowship of the brothers and sisters of the household of faith.

Therefore we pray, '''Our Father in heaven, hallowed be Your name. Your kingdom come. Your will be done on earth as it is in heaven. Give us this day our daily bread. And forgive us our debts, as we forgive our debtors. And do not lead us into temptation, but deliver us from the evil one. For Yours is the kingdom and the power and the glory forever''' (Matthew 6:9-13).

REFLECT AND MEDITATE

Go back now and pray the Lord's Prayer, thinking about each expression in relation to God as Father. Do you believe He will grant this prayer to you even now?

REACT AND RESPOND

God forgives us as we forgive one another. Search your own life. Have you been hurt by someone, or do you hold a grudge against someone? If so, determine to go to that person and express your true love that forgives.

REJOICE AND WORSHIP

Read again John 17. Offer praise to God for making you one with Him and Christ, even as God and Christ are one.

Study 3

GOD IS LOVINGLY GOOD

READ AND RESEARCH (Psalm 145; Matthew 19:17)

When the rich young ruler came to Christ, he called Him, '''Good Teacher.''' Jesus asked him, '''Why do you call Me good?''' and went on to say, '''No one is good but One, that is, God''' (Matthew 19:16, 17).

Jesus was not denying that He himself is good. Rather, He was emphasizing to the young man that if he truly meant that Jesus is good, then in essence he was also declaring that Jesus is God.

When we say that God is lovingly good, we are saying much more than when we refer to a human as being good. Because of sin, man is not basically good. Paul described man: '''There is none righteous, no, not one; There is none who understands, there is none who seeks after God. They have all gone out of the way; they have together become unprofitable; there is none who does good, no, not one''' (Romans 3:10-12).

In his book *Systematic Theology*, Professor Louis Berkhof defines the goodness of God as "that perfection of God which prompts Him to deal bountifully and kindly with all His creatures" (p. 70).

Notice that he does not say God's goodness is His activity of doing good. Rather, God's goodness is in His very nature, which elicits the acts of goodness. In contrast to the pitiful state of man who is depraved by sin, God is good in the very nature of His eternal existence.

Because God is good, He does good. When His goodness is expressed toward man, God is loving, gracious, merciful and long-suffering.

God proved His love for man by giving His Son in death (John 3:16). John said in his epistle, "In this the love of God was manifested toward us, that God has sent His only begotten Son into the world, that we might live through him. In this is love, not that we loved God, but that He loved us and sent His Son to be the propitiation for our sins" (1 John 4:9, 10).

The love of God for man is also full of grace. This was not just a love for man in a state of goodness but rather a love for man in total depravity. Paul described it like this: "For when we were still without strength, in due time Christ died for the ungodly. For scarcely for a righteous man will one die: yet perhaps for a good man someone would even dare to die. But God demonstrates His own love toward us, in that while we were still sinners, Christ died for us" (Romans 5:6-8).

As God manifests His loving goodness toward man, He shows forth His mercy. Therefore the psalmist said, "Oh, praise the Lord, all you Gentiles! Laud Him, all you peoples! For His merciful kindness is great toward us, and the truth of the Lord endures forever. Praise the Lord!" (Psalm 117:1, 2).

In Psalm 136 the poet declared it is because of God's goodness that He is merciful. "Oh, give thanks to the Lord, for He is good! For His mercy endures forever" (v. 1). In this psalm alone the psalmist says 26 times, "His mercy endures forever."

Because of God's mercy, He not only made the heavens (v. 5), the earth (v. 6), the sun, the moon and the stars (vv. 7-9), but He also struck Egypt (v. 10) in order to deliver Israel (vv. 11, 12). While He divided the Red Sea (v. 13) so Israel could walk through (v. 14), in the same sea He overthrew Pharaoh and his army (v. 15). He led Israel through the wilderness (v. 16), struck down great kings (vv. 17-20) and gave their land to Israel as a heritage (vv. 21, 22), all because "His mercy endures forever." And today God "remembered us in our lowly state" (v. 23), "rescued us from our enemies" (v. 24) and "gives food to all flesh" (v. 25) because "His mercy endureth forever."

We should also know that because of His goodness, God is long-suffering. This is why Paul said we should never judge another person. When we judge, regardless of man's wrongdoing, it degrades the long-suffering of God. "Or do you despise the riches of His goodness, forbearance, and longsuffering, not knowing that the goodness of God leads you to repentance?" (Romans 2:4). As God bore with us in our sins, so He also bears with others.

In summary, let us remember that God is lovingly good. Because of His goodness He loves us even while we are sinners. He graciously gives to us of Himself even though we have no merit for such goodness. In mercy He works for us in the course of events in the world in which we live, and He extends this loving goodness in long-suffering.

Because God loves us, we can seek for His goodness. "Let us therefore come boldly to the throne of grace, that we may obtain mercy and find grace to help in time of need" (Hebrews 4:16).

REFLECT AND MEDITATE

Read again the verse in Hebrews 4:16. Knowing that God's throne is one of grace, think of those needs in your life that can be met by obtaining His mercy.

Discipleship

REACT AND RESPOND

Perhaps you have thought of a person that you judged. Write on a piece of paper the way you feel that such a judgment from you actually brings condemnation to you.

REJOICE AND WORSHIP

Read the words of the song "At Calvary" (*Church Hymnal*, p. 139). As you reflect upon its truths, give praise to God for His loving goodness whereby He has given you His mercy, grace and long-suffering.

Study 4

GOD IS SOLE REDEEMER

READ AND RESEARCH (1 Peter 1:13-25)

In the majority of Old Testament, the idea of *redemption* is mainly that of "buying back" that which has been sold. In the New Testament the word *redemption* is predominantly used in the sense of "ransom."

Two different Greek words used in the New Testament are translated "redeem." *Luo* means to "loosen" or "to free," while *exagorazo* means "to buy out of the marketplace." But the underlying thought for both of these words is the same. Both refer to the awful practice of slavery which was common at that time. When a slave was purchased from an owner and manumitted, he was "bought out of the marketplace" where the slave auctions were held (*exagorazo*), and at the same time he was "loosed" from the chains (*luo*) which kept him bound.

There is a beautiful picture of New Testament redemption in the book of Hosea. The prophet's wife, Gomer, was unfaithful to her husband and "played the harlot." It seems that she was then abandoned by her lovers and had to sell herself as a common slave. God told Hosea to purchase her back to himself for 15 pieces of silver.

God said this kind of love demonstrated "the love of the Lord for the children of Israel" (Hosea 3:1). Men and women today forsake God and sell themselves to the idol gods of this world. Spiritually, this is to "play the harlot" and "commit whoredoms."

After selling ourselves to sin, we become the slaves to sin (John 8:34). Our "lovers" in this world forsake us, and our existence is nothing more than that of a slave placed on the auction block to be sold to the highest bidder.

However, ours is a slavery that is even worse. Like Onesimus, who had fled from his master Philemon, we are not simply slaves; we are runaway slaves, thieves and unprofitable. We are sold out to sin and cursed by the law itself.

After Paul found Onesimus in Rome and ministered to him through the gospel, he knew the runaway slave could not pay back the money he had stolen from his master. Therefore he told Philemon, "If he has wronged you or owes you anything, put that on my account. I, Paul, am writing with my own hand. I will repay" (Philemon 18, 19).

Man's debt of sin is an awful debt. God said that for one sin "'You shall surely die'" (Genesis 2:17). This is not simply physical death that comes to all mankind; rather it is that second death described in Revelation 20:13-15. "The sea gave up the dead who were in it; and Death and Hades delivered up the dead who were in them. And they were judged, each one according to his works. Then Death and Hades were cast into the lake of fire. This is the second death. And anyone not found written in the Book of Life was cast into the lake of fire."

Every sin, every transgression, every iniquity carries with it the penalty of eternal damnation. This is man's debt. Who can pay the penalty? Not simply another man, because he already owes more than he can pay for himself (Psalm 49:7).

However, only a man can pay our debt. The angels cannot pay the debt of sin because they are no longer subject to sin. The demons cannot pay the debt of sin because they cannot experience death. Where is the redeeming Savior?

There is only one Redeemer. There is only One who can stand for us before God as Paul stood for Onesimus before Philemon. Christ is the only One who can say, "If he owes You anything, put that on My account." As Paul explained to the Galatians, "Christ has redeemed us from the curse of the law, having become a curse for us (for it is written, 'Cursed is everyone who hangs on a tree')" (Galatians 3:13).

Christ became man, born of a virgin, "in all points tempted as we are, yet without sin" (Hebrews 4:15). Isaiah saw Christ in a prophetic vision and said, "All we like sheep have gone astray; we have turned, every one, to his own way; and the Lord has laid on Him the iniquity of us all" (Isaiah 53:6). John the Baptist rejoiced when he saw Him coming and said, "'Behold! The Lamb of God who takes away the sin of the world'" (John 1:29).

Peter described how this redemption was accomplished: "Knowing that you were not redeemed with corruptible things, like silver or gold, from your aimless conduct received by tradition from your fathers, but with the precious blood of Christ, as of a lamb without blemish and without spot. He indeed was foreordained before the foundation of the world, but was manifest in these last times for you" (1 Peter 1:18-20).

God himself is sole redeemer of mankind. Thank God "for His indescribable gift!" (2 Corinthians 9:15).

REFLECT AND MEDITATE

Read Psalm 103 and meditate on all those blessings of redemption which are yours through Christ Jesus.

REACT AND RESPOND

Go visit a prison inmate, and share your testimony of being set free from chains worse than prison bars.

REJOICE AND WORSHIP

Sing the song "Redeemed" (*Church Hymnal*, p. 277) as a praise to God for delivering you from the slavery of sin.

Study 5

GOD IS RIGHTEOUS JUDGE

READ AND RESEARCH (Genesis 18:16-33)

God visited Abraham and Sarah in their old age and promised that she was going to have a son. At the same time He also revealed to Abraham that He was about to judge the wicked cities of the plain, Sodom and Gomorrah.

Abraham's conversation with the Lord is very revealing: "And Abraham came near and said, 'Would You also destroy the righteous with the wicked? Suppose there were fifty righteous within the city; would You also destroy the place and not spare it for the fifty righteous...? Far be it from You to do such a thing as this, to slay the righteous with the wicked, so that the righteous should be as the wicked; far be it from You! Shall not the Judge of all the earth do right?' And the Lord said, 'If I find in Sodom fifty righteous within the city, then I will spare all the place for their sakes'" (Genesis 18:23-26).

After a relatively lengthy conversation, the Lord finally agreed, "'I will not destroy it for the sake of ten'" (v. 32). Nevertheless, after warning Lot's family, "the Lord rained brimstone and fire on Sodom and Gomorrah, from the Lord out of the heavens. So He overthrew those cities, all the plain, all the inhabitants of the cities, and what grew upon the ground" (Genesis 19:24, 25).

The ancient cities of Sodom and Gomorrah stand as a vivid testimony of the righteous judgment of God. Because of His righteousness, God would have spared the entire metropolitan area of the plains if only 10 righteous people could be

Discipleship

found. But on the other hand, because of His righteousness the cities were absolutely destroyed in judgment due to their gross sins.

When Jesus looked on the wickedness of the city of Capernaum, He said, "'And you, Capernaum, who are exalted to heaven, will be brought down to Hades; for if the mighty works which were done in you, had been done in Sodom, it would have remained until this day. But I say to you that it shall be more tolerable for the land of Sodom in the day of judgment than for you'" (Matthew 11:23, 24). Therefore, we see God's righteous judgment is still pending on the wicked cities of the modern world.

Throughout Scripture, God is repeatedly referred to as being righteous (Ezra 9:15; Nehemiah 9:8; Psalm 119:137; 145:17; Jeremiah 12:1; Lamentations 1:18; Daniel 9:14; John 17:25; 2 Timothy 4:8; 1 John 2:29; 3:7; Revelation 16:5).

If God is righteous, then there must be some type of law and some type of accountability for that law. As Professor Berkhof says, "The fundamental idea of righteousness is that of strict adherence to the law" (*Ibid.*, p. 74).

God has spoken to the whole world through the unwritten laws of nature of man's conscience. As Paul said, "For the wrath of God is revealed from heaven against all ungodliness and unrighteousness of men, who suppress the truth in unrighteousness, because what may be known of God is manifest in them, for God has shown it to them" (Romans 1:18, 19).

Even though judgment is, to a degree, an ongoing process, there is a final great judgment in which mankind will be brought before the tribunal of the eternal Godhead. Every person must face the laws of God in judgment. As the writer to the Hebrews said, "It is appointed for men to die once, but after this the judgment" (Hebrews 9:27).

This scene is described by the Revelator: "Then I saw a great white throne and Him who sat on it, from whose face the earth and the heaven fled away. And there was found no place for them. And I saw the dead, small and great, standing before God, and books were opened. And another

book was opened, which is the Book of Life. And the dead were judged according to their works, by the things which were written in the book. . . .And anyonenot found written in the Book of Life was cast into the lake of fire" (Revelation 20:11, 12, 15).

This is the final judgment of the Righteous Judge. Those whose names have been written in the Book of Life are those who have accepted the gift offered by Christ. He prayed, "'Father, forgive them'" and then died for our sins, and the righteousness of God is satisfied. As Isaiah said, "He shall see the travail of His soul, and be satisfied. By His knowledge My righteous Servant shall justify many, for he shall bear their iniquities" (Isaiah 53:11).

However, those who have not accepted the gracious gift of the sacrifice of the Son of God must pay the penalty for their own sins. God is love, and He gave His Son to pay for our sins. But God is also the righteous judge.

READ AND MEDITATE

Read Psalm 32 and search your own heart to see if there is any hidden sin. If so, read Psalm 51 as a prayer for God's forgiveness.

REACT AND RESPOND

Visit a known sinner in your community, and share with him/her your testimony of how God in righteousness accepted the gift of Calvary for your sins when you believed in Christ.

REJOICE AND WORSHIP

After reading the words of "The Great Judgment Morning" (*Church Hymnal*, p. 208), worship God by singing "My Sins Are Gone" (p. 318).

DISCIPLESHIP COMMITMENT

As a result of this week's study, I will strive for a deeper understanding of who God is so that I can be a better disciple.

CHAPTER 2

Who Am I?

INTRODUCTION

In last week's lessons we studied about God--who He is and what He does in order for man to have fellowship with His Creator. God is Creator, He is heavenly Father, He is lovingly good, He is sole redeemer, and He is Righteous Judge. Because of who God is and because of what He has done, you and I are able to come to grips with the question "Who Am I?"

As a human being you should recognize and appreciate the high dignity of your personhood. God himself fashioned you and breathed into you the breath of life. The spirit within you came directly from God, who is the "Father of spirits" (Hebrews 12:9). You are "fearfully and wonderfully made" (Psalm 139:14). Your soul is of more value than all the world (Matthew 16:26).

However, sin is a most heinous disease and an awful crime. Unforgiven sin severs our personal relationship with God and brings us into a state of total depravity. Without Christ all are lost, and the so-called "good moral person" is no better than the worst of criminals before the righteous God (Romans 3:9-20).

But there is marvelous forgiveness available through Jesus Christ, the Savior of mankind. There is no sin so black that He will not forgive. There is no crime so evil that He will not make atonement for.

However, since God is righteous, He does not simply look away from the sins of your past. Rather, those sins are paid for by Jesus, who had no sins of His own. In Christ Jesus you are not excused and forgiven; you are justified and forgiven. Your debt is paid in the courtroom of heaven.

Once the debt of sin has been paid, you are redeemed back to your rightful position as child of God. As His child you have all the privileges of the heavenly family and are an heir of the household of Christ.

Because you are His child, God gives you His Spirit so that you are enabled to live a life that is a testimony of the truthfulness of Jesus of Nazareth. Your witness is not a forced one; you simply place your life before the world and confirm that what the Lord said was true.

In our lessons this week we will study the following topics that address the question "Who Am I?"

1. I Am an Image of God by Creation
2. I Am Utterly Lost by Sin
3. I Am Justified and Forgiven
4. I Am a Child of God by Redemption
5. I Am a Witness of God by Calling

DISCIPLESHIP GOAL

Regardless of your status in life, as a human being you are equal in value to any other human being. You are worth more than the entire natural world with all its riches. The goal this week is to come to an understanding of who you are and of your high privileges obtained through Jesus Christ.

READING ASSIGNMENT
The Living Book, pp. 25 - 31

Discipleship

I AM AN IMAGE OF GOD BY CREATION

READ AND RESEARCH (Genesis 1; Psalm 8)

After God had created the heavens, the earth, and plant and animal life, He fashioned His final work of creation after His own image. When man stood upright from the dust of the earth, there was a dignity in his being that set him apart from the rest of creation. As the psalmist said, ''For You have made him a little lower than the angels, And You have crowned him with glory and honor'' (Psalm 8:5).

In describing the creation of man, the author wrote, ''Then God said, 'Let Us make man in Our image, according to Our likeness; let them have dominion over the fish of the sea, over the birds of the air, and over the cattle, over all the earth and over every creeping thing that creeps on the earth.' So God created man in His own image; in the image of God He created him; male and female He created them'' (Genesis 1:26, 27).

In Genesis 5:1, 2 the author wrote again, ''This is the book of the genealogy of Adam. In the day that God created man, He made him in the likeness of God. He created them male and female, and blessed them and called them Mankind in the day they were created.''

The image of God extended to every part of man's personhood. Even though it cannot properly be said that man is the physical image of God since God does not have physical limitations, yet even man's physical body was made to be compatible with the image of God. Since God is three-in-one Godhead of Father, Son and Spirit, man in the image of God also has a three-in-one nature of body, spirit and soul (1 Thessalonians 5:23).

The image of God in man is a spiritual image. Not only is man able to comprehend the spirit of goodness as opposed to the evil spirits, he is able also to actually be good in spirit or if he so chooses to be evil in spirit. Man is not as the beasts that simply follow an instinct of nature. Man has a moral spirit that enables him to judge a matter as to whether it is inherently right or wrong.

Man is made in God's image mentally. Even though man is not omniscient (all-knowing), he is able to think in the same manner in which God thinks. Not only can he distinguish between the past, the present and the future, but he can also determine the quality of a concrete existence (such as a good house) or of an abstract thought (such as telling a lie). Because of this mental capability, he can judge if a house is a good bargain at a certain price and at the same time judge if the salesman is telling him the truth about the house.

Because man has emotional feelings like God, he is able to experience such abstract sensations as love, joy, and peace or, in a negative sense, hate, sadness and turmoil. His love can be simply an emotion of receiving from another, or it can rise to a higher plane of sharing with another, or it can assume the highest form of receiving pleasure from giving oneself to another.

God's image in man is also a social image; therefore man has the capability of communication. Man does not like to be alone but enjoys the companionship of other humans. In fact, if a baby is left completely alone with only its essential physical needs met, inevitably its natural growth will be stymied. Isolation for an adult carries the risk of insanity.

On the other hand, man has successfully developed languages, writing and reading, and such technological inventions as the radio, television and computer to enhance his social interaction.

All of these natural capabilities are good, and men and women should be encouraged to develop them to their fullest potential. In the next lesson we will see how sin had a deadly effect on the image of God in man and therefore must be remedied in order for man to live a fruitful and fulfilling life. But we should remember that even in his sinful state, man still has much of God's image.

Even in his most pitiful condition, man is far superior to the animal or plant life. We feel much sympathy for a physically or mentally handicapped person. But even in a state of blindness or deafness or dumbness or mental retardation, a human being is so far superior to the best of the beasts of the field that it would be a shame to make a comparison.

God recognized this image of Himself in man by placing him over all creation. Therefore the psalmist said, ''You have made him to have dominion over the works of Your hands; You have put all things under his feet, All sheep and oxen-- Even the beasts of the field, The birds of the air, And the fish of the sea That pass through the paths of the seas'' (Psalm 8:6-8).

REFLECT AND MEDITATE

Read Isaiah 65:17-25 and consider how mar-velous it will be when God has fully brought in the kingdom of God on earth.

REACT AND RESPOND

Try to communicate as best you can with your own pet or with some animal. Then have a conversation with a 2-year-old child. Write down on a piece of paper your different feelings as you try to communicate with each.

REJOICE AND WORSHIP

Sing the Doxology several times (*Hymns of the Spirit,* p. 21). Worship God for creating us in a way that we can even know how to worship and serve Him.

Study 2

I AM UTTERLY LOST BY SIN

READ AND RESEARCH (Romans 1:18--3:20)

It is very important to distinguish between the personhood of each human being and the sin which plagues each and every individual. The failure to make this distinction will be that our love for fellow humankind will actually be dimin-ished. But God's commandment is that we love our neighbor even as we love our own self (Luke 10:27).

However, once we are able to make this dis-tinction between the sin and the person, the awful-ness of sin strikes us with a pain that is almost unbearable. When Paul wrote to the Romans concerning the gospel, he knew that his first task was to show that all men outside of the gospel are hopelessly lost because of sin. Only through faith in Jesus Christ can man be saved.

The first step in Paul's argument is to remind us of the obvious evil that abounds in the heathen world. Even without the gospel the heathen have the law of nature and conscience to guide them. But because of sin they violate those laws, and consequently every civilization has experienced a downward spiral of depraving sins.

As mankind continues in sin, God eventually ''gives them over'' to their own lusts, to their own sinful affections, and eventually to a ''reprobate mind'' (Romans 1:28, *KJV*) that essentially feels that nothing is wrong in itself.

This downward progression of the societies of mankind can be confirmed over and over again in the histories of civilizations. Man turns from God to idols, worships and serves the creature, seeks for affection in the unnatural uses of the body, burns in his lust and is filled with all types of unrighteousness.

However, even though this downward spiral becomes characteristic of all societies who turn from God, Paul recognized that in every society there would still be some people who would retain their outward front of morality. The second step of his argument is to show that when a man is capable of judging another man, he proves himself to be guilty.

A child that has never lied is incapable of judging a liar. The child simply does not have the understanding of a lie until the child has told a lie itself. Therefore, the judge who condemns the murderer must know from inner experience the evil of those murderous intents. Otherwise he would never condemn a person of being a mur-derer. The judge is likewise guilty of sin.

The third step in Paul's argument is against those religious individuals who think that they have worked out a system of being good within themselves but outside of Jesus Christ. So Paul asked those who trust in religious practices (especially the Jews), "Are we better than they?" It is a rhetorical question and he quickly answers, "Not at all. For we have previously charged both Jews and Greek that they are all under sin" (Romans 3:9).

Paul did not simply rely on his own reasoning to show the sinfulness even of the Jews (or an adherent of any other religion). Rather, he turned to Old Testament scriptures.

Quoting from the Psalms and the prophet Isaiah, Paul showed that even man in his very best attempts at goodness falls woefully short of the righteousness of God. "There is none righteous, no, not one. . . . there is none that doeth good, no, not one . . . . Therefore by the deeds of the law there shall no flesh be justified in his sight" (from Romans 3:10-20).

Leprosy in the Old Testament was a most pitiful disease. It would gnaw away at the body until a hand would fall off, a foot would crumble, an eye would be eaten out of its socket, and the ear would fall from the side of the face. The leper was banned to the outside of the camp and forced to cover his face, screaming, "Unclean! Unclean!" (Leviticus 13:45, 46).

Without Christ I am utterly lost in my sins. My soul is eaten up with sin like leprosy eats away at the vital organs of the body it infects. Sin eats away the spiritual eyes until man cannot see spiritual things. Sin eats away the spiritual ears until man cannot hear the voice of God. Sin eats away the spiritual tongue until man cannot speak to the One who made him. Sin eats away at the spiritual hands and feet until man cannot raise his hands in worship nor walk in the way of holiness.

And when the sinner comes into the congregation of the righteous, there is a silent scream that proceeds out of his soul, "Unclean! Unclean!"

This is not simply the state of the criminal or the prostitute or the murderer or the terrorist. This is the awful condition of every person who has not looked to Christ for forgiveness of sins.

REFLECT AND MEDITATE

Read Leviticus 13 and 14. Meditate upon the state of the soul when it is like a man with leprosy, and then consider the wonderful relief when the disease is gone.

REACT AND RESPOND

Make a list of the ways that disease can handicap the body. Then one by one make a separate list of a similar way that sin can handicap the soul.

REJOICE AND WORSHIP

Take the lists you have already made of the handicaps caused by sin, and lay the list out before the Lord in prayer. Rejoice that He has forgiven you for every sin.

Study 3

I AM JUSTIFIED AND FORGIVEN

READ AND RESEARCH (Psalm 51; Philemon)

Even though we briefly looked at Philemon last week in relation to God as redeemer, let's take a closer look at this marvelous story in relation to forgiveness and justification. It is a powerful illustration of how God works in our own lives.

At some point in his missionary journeys, the apostle Paul had ministered to Philemon in a very special way. Probably he had brought the message of salvation to him because he said in verse 19, "Not to mention to you that you owe me even your own self besides." At that time Paul probably also had come to know Onesimus, one of the slaves of Philemon's household.

Toward the end of his ministry when Paul was in Rome, again he met and ministered to Onesimus, who had stolen some money from his master Philemon and fled to the Imperial City. Now that

Onesimus was free (at least physically) and the apostle was in chains, no doubt the runaway slave was struck by the message of the gospel he had previously rejected.

After Paul ministered to Onesimus, he convinced him that he needed to return to Philemon in order to ask forgiveness and to rectify the evil of his thefts. But there was a dilemma. As a runaway slave Onesimus had no way of paying back his master for the time he had "stolen" from him nor for the money he mayhave taken when he slipped away. Therefore Paul sent this brief letter with Onesimus when he returned to his master.

This is a pattern of what happens when the sinner comes face-to-face with Jesus of Nazareth. He ministers to us the joy of freedom even from a cross. He convinces us that though we have "run away," yet we remain slaves to the sins of our past.

The only way to happiness is to return to God our master and ask Him for forgiveness. However, we also face the same dilemma. We do not have the resources to repay that which we have stolen. We need a personal friend who will intercede on our behalf.

In the letter Paul readily admitted that Onesimus had been unprofitable (v. 11), had done wrong (v. 18), and owed a debt that he could not repay (v. 18). Therefore Paul interceded on behalf of the runaway slave "for love's sake" (v. 9).

"I appeal to you for my son Onesimus, whom I have begotten while in my chains," the apostle wrote in verse 10, informing the master of the change that had taken place. Paul now had a deep affection for the slave as for one who was now his own son.

"If then you count me as a partner, receive him as you would me," Paul continued. "If he has wronged you or owes you anything, put that on my account. I, Paul, am writing with my own hand. I will repay" (vv. 17-19).

It is in this same manner that Jesus makes intercession for us. Through the Holy Spirit, He makes intercession for us in our own inner soul (Romans 8:26), and writes a personal letter of forgiveness upon our own hearts (Hebrews 10:15-18). But instead of sending us to the Father alone with words written by pen on parchment, as the Living Word, Jesus goes personally into the presence of the Master to make intercession for us (Romans 8:34).

What a comfort it must have been for Onesimus, an unprofitable runaway slave, to know that when he stood at the door before his master Philemon, he could simply hand him the letter from Paul, offering to pay his debts and interceding for him! When Philemon read those words from his aged and dear friend, in no way could he refuse to accept Onesimus into his own arms even as he would have accepted Paul had he come in his own flesh.

But how much more comforting it is to you and me when we are escorted by the Spirit of the Son into the presence of the heavenly Master!

"Father, I appeal to You for My son, whom I have begotten by the Cross. He was once unprofitable to You, but now is profitable to You and to Me. Perhaps he departed for a while that You might receive him forever--no longer as a slave but above a slave, a brother beloved. Receive him as My own self. If he has wronged You or owes You anything, put that on My account."

It is through this personal intercession by the Son of God that as runaway slaves we are to return to the heavenly Master. When we stand at the door before Him, we simply bow and offer Him the "letter," the Living Word, who already sits at His own right hand.

As the Father embraces us with His love, at that very moment He forgives and justifies us, accepting the price that has already been paid on our behalf at Calvary. "Therefore, having been justified by faith, we have peace with God through our Lord Jesus Christ" (Romans 5:1).

REFLECT AND MEDITATE

Once more read the entire story of Onesimus and Philemon. As you read, put yourself in the place of the slave, Jesus in the place of Paul, and the Father in the place of Philemon.

Discipleship

REACT AND RESPOND

Write a letter to a person you know is enslaved to a particular type of sin (such as an alcoholic, drug addict, prostitute, homosexual, etc.), confessing that you too were at one time enslaved. Then share your personal testimony of forgiveness and justification.

REJOICE AND WORSHIP

Before his conversion, John Newton was a slave trader. Read the words of his famous hymn, ''Amazing Grace,'' and rejoice for God's deliverance in your own life.

Study 4

I AM A CHILD OF GOD BY REDEMPTION

READ AND RESEARCH (Book of Ruth)

Last week we looked at redemption when we considered who God is as the sole redeemer of mankind. Now we will consider redemption in light of our own experience, whereby we become part of God's family as His own child.

In the Old Testament the story of Ruth, the Moabitess, gives a beautiful picture of redemption. We can only highlight its truths in such a brief study. First, let us notice the conditions of Ruth at the time of her redemption:

1. She was a despised stranger, a Moabitess. Moab was the son that was born out of the drunken and incestuous encounter between Lot and his firstborn daughter after fleeing from Sodom (Genesis 19:31-38). Moabites were forbidden by law to enter into the congregation of Israel (Deuteronomy 23:3).

2. It was the time ''when the judges ruled'' (Ruth 1:1). This time is described in the last verse of the book of Judges. ''In those days there was no king in Israel; everyone did what was right in his own eyes'' (Judges 21:25).

3. It was a time of famine (Ruth 1:1) and indebtedness which caused Naomi to say, '''I went out full, and the Lord has brought me home again empty''' (Ruth 1:21).

4. It was a time of loneliness. Naomi's husband and two sons had all died, causing her to say, '''The Lord has testified against me, and the Almighty has afflicted me''' (Ruth 1:21).

5. It was a time of extreme bitterness, causing Naomi (which means ''pleasant'') to say, '''Do not call me Naomi, call me Mara [which means ''bitter''], for the Almighty has dealt very bitterly with me''' (Ruth 1:20).

So also today the sinner finds himself/herself a stranger in the congregation of the righteous, a ''Moabitess'' descendant of an illicit spiritual relationship, fleeing from the burning of Sodom but unable to resist the drunken impulses of this world.

Furthermore, it is a time when there is no king who rules over the heart, but rather every man does what is right in his own eyes. It is a time of spiritual famine and debt, a time of loneliness in which even companions and children are cut off from us, and a time of excessive bitterness in which the cry is heard over and over, ''Call me not Naomi [pleasant], but call me Mara [bitter].'''

But there were two events of redemption that took place in the heart of the Moabitess Ruth that enabled her to become a daughter of Israel, so that Matthew would even record in his genealogical record of Christ, ''Boaz begot Obed by Ruth, Obed begot Jesse, and Jesse begot David the king'' (Matthew 1:5, 6).

The first redemption event was the coming of love into her heart. Her poetic words are sung in weddings the world over even 3,000 years later. '''Entreat me not to leave you, Or to turn back from following after you; For wherever you go, I will go; And wherever you lodge, I will lodge; Your people shall be my people, And your God, my God. Where you die, I will die, And there will I be buried''' (Ruth 1:16, 17).

The second redemption event was the marriage

relationship that was established between herself and Boaz the redeemer. Boaz called the elder witnesses to the gate of the city and swore with the oath custom of that day, "'Moreover, Ruth the Moabitess, the wife of Mahlon, I have acquired as my wife, to raise up the name of the dead on his inheritance, that the name of the dead may not be cut off from among his brethren and from the gate of his place. You are witnesses this day'" (4:10).

So today the "estranged Moabite(ss)" can have two redemption events that brings him/her into the heavenly family as a daughter/son of Israel.

The first redemption event is that of love--a love that causes us to reach out to our fellowman, even with the love that God has bestowed on us. In the midst of a world of self-will, illicit relationships, famine, loneliness and bitterness, the child of God reaches out to feed the hungry, comfort the lonely and encourage those who are bitter.

The second redemption event is that of a personal relationship with Jesus Christ. It is a marriage relationship to the Redeemer himself (Ephesians 5:21-33). Now we are able to enjoy the full fellowship of the congregation of Israel and are heirs of the household of faith.

Our inheritance is no longer as a despised stranger, born of the drunken relationships of this world, fleeing from the wrath of Sodom. We cuddle in the arms of our loving Redeemer, who provides for our needs and declares before many witnesses that we are His beloved, a child of the Kingdom through redemption.

REFLECT AND MEDITATE

Read again the story of Ruth (it's only four pages in most Bibles), and place yourself in her place. Think of the ways you now are able to enjoy "being in Israel" as a child of God.

REACT AND RESPOND

Look in today's paper and find a story of an individual that seems to be bitter. Either call or write him/her and share how he/she can become a child of God through redemption.

REJOICE AND WORSHIP

Spend time in prayer, thanking God for those you know have been redeemed whom you personally prayed for to be redeemed while they were still sinners. Rejoice and worship God for redemption.

Study 5

I AM A WITNESS OF GOD
BY CALLING

READ AND RESEARCH (Acts 1:8; 6:8--7:60)

The Greek word marturoi which is translated "witnesses" in Acts 1:8, is a legal term that was used in the courtrooms of that day. It referred to a person who would "take the stand" before the judge and give testimony either for or against the accused.

Because so many of Christ's witnesses (marturon) were killed because of their affirmation of the Lord, those who lost their lives in this manner came to be called "martyrs." Thus it is said that Stephen was the Lord's martyr (Acts 22:20).

Stephen's sermon is one of the greatest apologetic defenses of the Christian gospel that has ever been written. However, it was not because of the greatness of his oratory that Stephen became the first martyr-witness of the church. As he stood before the council, his very life was placed on the witness stand as a testimony concerning Jesus of Nazareth.

Stephen was not the person on trial. Jesus was on trial. Stephen was summoned as a witness, "'for we have heard him say that this Jesus of Nazareth will destroy this place and change the customs which Moses delivered to us'" (Acts 6:14).

Stephen's life was described as "a man full of faith and the Holy Spirit (Acts 6:5), who "did great wonders and signs among the people" (v. 8).

These skeptical unbelievers "were not able to resist the wisdom and the Spirit by which he spoke" (v. 10), and when the council looked at him, they "saw his face as the face of an angel" (v. 15).

After reviewing the work of God among the people of Israel in the past, Stephen then spoke directly to the ones who sat in judgment against his Lord.

When the listeners heard those condemning words, they "were cut to the heart" and "gnashed at him with their teeth" (v. 54). But Stephen "gazed into heaven and saw the glory of God, and Jesus standing at the right hand of God" (v. 55). When Stephen told them what he was seeing, they screamed, closed their ears, ran at him, dragged him out of the city, laid their cloaks at the feet of Saul of Tarsus and stoned him (vv. 56-59).

Even as the stones were piling up around him and pounding his fleshly body to death, Stephen "knelt down and cried out with a loud voice, 'Lord, do not charge them with this sin. And when he had said this, he fell asleep" (v. 60).

This is a witness. This is a *martus*.

This is what we are called to be. Jesus said, "'But you shall receive power when the Holy Spirit has come upon you; and you shall be witnesses to Me in Jerusalem, and in all Judea and Samaria, and to the end of the earth'" (Acts 1:8).

It is true that a witness is often called upon to testify on behalf of or against the accused. However, the greatest force of one's testimony is not the words that are spoken but one's own physical presence.

Should a doctor be accused of malpractice, his greatest defense would be a series of witnesses who would take the stand and testify that at one time they were ill, or diseased, or blind, or deaf, or lame, but this physician had ministered to them. "Look at me," the convincing witness would say, "I am no longer blind. Now I can see. This man is a good surgeon." The piercing living eyes would themselves be the greatest witness.

The Great Physician is on trial before this world. As legal witnesses we stand before the world, not so much with our words but with our entire bodies, our entire lives. We give our testimony. "I was a slave to sin." "I was an alcoholic." "I was a drug addict." "I was a lying wretch." "I was a hateful leech." "I was an envious tyrant." The list is endless.

"But look at my life now," we say to the courthouse world. "I am free. I've been delivered from such addictions as alcohol and drugs. I love the truth. Jesus of Nazareth is the Great Physician who has cured me of my sinful diseases."

The question is not *if* you want to be witness for Christ. You *are* a witness. You *are* on the stand. The world is judging; Jesus is on trial in your life.

The question we must face day by day is simply "What kind of witness does my life give? Does it truly reflect the work of the Master Physician?"

REFLECT AND MEDITATE

Read the story of the two witnesses in Revelation 11:3-12. Do you think the world is swiftly coming to the time that such a scene could take place?

REACT AND RESPOND

If possible, visit a courtroom. If that is not possible, read a book or watch a TV program with a courtroom setting. Notice how the witnesses give testimony, and compare your own life as a witness of Jesus Christ.

REJOICE AND WORSHIP

Most Christians remember vividly the time they were saved or sanctified or filled with the Holy Spirit. Recall one of those experiences in your own life, and read the words of the old gospel song "I Can Tell You the Time" (*Church Hymnal*, pp. 34, 35).

DISCIPLESHIP COMMITMENT

I will believe God has made me His child and determine to live by His grace that my life will bear witness to the truth of Jesus of Nazareth, the Son of God.

CHAPTER 3

How Can I Follow God?

INTRODUCTION

During the last two weeks we examined the questions "Who is God?" and "Who am I?" This week we will ask the question, "How can I follow God?"

The first step in following God is to know Him in such a way that we understand what His will is for our own individual life and *willingly* submit to His *will*. God is not a tyrant who dictates to human beings what they are to do. He is a Father who reveals His desires. We are children who consciously choose either to follow or reject His desire for our own life.

God has not left us with no indication of His will. When Jesus prayed on the night He was betrayed, He said He was not just praying for the disciples who were with Him at that time; but He prayed also for those who would believe on Him through their word (John 17:20). Therefore, the teachings of the apostles tell us how to believe on Christ and how to follow Him.

Even though each person must choose for himself/herself whether he/she will follow, we are not left alone in our Christian walk. God has set each of us as members in the body of Christ, and we have fellowship and communion with our brothers and sisters. Through the Holy Spirit, God uses this relationship with one another to help us understand His will.

One of the greatest means of fellowship is through the "breaking of bread," that is, the sacrament commonly referred to as Communion, or the Lord's Supper or the Holy Eucharist. This is a communion not only with one another but with the Lord himself. The Communion service has

been one of the most sacred times of worship for the Christian church throughout its history in all parts of the world.

In the final analysis, to know God's will one must be able to seek God through prayer. This week we will only begin to consider prayer in its most elementary form since next week the entire five lessons are on communing with God in prayer. A person does not, however, have to know the depths of prayer to begin to know God's will. He will meet you where you are if you will simply say as the woman of Sidon, "Lord, help me!"

Therefore, we will consider the following five topics in anattempt to answer the question, "How can I follow God?"

1. I Follow God by Submitting to His Will
2. I Follow God by Considering the Apostles' Teaching
3. I Follow God by Fellowship With the Believers
4. I Follow God by the Breaking of Bread
5. I Follow God by Prayer

DISCIPLESHIP GOAL

Our goal this week will be to come to know how to follow God as we submit to His will, as we search the apostles' teaching, as we have fellowship with the saints, as we partake of the Communion service, and as we seek Him for our everyday needs.

READING ASSIGNMENT
The Living Book, pp. 32 - 48

Discipleship

Study 1

I FOLLOW GOD BY SUBMITTING
TO HIS WILL

READ AND RESEARCH (Luke 9:23-26; 14:26-33; Romans 12:1, 2)

Most Christians will readily agree that they desire to follow God according to His will. "But how can we know His will?" is a common plea for help. Let's look at how Jesus explained to His disciples what it meant to know His will and follow Him.

Jesus asked His disciples, "Who do the people say that I am?" They replied that some said He was John the Baptist; some, Elijah; and others, one of the prophets. Jesus then asked, "'But who do you say that I am?'" Peter replied and the others agreed, "'You are the Christ, the Son of the living God'" (Matthew 16:13-20; Mark 8:27-30; Luke 9:18-21).

Then Jesus gave the invitation to follow Him: "'If anyone desires to come after Me, let him deny himself, and take up his cross daily, and follow Me'" (Luke 9:23; see also Matthew 16:24 and Mark 8:34.) In the King James Version Luke 9:23 is rendered, "If any man *will* come after me, let him deny himself, and take up his cross daily, and follow me."

Notice particularly the phrase "if any. . .will come." Its truer meaning is revealed when it is translated "if anyone *wills to come* to Me" or, as it is translated in the *New King James Version*, "'If anyone desires to come after Me.'"

The word *will* in the English language is used in two different ways. Its most common usage is as a helping verb to express the future tense (for example, "I will go to town tomorrow"). However, *to will* is also a verb that stands alone, meaning "to purpose, determine on, or elect by act of will; to choose; to decide upon or ordain" (Webster).

In the Lord's expression "if any...will come," He uses two different Greek words and not simply the future tense of the verb *come*. Jesus was not saying, "if any will come" tomorrow or some time in the future. He was saying to His disciples, "If anyone *wills to come* after Me right now, then let him deny himself and take up his cross daily and follow Me."

Therefore, to follow God by submitting to His will must begin with a conscious decision on the part of the disciple. You must *will* to come to Him, you must choose, you must purpose within your own self that you are going to follow Him. God's will is not forced upon His followers.

After the disciple has consciously willed to follow after Christ, then, Jesus said, "let him deny himself." Now some would say you deny yourself by giving up a certain food or by denying yourself a new car or a new dress. However, such an action is to deny the food or the car or the dress. Jesus did not say to simply deny things. He said to deny your *self.*

This denial of self is illustrated in Jesus' words in Luke 14:26: "'If anyone comes to Me and does not hate his father and mother, wife and children, brothers and sisters, yes, and his own life also, he cannot be My disciple.'"

Jesus did not mean that His followers had to have an emotional feeling of hate toward family members. God is love (1 John 4:16) and demands that we love one another (v. 11).

Jesus illustrated what he meant by *hate* with the two parables that follow. If a man is going to build a tower, he should have enough many to complete the tower, or it would be better to never begin to build. If a man is going to war, he must have enough strength to win, or it would be better to make peace. The Christian life is like building a tower and at the same time fighting in a war. What type of tower do you want your life to be? Who is the enemy you are fighting? What resources do you possess?

Jesus is saying that if you count up all you own and all your father and mother and children possess, you will discover you do not have enough materials or strength to build the tower or win the war against Satan. You must set aside your own strengths and gifts, you must "hate" even what

28

your own loved ones give to you, you must deny your own self and ''take up your cross daily'' and follow Christ.

Having made the conscious choice to come to God and having placed our own selfish desires on the Cross, we are then ready to do as Paul said in Romans 12:2. ''And do not be conformed to this world, but be transformed by the renewing of your mind, that you may prove what is that good and acceptable and perfect will of God.''

The word *transformed* is the same word translated in the Gospels *transfigured* or *transfiguration*. We are to have a ''mountain of transfiguration experience'' (Matthew 17:1-8; Mark 9:2-8; Luke 9:27-36), whereby we are ministered to by the law (Moses) and the prophets (Elijah). Our minds, instead of simply being conformed to this world, are renewed or renovated so that we are able to know the will of God, which is always good, acceptable and perfect.

REFLECT AND MEDITATE

Read the story of the Lord on the Mount of Transfiguration (see scriptures above) and the description of the living Lord in Revelation 1:10-20. Consider how you can be like Him.

REACT AND RESPOND

Write down on paper the five things in this world you would like to do more than anything else. Go over the list again, and see if you are willing to change your own plans to follow God's will.

REJOICE AND WORSHIP

Worship God with the words of the song ''Have Thine Own Way, Lord'' (*Church Hymnal*, p. 375).

Study 2

I FOLLOW GOD BY CONSIDERING THE APOSTLES' TEACHING

READ AND RESEARCH (John 17:17-23; 2 Timothy 3; 2 Peter 1)

In Jesus' last recorded prayer for His disciples, He said He was sending them into the world now even as the Father had sent Him into the world (John 17:18). Then He prayed, '''I do not pray for these alone, but also for those who will believe in Me through their word''' (v. 20). The reason He prayed thus was '''that they also may be one in Us''' (v. 21).

Therefore, if we want to follow God in such a closeness that our relationship can be described as ''made perfect in one'' with Him (v. 23), it is necessary that we believe on Him through the word He gave to the apostles and which they have given to us.

The apostle Peter told how the Scripture was revealed to the prophets of the Old Testament (2 Peter 1:15-21). With the canonization of the New Testament books, the early church agreed that the Spirit worked in the heart of the apostles in the same manner to give us the teachings of the apostles.

Peter shared with his readers the marvelous experience he, James and John had known with the Lord on the Mount of Transfiguration. He said, ''We also have the prophetic word made more sure'' by such a spiritual experience as that on the mountain with the Lord himself (v. 19).

These spiritual moments we share in the Spirit with the Lord confirm the word of the prophets even as the prophecies themselves give validity to our spiritual experiences. The ''prophetic word made more sure''--that is, ''the prophecy of Scripture'' (v. 20)--is not simply a ''private interpretation'' (v. 20) that came by ''the will of man'' (v. 21). The Scriptures were given to us by ''holy men of God. . .as they were moved by the Holy Spirit'' (v. 21).

The word *moved* means ''picked up and carried along.'' The Holy Spirit moved on the apostles when they wrote to us the Scriptures in such a manner that He ''carried them along'' with the very message He wanted them to write down for all followers of Christ to hear. The same Holy Spirit now moves on the believer as he reads the Scriptures and through them reveals "the deep things of God" (1 Corinthians 2:10).

The apostle Paul said, "All Scripture is given by inspiration of God" (2 Timothy 3:16). This does not mean simply a type of inspiration that is similar to when a person sits down at the piano and is "inspired" to write a song. Paul didn't say the Scriptures were by the "inspiration of man."

He said the Scripture is given "by inspiration *of God.*" God himself is the origin of Scripture. The expression "inspiration of God" is actually one word in Paul's language (*theopneustos*). It literally means "God-spirited" or "God-breathed." The Word of God proceeds from the heart of God himself as the living Logos (John 1:1-4).

This same living Word also is "breathed out from God" as the Scripture or "the Word which stands written" (see Matthew 4:4, 7, 10; Romans 1:17; Hebrews 10:7). This written Word is "profitable for doctrine, for reproof, for correction, for instruction in righteousness, that the man of God may be complete, thoroughly equipped for every good work" (2 Timothy 3:16, 17).

In giving these final instructions to his son Timothy, Paul said that "in the last days perilous times will come" (3:1). It will be a time in which men and women will be extremely wicked. They will have a "form of godliness" but will deny "its power" (v. 5). They will have a type of knowledge, "always learning," but not true knowledge, "never able to come to the knowledge of the truth" (v. 7).

In such a time Paul commended Timothy and all of the Lord's followers today to follow God by putting their trust in the "Holy Scriptures" (v. 15). He said, "Continue in the things which you have learned and been assured of, knowing from whom you have learned them" (v. 14).

The early church, under the guidance of the Holy Spirit, carefully scrutinized the various writings of their day which claimed to be given by inspiration of God. Many false prophets claimed they had received a revelation from God, but their words were rejected. The books of the New Testament that we have in the King James Version and most of the modern translations of the Bible are those writings which the early church agreed upon as being Holy Scripture.

These are those same Scriptures which "are able to make you wise for salvation through faith which is in Christ Jesus" (v. 15). If we desire to follow God, we must search the Scriptures which have eternal life and testify of Jesus Christ (John 5:39).

REFLECT AND MEDITATE

Read Psalm 119 and consider how the Word is alive today just as much as when the psalmist wrote those wonderful verses.

REACT AND RESPOND

Read several different passages of Scripture from both the King James Version and another version such as the *New International Version.* Which do you feel better enables you to understand the voice of the Spirit of God speaking to you?

REJOICE AND WORSHIP

The words in many of the psalms have been put to music so that we can sing them. Other songs are based on one particular scripture. If possible, sing one or more of the Scripture choruses. If you do not know any of them, read the words of "Come Unto Me" (*Church Hymnal*, p. 44) and sing the chorus.

Study 3

I FOLLOW GOD BY FELLOWSHIP WITH THE BELIEVERS

READ AND RESEARCH (Romans 12:1-16; 1 Corinthians 12-14; Philippians 2:1-16)

The apostle Paul explained in his writings that Christians are a part of the one body of Jesus Christ. We are not simply individual believers that "do our own thing" without ever coming in contact with other believers. We are members of the family of God. The family fellowship that we have with our brothers and sisters in Christ is very important in following God.

Paul said, "For I say, through the grace given to me, to everyone who is among you, not to think of himself more highly than he ought to think, but to think soberly, as God has dealt to each one a measure of faith. For as we have many members in one body, but all the members do not have the same function, so we, being many, are one body in Christ, and individually members of one another" (Romans 12:3-5).

Those Christians who feel that they do not need the fellowship of the saints of God are extolling themselves in a strength which they do not really possess. As Paul said, they're thinking more highly of themselves than they ought to think.

Each member of the body will have a gift or gifts from God which is intended to be helpful to all members of the body. You need the gift(s) that other members of the body have been blessed with in order to help you; and they need the gift(s) God has blessed you with. We all need this fellowship with one another.

As we continue reading Paul's explanation of these gifts, it becomes obvious that he was not simply talking of the individual natural talents that we all possess to a degree. *Prophecy* (v. 6) is not just a word of God to an individual person; rather, it is an utterance that is given "in the church" (1 Corinthians 14:19). Ministering, teaching, exhorting, giving, leading and showing mercy all have their ultimate fulfillment in the body of Christ.

This does not mean that the spiritual gifts will not be effective in our lives outside the church. Many of the other items listed in Romans 12 are either inward virtues (such as "fervent in spirit") or could certainly be fulfilled between just two people (such as "given to hospitality").

But while the effect of the spiritual gifts will continually work in our lives day by day, there can be no doubt from the book of 1 Corinthians that the Spirit works in a special way when the body of Christ has come together as the church.

Even though Paul earlier in the letter talked of several individual matters, he said in chapter 11 "since you come together" (v. 17), "when you come together as a church" (v. 18), "when you come together in one place" (v. 20), "when you come together to eat" (v. 33) and "lest you come together for judgment" (v. 34). He used the expression two additional times in chapter 14 (vv. 23, 26).

Furthermore, he called this coming together "the church" and used the word *church* 13 times in these three chapters (1 Corinthians 11:16, 18, 22; 12:28; 14:4, 5, 12, 19, 23, 28, 33-35).

This fellowship in coming together in the church is more than simply the fellowship of the saints. Paul said it is the fellowship of the Spirit himself (Philippians 2:1).

Again, some argue that the individual can have fellowship with the Spirit when he is alone. Since the Holy Spirit is a personal being, this is true; but that is not the type of fellowship Paul was speaking of. He said that if there is any fellowship of the Spirit, "fulfill my joy by being like-minded, having the same love, being of one accord, of one mind" (v. 2).

As the believers as one body are able to bring their minds together and to have the same love for one another and truly become in "one accord," then the fellowship with the saints is anointed in such a way that it becomes the fellowship of the Spirit.

Individually, our responsibility is to "let this mind be in...[us] which was also in Christ Jesus"

(v. 5). Just as Jesus "humbled Himself and became obedient to the point of death" (v. 8), so also we are to "look out not only for. . .[our] own interests, but also for the interests of others" (v. 4). If Jesus could so humble Himself to come from heaven to earth, we should not hesitate to kneel in fellowship with our brothers and sisters.

As we enjoy the fellowship of the body when the church gathers in His name (Matthew 18:19, 20), we are also able to "work out. . .[our] own salvation with fear and trembling" (Philippians 2:12). This then becomes the means for us to know the will of God, "for it is God who works in you both to will and to do for His good pleasure" (v. 13).

REFLECT AND MEDITATE

Read the story of Judas in Matthew 26:1-4, 14-16, 27:1-10 and John 13:21-30. What do you think would have happened if he had shared his plans and feelings with at least one of the other disciples?

REACT AND RESPOND

Write a letter to your pastor, telling him why you appreciate the fellowship you are able to have with the members of your local church.

REJOICE AND WORSHIP

Thank God for your church, and worship Him through the old hymn, "Blest Be the Tie" (*Church Hymnal*, p. 130).

Study 4

I FOLLOW GOD BY THE BREAKING OF BREAD

READ AND RESEARCH (Matthew 26:26-29; Mark 14:22-25; Luke 22:17-20; John 13:1-35; 1 Corinthians 11:23-26)

Even though some scholars say that the book of Acts refers to a custom of "breaking of bread" that has to do with household meals at home, we are using the expression as it refers to the service commonly called the Lord's Supper, Communion, the Holy Eucharist or the Feast. For the child of God this is one of the most sacred of all services and unites us in communion both with the Lord and with the body of believers.

Paul specifically called this sacrament the Lord's Supper (1 Corinthians 11:20), the Communion (1 Corinthians 10:16) and the Feast (1 Corinthians 5:8). The word *eucharist* is simply a Greek transliteration meaning "thanksgiving." Since Matthew, Mark, Luke, John and Paul all mention the Lord's giving thanks when He gave to us the service, many churches refer to it as the Holy Eucharist, or the holy thanksgiving.

This service is closely related to the Old Testament Passover Feast (Exodus 12:1-28). Paul said, "For indeed Christ, our Passover, was sacrificed for us" (1 Corinthians 5:7).

On the evening the children of Israel were delivered from Egypt, God told the people to slay and eat a lamb for each household (or one lamb for two households if their number was small). The blood was to be taken in a vessel and sprinkled over the lintel and on the doorposts of the house.

God had already said that on that night the death angel would go throughout Egypt and slay all the firstborn in every house, "'from the firstborn of Pharaoh who sits on his throne, even to the firstborn of the maidservant who is behind the handmill, and all the firstborn of the beasts'" (Exodus 11:5).

Now He told the children of Israel the lamb they were to eat "'''is the Lord's Passover'''" (Exodus 12:11) because "'''when I see the blood, I will pass over you; and the plague shall not be on you to destroy you when I strike the land of Egypt'''" (v. 13).

While Jesus and His disciples were partaking of this Passover meal, "Jesus took bread, blessed it and broke it, and gave it to the disciples, and said, 'Take, eat; this is My body.' Then He took the cup, and gave thanks, and gave it to them, saying, 'Drink from it, all of you; For this is My blood of the new covenant, which is shed for many for the remission of sins'" (Matthew 26:26-28).

In the setting of the Passover meal, there can be no doubt as to the meaning of Jesus' words. The bread is His body, which is our Passover Lamb. We eat it as a memorial for that night of deliverance when we were delivered from the Egyptian bondage of slavery to sin. It gives strength to us to make the long journey to the Promised Land.

The cup of "'the fruit of the vine'" (Matthew 26:29) is His blood of sacrifice. Even as we drink it, it is "sprinkled over the doorposts" of our souls through faith. When the death angel passes throughout the land, he "passes over" our souls because of the blood. This is the "new testament," or the new covenant, that God has made with us through the blood of Christ.

A testament or will is the strongest of all man-made covenants. For it to take effect, there must be the death of the testator (Hebrews 9:16, 17). Jesus was referring to His own death when He said His blood "'is shed for many for the remission of sins'" (Matthew 26:28). The word *remission* simply means "forgiveness."

Through the death of Christ the new testament, or new covenant as it is called in the book of Hebrews (8:8), has been ratified, whereby He said, "'I will put My laws in their mind and write them on their hearts; and I will be their God, and they shall be My people'" (Hebrews 8:10 from Jeremiah 31:33).

Through the new testament of His blood and the breaking of the bread of His body, we sit at the Lord's supper table. The Father himself is present in Spirit, and the Son is present in the broken bread and poured-out cup. In communion with God, we are directed by the Holy Spirit in His will for our daily lives.

The partaking of the meal is His will for a threefold reason. First, it is His direct command. Second, as Paul said, when you eat of the bread and drink of the cup, "you proclaim the Lord's death till He comes" (1 Corinthians 11:26). Third, as we partake of the Communion meal, we are giving testimony of our hope in the coming Kingdom.

Jesus said, "'But I say to you, I will not drink of this fruit of the vine from now on, until that day when I drink it new with you in My Father's kingdom'" (Matthew 26:29). To drink the cup and eat the bread is to demonstrate our faith that God is directing our lives toward the kingdom of heaven.

REFLECT AND MEDITATE

Read Exodus 14-16 and reflect upon how people today soon complain after God has brought about great victories in their lives.

REACT AND RESPOND

Try to find a Jewish person in your community who can explain to you how they still observe the Passover. Discuss with him/her the relationship between the Passover and the Communion service of the Christian church.

REJOICE AND WORSHIP

Read the words of the song written by M.S. Lemons, "Remember" (*Church Hymnal*, p. 274), and worship God as you consider again the work of Calvary.

Study 5

I FOLLOW GOD BY PRAYER

READ AND RESEARCH (Matthew 15:1-28)

Next week we will consider the question "How can I commune with God in prayer?" This will help us in dealing with the problem of how the Christian can come to a depth in prayer that is pleasing to the Lord for a mature child of God. However, now we would like to take a look at prayer in an introductory manner as it relates to every Christian's desire to follow God.

The first 28 verses of of Matthew 15 draw a

vivid contrast between people who simply keep the observances of a formalized religion and a woman who cried out to God because of her desperate need.

The scribes and Pharisees of Jerusalem were very proud of their strict religious observances. When they came to Jesus, they wanted to know why His disciples transgressed the '''tradition of the elders''' by not washing their hands when they ate bread (v. 2).

In answering them, Jesus said that their traditions were not as important as the Word of God and showed them that one of their traditions actually made void the commandment of God (vv. 3-6). Such religious observances were described in the words of Isaiah: ''''These people draw near to Me with their mouth, and honor Me with their lips, but their heart is far from Me''''' (v. 8). This is vain worship (v. 9).

Jesus explained that the ritual of washing the hands was not nearly as important as the cleansing of the inner heart. While dirty hands may contaminate the body to a degree, in the heart all types of filth are conceived, and this is what truly defiles a man (Matthew 15:10-20). Therefore, religious observances are not nearly as important as the hypocrites thought they were.

Then Matthew gave the story of a Syrophoenician woman who came to Christ with a desperate need. Her daughter was demon-possessed (v. 22).

It seems strange at first glance that when the woman first cried out to Him, Jesus ''answered her not a word.'' However, it seems likely that her prayer was mostly a repetition from someone else's prayer that she had been taught or overheard. It is rather stilted for a stranger: '''Have mercy on me, O Lord, Son of David!''' (v. 22).

After Jesus did not answer and after the disciples had tried to run her away, she came and worshiped Him and said simply, '''Lord, help me!''' This is probably the simplest prayer to be found in all of Scripture.

But the word the woman used is laden with meaning. It is what I would call a ''picture word.'' It has two pictures because it is a compound word.

First, picture in your mind a person screaming from the depths of his being. Second, picture in your mind a person running to help. Now, draw the pictures together. The word *help* then becomes ''Oh, that someone would come running to my screams!'' This was her request.

When a person is in deep distress or when there is an awful fear present, it is very difficult to speak intelligible words. Instead, more than likely there will come from the mouth nothing more than a scream. This woman was saying by using this particular word for *help*, ''Lord, I'm hurting so much I can't really talk about it. All I can do is scream. Would You please come running to my screams?'' '''Lord, help me!'''

The Lord replied, '''It is not good to take the children's bread and throw it to the little dogs''' (v. 26). Now the Lord was not really calling the woman a dog, even though it seems that way at first. Rather, He knew she herself felt like a dog, and this she did not deny. How would you feel if you had to tell people your daughter was demon-possessed?

But then she remembered the picture of the dogs under the table, eating the crumbs that fell to the floor. '''True, Lord, yet even the little dogs eat the crumbs which fall from their masters' table''' (v. 27).

''Just a little crumb like the dogs eat is all I want. But that will be enough to heal my daughter.'' When Jesus heard her words, He said to her, '''O woman, great is your faith! Let it be to you as you desire.''' And as Matthew said, ''Her daughter was healed from that very hour'' (v. 28).

Like the woman, we too find ourselves in such desperate needs that all we can say is, ''Lord, help me!'' But when that simple prayer becomes a scream from the heart, ''Oh that someone would come running to my screams!'' He answers, ''Let it be to you as you desire.''

REFLECT AND MEDITATE

Read Psalm 12, which begins, ''Help, Lord.'' Meditate on the words as you consider what this psalm is saying to you in today's world.

REACT AND RESPOND

Think back to your childhood to a time when you were so frightened all you could do was scream. Write down on paper the story of that incident, and let it be a parable of how today you sometimes scream in your spirit.

REJOICE AND WORSHIP

One of the most peaceful feelings a human being can experience is in those moments right after being delivered from a very frightening experience. Rejoice in the words of the song ''Wonderful Peace'' (*Church Hymnal*, p. 290).

DISCIPLESHIP COMMITMENT

I will strive to follow God by submitting to His will, by considering the apostles' teaching, by fellowship, by breaking of bread and by simple prayer.

CHAPTER 4

How Can I Commune With God in Prayer ?

INTRODUCTION

In the previous three weeks of study, we have considered "Who is God?" "Who am I?" and "How can I follow God?" Now we will consider how we can commune with God through prayer.

God is not an impersonal being who stands aloof from the cries of mankind. As we noted the first week, He is the heavenly Father who desires to have a close personal relationship with His sons and daughters.

In a general sense, the first prayer most people think of is what we commonly call the Lord's Prayer. This prayer was taught to the disciples by the Lord and contrasted with against those types of prayers that amount to no more than "vain repetitions." As disciples we will consider how to pray in the manner the Lord taught His disciples.

However, the longest recorded prayer the Lord himself actually prayed is found in John 17. This is the prayer Jesus prayed for His disciples on the night He was later betrayed and taken into custody. We have the privilege of also praying in the manner our Lord modeled for us.

The writer of the book of Hebrews said, "Let us therefore come boldly to the throne of grace, that we may obtain mercy and find grace to help in time of need" (Hebrews 4:16). We will examine how to come to "the throne of grace" by looking at the manner in which the Old Testament high priest was able to come before the ark of the covenant. It was before the mercy seat of that ark that God said, "'There I will meet with you, and I will speak with you from above the mercy seat'" (Exodus 25:22).

Paul described for us in Ephesians 6 how we can be a child of God "praying always with all prayer and supplication in the Spirit" (Ephesians 6:18). When the enemy resists us, we must "be strong in the Lord and in the power of His might" (v. 10). Our enemy is not the flesh, but rather the principalities, the powers, the rulers of the darkness of this age, the spiritual wickedness in the heavenly places.

However, because of our infirmities of the flesh, there are times we simply do not know how to pray as we should. Then the Holy Spirit will intercede for us with our very "groanings which cannot be uttered" (Romans 8:26).

Therefore, we will see that we can commune with God by praying as the Lord taught His disciples, by praying as the Lord himself prayed, by going boldly to the throne of grace, by praying in the Spirit, and by allowing the Spirit to make intercession for us.

DISCIPLESHIP GOAL

As a child of God, Jesus has made you a priest to serve His God and Father (Revelation 1:6). The goal this week is to come to a better understanding of the priestly privilege of prayer and its powerful ministry in the world and that you as an individual may be able to participate in the marvelous ministry of prayer.

READING ASSIGNMENT
The Living Book, pp. 32 - 48

Study 1

PRAYING THE LORD'S PRAYER
(AS TAUGHT TO THE DISCIPLES)

READ AND RESEARCH   (Matthew 6:1-13; Luke 11:1-13)

The first recording of what we commonly refer to as the Lord's Prayer is given in Matthew as part of the Sermon on the Mount. On the one hand we must not isolate this part of the sermon but keep it in the context of the entire message. On the other hand we see from Luke that Jesus must have repeated this model prayer on at least one other occasion and probably several other times. Therefore, there are some simple truths about the Lord's Prayer that are able to stand by themselves.

First, let us note the context of the entire sermon.

Jesus began the sermon with the Beatitudes. Therefore, our prayers should recognize our own self-poverty (Matthew 5:3), express an emotion of mourning (v. 4), be filled with the spirit of meekness (v. 5), seek for a righteous answer (v. 6), express mercy (v. 7), be made with a pure heart (v. 8), and culminate with the desire for peace among those for whom we pray (v. 9).

We should also remember that the sermon is full of commands for action. Prayer must never become a substitute for obeying the Lord's directives. Even if you are at the altar of prayer and remember that "'your brother has something against you,'" the Lord said, "'Leave your gift there before the altar, and go your way. First be reconciled to your brother, and then come and offer your gift'" (Matthew 5:23, 24).

There are many other injunctions. "'Let your life so shine before men'" (5:16). "'Agree with your adversary quickly, while you are on the way with him'" (5:25). "'Do not swear at all'" (5:34). "'Whoever slaps you on your right cheek, turn the other to him also'" (5:39). "'Give to him who asks you" (5:42). "'Love your enemies, bless those who curse you, do good to those who hate you, and pray for those who spitefully use you

and persecute you'" (5:44). "'Do not do your charitable deeds before men, to be seen by them'" (6:1). "'When you pray, go into your room. . . .do not use vain repetitions'" (6:6, 7).

It is in this context of the spirit of the Beatitudes and commands for righteous actions that the Lord said, "'In this manner, therefore, pray.'"

Now let us note the prayer itself.

1. "Our Father in heaven, hallowed be Your name" (v. 9). Prayer should begin with the recognition of God as our heavenly Father and a plea that His name may be sanctified within us.

2. Overriding all of our requests should be the prayer for God's will to be done right here on earth where we live even as it is done in heaven itself. Such a prayer is essentially saying, "Let Your kingdom come to earth" (v. 10).

3. We should pray for our own physical needs but should not pray that we would have enough to hoard for the future. "'Give us this day our daily bread'" (v. 11), or as Luke says, "'Give us day by day our daily bread'" (Luke 11:3).

4. We should pray for our spiritual needs, recognizing the sins within our own lives and expressing the willingness to empathize with people who have evil in their lives. "'And forgive us our debts, as we forgive our debtors'" (v. 12). These "debts" are debts of sin as shown by Luke, who simply says, "'Forgive us our sins'" (Luke 11:4).

5. We should pray that the very way in which we walk today might be according to God's leading so that we would not fall into temptation but that we might be rescued away from every evil which confronts us. "'Do not lead us into temptation, but deliver us from the evil one'" (v. 13).

6. Finally, even though Luke does not mention this part of the prayer and some might question its validity, we should recognize that all things belong to God, the Creator, and it is His power that will usher in the final glory of both heaven and earth. "'For Yours is the kingdom and the power and the glory forever. Amen.'" (v. 13).

Later in the sermon Jesus said, "'Ask, and it will be given to you; seek, and you will find; knock, and it will be opened to you. For everyone who asks receives, and he who seeks finds, and to him who knocks it will be opened'" (7:7, 8).

Many times Christians feel that if they ask God for something that they have previously asked for, it is a sign of unbelief. But the verb tenses that Jesus uses in verse 8 (*asks, seeks, knocks*) are in the Greek imperfect tense. This means literally one who "keeps on asking and asking and keeps on seeking and seeking and keeps on knocking and knocking" will receive and finally have the door opened, just like a child who asks again and again.

REFLECT AND MEDITATE

Read Matthew 6:19-34. Think about how God cares for you even as He cares for the birds of the air and the lilies of the field.

REACT AND RESPOND

As you pray today, turn on a tape recorder, but try not to think of its being there while you pray. After your prayer, listen to the recorder, and see if you included all six of the elements mentioned above in the Lord's Prayer.

REJOICE AND WORSHIP

The Rev. W.H. Ward was a great prayer warrior who spent many years teaching singing schools in local Church of God congregations. After reading the words of his song "Prayer Bells of Heaven" (*Church Hymnal*, p. 276), rejoice that God has enabled us to come before Him in prayer.

Study 2

PRAYING THE LORD'S PRAYER (AS PRAYED BY CHRIST IN JOHN)

READ AND RESEARCH (John 17:1-26)

The synoptic writers recorded the Passover meal Jesus shared with His disciples during the evening of the night He was betrayed. John described how the Lord washed each of the disciples' feet (John 13), gave us in detail how He promised the coming of the Holy Spirit of Comfort (John 14, 16), and recountedthe words of His prayer for the disciples just before He entered the Garden of Gethsemane (John 17).

It is this prayer in John 17 that is truly "the Lord's Prayer." This is the prayer He prayed. This is a model prayer that we should consider when praying for one another.

We are not being presumptuous in saying that we have the privilege of praying even as the Lord prayed. In praying for the glory of the Father in His own life, Jesus said that the very purpose for which He had come was that the disciples might have eternal life, and eternal life is '"that they may know You, the only true God, and Jesus Christ whom You have sent'" (vv. 1-3).

One might say it is impossible for us to pray the prayer that Jesus prayed when He said, '''And now, O Father, glorify Me together with Yourself, with the glory which I had with You before the world was'" (v. 5). After all, you and I did not share in the pre-Creation glory because we were not even there.

In one sense that is true. But on the other hand, this does not mean we pray that we ourselves may be glorified with the glory which *we* had. Rather, it means we pray that *in* Jesus we may be glorified even with the glory which He had before the world was formed.

We can pray the prayer because He has given us the authority to do so (v. 2) through the work He himself has already completed (v. 4). It is His word that we keep (v. 6), words which came from the Father (v. 7), and which we have received and believed (v. 8). Therefore, even as He prayed for us, we can now pray for one another because through Christ we belong to God (v. 9). Even as we pray, He is glorified through us (v. 10).

Now let us note more particularly how we should pray for our fellow brothers and sisters in Christ.

1. Pray that the Father will keep them (vv. 11, 15). It is true that we recognize that some are as

"the son of perdition" (v. 12). God will not keep those who betray His Son and sell Him to the Pharisees of this world. But we should pray that He will keep those who "are not of the world" (vv. 14, 16). Our prayer is not that God will "take them out of the world" but that He will "keep them from the evil one" (v. 15).

2. Pray that the Father will sanctify them (vv. 17-19). The work of sanctification is the perfection of truth, and it is the Word of God that is truth (v. 17). The word *sanctify* means "to set forth in purity." Jesus said that He came to the earth and set before us a holy life (vv. 18, 19). Therefore, we should pray that through His Word, God will sanctify His disciples even as Jesus was sanctified while on earth.

3. Pray that God will give unity through the Word (vv. 20-23). The prayer for unity is not simply between the believer and the ones he/she may personally know in a local congregation or in a denomination, nor even in a particular generation. Rather the prayer for unity is for all believers in the Word (v. 20).

The reason for this prayer for oneness is "'that the world may believe that You sent Me'" (v. 21). When we are "'made perfect in one'" (v. 23) even as God is one, then "the world may know that You have sent Me, and have loved them as You have loved Me" (v. 23).

4. Pray that we all may be with Christ (v. 24). This is not simply a prayer for future glorification when we will see Jesus face-to-face. That will take us out of this world, and Jesus had already prayed, "'I do not pray that You should take them out of the world, but that You should keep them from the evil one'" (v. 15).

Rather, we pray that even now we may be with Christ where He is through the Paraclete (the Comforter, the Holy Spirit). Even now let us behold His glory (v. 24) which is the glory of love before the foundation of the world (v. 24).

The result of such praying will be that love will abound and the presence of Jesus Christ will be real in our midst. It will be, as Jesus said, "'that the love with which You loved Me may be in them, and I in them'" (v. 26). You have the privilege to pray as the Lord himself prayed and thereby glorify the Father on earth.

REFLECT AND MEDITATE

Read and meditate on the story written by John in chapter 13 about how Jesus had washed the feet of the argumentative disciples earlier in the evening before praying the prayer in chapter 17.

REACT AND RESPOND

Request that your church have a Communion service in which the saints wash one another's feet.

REJOICE AND WORSHIP

The true depth of praying as Jesus prayed in John 17 can only be reached through the Holy Spirit. Worship God by singing the song "The Comforter Has Come" (*Church Hymnal*, p. 406).

Study 3

COMING BOLDLY TO THE THRONE OF GRACE

READ AND RESEARCH (Hebrews 4:9-16; 9)

Throughout the book of Hebrews the writer continually refers to the Old Testament Scriptures in order to teach us about the Lord Jesus Christ. Therefore, we must look at the Old Testament patterns to understand what he means when he says, "Let us therefore come boldly to the throne of grace, that we may obtain mercy and find grace to help in time of need" (4:16).

After leaving Egypt, Israel was recognized as a nation whose God dwelt in the midst of their camp. God gave Moses instructions as to how he was to build a tabernacle. There would be an outer courtyard, where the people could come and offer sacrifices before the Lord.

Just inside the courtyard was the tabernacle upon which the sacrificial offerings were to be made. Before the entrance of the tabernacle was the laver in which the priests would wash their hands and feet.

The tabernacle was divided into two sections, the Holy Place and the Holy of Holies. In the Holy Place were the golden candlesticks, the table of showbread, and the altar of incense. Just beyond the Holy Place, separated by a thick curtain called the veil, was the Holy of Holies in which the ark of the covenant was placed. Few scholars doubt that the writer of Hebrews had this ark of the covenant in mind when he used the expression "throne of grace."

The writer was not saying that we must go to the physical temple in Jerusalem or the literal tabernacle in the wilderness. Rather, as he explains in chapter 9, these were "the copies of the things in the heavens" (v. 23).

There is a heavenly sanctuary, "the greater and more perfect tabernacle not made with hands" (v. 11), and now Christ has entered "into heaven itself, now to appear in the presence of God for us" (v. 24). This is what the writer was referring to when he said, "Let us. . .come boldly to the throne of grace."

As a child of God "washed. . .from our sins in His own blood" Jesus has "made us kings and priests to His God and Father" (Revelation 1:5, 6). It is your privilege as a priest of God in Christ to come to His priestly throne, before the mercy seat, overshadowed by the cherubim of heaven, to obtain mercy and find grace to help in the time of need.

We begin our entrance by offering the sacrifice of the Lamb of God that has already been slain to take away the sin of the world (John 1:29). We proceed to the laver where the Lord himself washes away the dirt of our earthly journey (John 13:10).

By faith we enter the Holy Place of communion with God. The light is from a golden candlestick whose oil is the Holy Spirit himself. The light reveals to us those things which "'eye has not seen, nor ear heard, nor have entered into the heart of man,'" even the "deep things of God" (1 Corinthians 2:9, 10).

We have Communion at the table of showbread on which the Lord placed Himself, and on which we lay our own lives, praying that God will work things not according to our will but according to His purpose (Romans 8:28, where the word *purpose* is the same as the *setting forth* of the show-bread in the Gospels).

In faith we approach the golden altar where we offer up the incense of praise. "Therefore by him let us continually offer the sacrifice of praise to God, that is, the fruit of our lips, giving thanks to His name" (Hebrews 13:15).

Without trembling we continue onward past the veil, which now has been "torn in two from top to bottom" (Matthew 27:51; Mark 15:38; Luke 23:45) and which is "His flesh" (Hebrews 10:20).

Now we stand before the throne of grace. This is the place concerning which God said, "And there I will meet with you, and I will speak with you from above the mercy seat, from between the two cherubim which are on the ark of the Testimony, of all things which I will give you in commandment unto the children of Israel" (Exodus 25:22).

At such a sacred time let us not dare to spend our time in trifling matters. As priests we have written upon the breastplate of our hearts the very names of our brothers and sisters (Exodus 28:29). Upon our shoulders are the precious stones with the burdens of the children of Israel (Exodus 28:9-12).

It is a throne of grace and therefore a place where mercy and grace are to be sought. It is not a judgment throne. We do not seek here for the condemnation of sinners. We seek for that mercy which is everlasting, which is extended to all generations (Psalm 136). We seek for that grace which is able to sustain us and which is always sufficient (2 Corinthians 12:9).

REFLECT AND MEDITATE

Read Exodus 25-27, which describes the building of the tabernacle in the wilderness. Apply the principles of the tabernacle to your own praying.

REACT AND RESPOND

Make an outline drawing of the courtyard, the tabernacle, the altar, the laver, the candlestick, the table of showbread, the altar of incense and the ark of the covenant. How do they relate to your praying?

REJOICE AND WORSHIP

Sing the song "Just As I Am" (*Hymns of the Spirit*, p. 300), and worship God because you are able to approach His throne through the atoning grace of Jesus Christ.

Study 4

PRAYING IN THE SPIRIT

READ AND RESEARCH (Ephesians 6:10-18)

In the Ephesians 6 the apostle Paul described for us the Christian armor which rightly belongs to every born-again believer. While it is true that there are many situations in which we are fighting against the spiritual enemy, we cannot forget that the context in which Paul describes the warfare is that of "praying always with all prayer and supplication in the Spirit" (v. 18).

The believer should not feel that it is always a simple and easy matter to be "praying in the Holy Spirit" (Jude 20). The Enemy uses many different strategies in attacking our prayers before they even begin. These include our jobs, our families, the weaknesses of our own flesh, the church, doing good deeds and time itself. That is not even mentioning such distractions as television, the newspaper and various types of relaxation.

We should begin our prayer, "in the Lord and in the power of His might" (v. 10) and "put on the whole armor of God, that. . .[we] may be able to stand against the wiles of the devil" (v. 11). Paul said again in verse 13, "Therefore, take up the whole armor of God, that you may be able to withstand in the evil day."

Remember, our enemies are not those people who might persecute us or say evil against us. But we fight "against principalities, against powers, against the rulers of the darkness of this age, against spiritual hosts of wickedness in the heavenly places" (v. 12).

There are six steps the Christian should be prepared to take when the Enemy would hinder your praying in the Spirit:

1. Gird your waist with truth (v. 14). On the Roman soldier this included both the clothing under the armor and the belt or girdle that bound the armor together. Spiritually, the "truth" in this verse is not referring just to the Word (which is described in verse 17) nor to our simply speaking words of truth. Rather, the meaning is that we must *be* truth. We come to God in honesty, without trying to pretend we are something that in reality we are not. We must be honest with God if we want to "pray in the Spirit."

2. Have on the breastplate of righteousness (v. 14). This is not simply the righteousness imputed to us through salvation. This also includes the righteousness of our daily lives as we commit our ways to God through the help of Jesus Christ our Lord. Again, it is not simply the deeds of our lives (these will follow our spiritual prayer), but it is the very desire for righteousness.

3. Put on your feet the gospel of peace (v. 15). The word *gospel* means "good news." If it is not good news, it is not gospel. You should have your feet shod with good news so that every step you take you will be telling people good news. Should we tell people about sin and judgment and hell? Yes, but not simply that they are sinners who must face judgment and hell. The good news about sin is that it can be forgiven. The good news about judgment is that Christ has already faced it for you. The good news about hell is that you do not have to go there.

4. Take the shield of faith in order to "quench

all the fiery darts of the wicked one'' (v. 16). The ''fiery darts'' refer to the burning arrows that had been dipped in pitch and used by the Romans to destroy the strongholds of the enemies by setting them on fire. Through faith we ward off the Enemy's attack.

5. Take the helmet of salvation (v. 17). This protects our mind so that, as Paul says, we can meditate on these things''--whatever things are true, noble, just, pure, lovely and of good report (Philippians 4:8). This is our virtue and praise in the Spirit.

6. Take the sword of the Spirit, ''which is the word of God'' (v. 17). When Satan came against Jesus in the wilderness, Jesus said to him at the first temptation, ''It is written...'' (Matthew 4:4); again at the second temptation, ''It is written...'' (v. 7); and again at the third temptation, ''It is written...'' (v. 10). This must not simply be an exercise of our lips. But rather the Holy Spirit himself must anoint us to say with piercing strength, ''It is written! It is written! It is written!''

With the armor intact we are then able to ''pray in the Spirit.'' We speak to God as honest children, not trying to act as though we are someone else. We are what we are. Our righteousness is in Christ, and we take it as our own will and desire. We are determined to share the good news. We believe Jesus will do exactly what He promised. Our minds are helmeted from the evil things of this world. Our might is by the sword of the Spirit himself, the Word of God. Now as we ''pray in the Spirit'' God answers, forcing the Enemy to flee.

REFLECT AND MEDITATE

Read the story of David and Goliath in 1 Samuel 17. Do you face Goliaths in your own spiritual life? What type of armor do you need to be victorious?

REACT AND RESPOND

If possible, visit with a soldier and find out what a modern soldier's outfit consists of. If this is not possible, consult an encyclopedia. How does the spiritual armor compare to the modern soldier's defenses?

REJOICE AND WORSHIP

Read the words of the song ''Onward, Christian Soldiers'' (*Hymns of the Spirit*, p. 158), and worship God because of the victory we have in the Christian fight as we pray in the Spirit.

Study 5

INTERCESSION BY THE HOLY SPIRIT

READ AND RESEARCH (Romans 8:14-39)

One of the most familiar verses of the book of Romans is 8:28--''And we know that all things work together for good to them who love God, to those who are the called according to His purpose.''

Many Christians take a shallow look at this tremendous verse and develop a personal theology that avoids all types of pain, suffering and persecution. The false reasoning says that if you love God, everything will go well--you won't have any problems or any type of suffering. Furthermore, such false reasoning says that if you do have problems or suffering or things don't go well, it's because you don't really love God.

However, in the verses preceding verse 28, Paul used several different words that talk about the Christians' suffering (sufferings, pain, travail, weaknesses, etc.). Paul was not at all saying that the Christian will not suffer. Rather, he was saying that the Holy Spirit will help us in our sufferings. The Spirit will take the evil happenings about us and make them work in such a way that it will eventually be for our own good.

The Spirit gives us the assurance that we are God's children. ''You have received the Spirit of adoption by whom we cry out, 'Abba, Father.' The Spirit himself bears witness with our spirit that we are the children of God, and if children, then heirs--heirs of God and joint heirs with Christ'' (vv. 15-17).

The Spirit uses the very sufferings we experience day by day to give us this assurance (vv. 17, 18).

The Spirit is able to accomplish this miracle of turning evil around for our good in a threefold manner. First, He reveals to us the hope of suffering. Second, He takes our infirmities unto Himself. And third, He makes intercession for us even with our own groanings which cannot be uttered.

In verses 19-25 Paul compared our own sufferings to the world of nature about us. There he says we can see the hope of pain just as the travail of a mother with child carries a hope that helps the suffering (John 16:21).

Second, Paul said, ''Likewise the Spirit also helps our weaknesses'' (v. 26). The word ''helps'' means that the Spirit takes our weaknesses (infirmities, *KJV*) unto Himself. In this verse our weaknesses are not our sufferings. The Holy Spirit does not always take our sufferings away. Rather, our weakness is that ''we do not know what we should pray for as we ought.'' We can't understand the pain, the sorrow, the suffering. Therefore, we simply do not know how nor do we have the strength to pray as we should.

It is this weakness that the Holy Spirit takes unto Himself. He uses our ''groanings which cannot be uttered'' to pray for us according to the will of the heavenly Father.

The word for *intercession* has a root that means ''to hit the center of the target.'' It is as though the Holy Spirit binds together all of our hurts, examines them carefully and then shoots His piercing arrow into the very center of our pain.

He does not simply kill the pain. He carefully takes the cause of our pain, attaches it again to His arrow of compassion and shoots it into the very center of the heart of God. The Holy Spirit not only intercedes in our own heart, but He also ''knows what the mind of the Spirit is, because He makes intercession for the saints according to the

will of God'' (v. 27).

It is with this intercession of the Holy Spirit that all things are fit together in such a way as to work for our good. The Holy Spirit gives us hope in the midst of our travail and takes our weaknesses on Himself when we do not know how to pray.

The goal of this intercessory work of the Spirit is that we might be ''conformed to the image of His Son, that He might be the firstborn among many brethren'' (v. 29).

What is the image of the Son? What was His life like? Did He experience sufferings, or was His life one of ease and comfort? As the writer of Hebrews said, ''For it was fitting for Him, for whom are all things and by whom are all things, in bringing many sons to glory, to make the author of their salvation perfect through sufferings'' (Hebrews 2:10).

REFLECT AND MEDITATE

Read Job 1 and consider how you would react if you lost your possessions and your children today.

REACT AND RESPOND

Write a letter to a friend you know is suffering, and explain to him how the Holy Spirit helps us during our times of grief, sorrow and pain.

REJOICE AND WORSHIP

Worship God in an offering of praise by praying for as many people you can think of who are suffering and then by thanking God that you are not presently enduring the same type of suffering.

DISCIPLESHIP COMMITMENT

As a result of this week's study, I will commit myself to a more dedicated prayer life, praying as the disciples prayed, as the Lord prayed, coming boldly to the throne of grace, praying in the Spirit and allowing the Spirit to make intercession for me.

CHAPTER 5

What Is the Word of God?

INTRODUCTION

The greatest truth in the world is the fact that God exists. The next greatest is the fact that God has revealed Himself to man. There is a God, and we can know Him . . . through His Word.

The Bible is the Word of God. It identifies itself as His Word. It has stood every test through the ages, proving that it is the true Word of God.

Listen to the joy of the Psalmist as he sings, "Forever, O Lord, Your word is settled in heaven" (Psalm 119:89). Hear him confidently proclaim, "Your word is a lamp to my feet and a light to my path" (Psalm 119:105). The Word of God, firmly established in heaven, gives clear guidance to our lives on earth. We have a reason to sing.

Everything we need to know about God, about salvation and about good living can be found in the Bible. It tells us about God--His power, His holiness and His love. It tells us about His standards, His judgment and His forgiveness. It tells us how to know Him, how to grow in Him, how to live for Him and how to please Him.

We are commanded to love God and to know His Word. Loving His Word is a direct result of loving Him. The Scripture passage that commands that we love the Lord with all our heart, soul, and strength, goes on to require, "'And these words which I command you today shall be in your heart'" (Deuteronomy 6:6).

Knowing the Word of God will produce wonderful results: "'This Book of the Law shall not depart from your mouth, but you shall meditate in it day and night, that you may observe to do according to all that is written in it. For then you will make your way prosperous, and then you will have good success'" (Joshua 1:8).

Many blessings come to us through the Bible: (1) It exposes our sin (Hebrews 4:12, 13; James 1:23, 24); (2) it offers salvation (John 6:47; Romans 1:16, 17); (3) it cleanses our conduct (Psalm 119:9; John 15:3; 17:17; Ephesians 5:25, 26); (4) it enables us to resist temptation (Psalm 119:11; Matthew 4:4, 7, 10; 1 Corinthians 10:13); (5) it nurtures spiritual growth (Deuteronomy 8:3; Job 23:12; Psalm 19:10; 119:103; Acts 20:32; 1 Peter 2:2, 3); (6) it protects from evil (Ephesians 4:14; 6:10-17; 1 John 2:14); (7) it equips for service (2 Timothy 3:16, 17); and (8) it produces joy (Jeremiah 15:16; John 15:11).

Jesus gave us a mission which requires us to know the Word of God. It is our duty to give witness according to the Scriptures (Luke 24:44-48), to proclaim His Word to every creature (Mark 16:15-20) and to teach others what we have learned from Him (Matthew 28:19, 20). Our duty to share His Word is a debt which we owe to every man (Romans 1:14-16). Someday we will stand before Christ in judgment and give answer according to this message we have received (Romans 2:12-16).

The lessons in this chapter will help us to see that the Bible is the Word of God and will help us to understand how God has spoken to us in His Word. We will learn five important truths about the Bible:

1. It Is a Divine Word
2. It Is a Written Word
3. It Is a Complete Word
4. It Is an Inspired Word
5. It Is a Dependable Word

DISCIPLESHIP GOAL

1. To recognize that God speaks to man
2. To respect the authority of God's Word
3. To rely on the faithfulness of God's Word

READING ASSIGNMENT

The Living Book, pp. 49 - 57

Study 1

IT IS A DIVINE WORD

READ AND RESEARCH (Romans 1:14-25; Hebrews 1:1-4)

Only God could have given the Bible to us. It is a book which man alone could never have written. It tells what man did not know, about things he did not understand, in ways he never would have imagined.

Man searches after truth. He has a curious mind and wants fresh answers. Sadly, man's most important questions cannot be answered by his own searching. He needs to know the origin of life, its meaning, its purpose and its future. He needs to know God. He needs a way to recognize truth. His great questions deal with the invisible and cannot be answered by man alone.

God has all the answers, and He *reveals* to us what we need to know. *Revelation* is the disclosure of truth that was previously unknown. Primarily, it is truth about God and about His will for man.

God discloses truth through nature. The Creator reveals Himself in His creation. This is a true revelation. It is called *general revelation* because it is known to everyone. It is called *natural revelation* because it is given through nature--the natural creation.

David claimed that the universe, day after day and night after night, displays the glory of God to every language so that its message reaches the whole earth (Psalm 19:1-4).

Paul said that "invisible attributes" of God are manifest by the creation to all men leaving them without excuse (Romans 1:20). Nature displays two specific truths: (1) God exists--"His . . . Godhead"; (2) He is powerful--"His eternal power." These two facts are important for us to know. They should be enough to make us curious-- enough to make us seek God. Sadly, they are not enough to help us find God.

Paul described the result of general revelation: "For the wrath of God is revealed from heaven against all ungodliness and unrighteousness of men, who suppress the truth in unrighteousness" (Romans 1:18).

Nature tells us there is a God and that He is a powerful, eternal God. It cannot tell us how to approach Him or please Him. The results of general revelation is "the wrath of God." Nature says enough to damn us but not enough to save us.

The problem is that sinful men do not know what to do with the revelation found in nature: (1) They ignore it because of their sinful condition-- they "suppress the truth in unrighteousness" (v. 18); (2) they fail to give true worship--"they did not glorify Him as God, nor were thankful" (v. 21); (3) they replace the true God with their own ideas about God--they "changed the glory of the incorruptible God into an image made like corruptible man" (v. 23).

God revealed Himself in another way that was clearly unambiguous. He came to earth as a man, disclosing truth by His words and by His perfect example. In Jesus Christ, God gave a *personal revelation*. This is the crowning revelation.

The epistle to the Hebrews asserts, "God, who at various times and in different ways spoke in time past to the fathers by the prophets, has in these last days spoken to us by His Son, whom He has appointed heir of all things, through whom also He made the worlds" (Hebrews 1:1, 2).

God's self-disclosure in Christ Jesus is the highest revelation. Christ is "the brightness of His glory and the express image of His person" (v. 3).

God, who reveals Himself in nature and in Jesus Christ, also "at various times and in different ways spoke. These "various ways" included dreams, visions, angels, audible voices, prophetic messages and sacred writings. These have been preserved for us in written form in the Bible as Holy Scripture. This is called *special revelation*.

The Bible identifies itself as the Word of God. The Old Testament uses expressions such as "Thus saith the Lord" 3,808 times. The New Testament makes many similar claims. It is a written record of His love for us--a love letter from God.

Discipleship

REFLECT AND MEDITATE

1. How has God expressed Himself to me?

2. When did I feel that He was speaking directly to me?

3. What is the most recent thing I did in response to His Word?

REACT AND RESPOND

Think of something God wants you to do, and begin doing it now.

REJOICE AND WORSHIP

God Almighty cares enough and is close enough to speak to us by His Word. We are not alone! We are not on our own! We are His own!

Study 2

IT IS A WRITTEN WORD

READ AND RESEARCH (Isaiah 30:8; Habakkuk 2:2, 3)

The general revelation in nature is universal but incomplete, and it does not save. The personal revelation in Christ is perfect, and it saves; but it was restricted by time and place.

The earthly life of Jesus lasted only 33 years--His ministry only three years--and they were only in Palestine. Jesus chose apostles and prepared them as witnesses, but their oral testimony was also limited by time and place (Luke 24:44-49; John 15:27).

A loving God who chooses to disclose Himself can surely find a way to bring His truth to all men everywhere in all eras of time. God can, and He did!

A written revelation is *universal*. It can be translated, printed and distributed all over the world, so that everyone can see what God has shown of Himself. The Bible is available in all the major languages of the world. Now it is being translated into languages spoken by smaller groups of people.

A written revelation is *permanent*. It does not end with the death of an apostle or a prophet, for his testimony lives in print, "and through it he being dead still speaks" (Hebrews 11:4).

A written revelation is *timeless*. It is available whenever we need it to guide our lives. Its message is always fresh.

A written revelation is *objective*. It does not depend on hearsay. Unlike folklore or tradition, it does not change as it is retold from one generation to the next. It is a consistent standard by which to recognize unchanging truth--and by which to judge the quality of our lives. Jesus warned, "'Do not think that I shall accuse you to the Father; there is one who accuses you--Moses, in whom ye trust. For if you believed Moses, you would believe Me; for he wrote about Me. But if you do not believe his writings, how will you believe My words?'" (John 5:45-47; see also Romans 16:25, 26).

A written record is *credible*. It allows us to see the actual testimony of the original witness. It can be examined closely, studied carefully and understood clearly. John proclaimed, "That which we have seen and heard we declare to you, that you also may have fellowship with us; and truly our fellowship is with the Father and with His Son Jesus Christ" (1 John 1:3). He stated his purpose in writing: "But these are written that you may believe that Jesus is the Christ, the Son of God, and that believing you may have life in His name" (John 20:31).

A written record is *communicable*. It can be shared with others. Scripture is the means to understanding Christ and His work (Luke 24:26, 27), and of preaching Him to the world (Luke 24:44-47).

Jesus often referred to the form of the divine revelation by saying, "'It is written'" (Matthew 4:4; John 2:17). He called it "'Scriptures,'" which means "writing" (Mark 12:24; 14:49; John 2:22). Paul quoted Christ and the Old Testament jointly as Scripture (1 Timothy 5:18) and identified his own teaching with the Scripture (2 Timothy 3:10-17). Peter made joint reference to Paul's epistles and Scriptures (2 Peter 3:15, 16). This totality of Scripture makes a person mature and completely equipped for service (2 Timothy 3:14-17).

From early days the Word of God was put into writing. Moses told the people what God had said, then he recorded the message (Exodus 24:3, 4). After Joshua delivered his farewell address, he "wrote these words in the Book of the Law of God" (Joshua 24:26). Samuel spoke to the people "and wrote it in a book and laid it up before the Lord" (1 Samuel 10:25). Many prophets wrote their messages.

Luke reported in the New Testament that "many have taken in hand to set in order a narrative of those things which are most surely believed among us, just as those who from the beginning were eyewitnesses and ministers of the word delivered them to us" (Luke 1:1, 2).

After these and other inspired books were written, they were read and honored by the people of God. There are other books and epistles mentioned in Scripture which are not included as part of the Bible (1 Corinthians 5:9; Colossians 4:16).

The *Old Testament* was addressed primarily to the people of Israel, and most of it was written in the Hebrew language. It prepared hearts for the coming of Christ. Jesus and His apostles preached it as the Word of God, held it to be an accurate revelation and quoted from it freely. For years, before the New Testament books were written, it was the only Bible of the early church.

The *New Testament* was written mainly by the apostles of Jesus Christ, who told about His life, proclaimed His saving work and applied His teaching to daily Christian life.

The relationship between the two testaments has been expressed by an unknown author:

"The New is in the Old contained; the Old is by the New explained; the New is in the Old concealed; the Old is by the New revealed.

REFLECT AND MEDITATE

Some issues of importance to us are not mentioned in the Bible. What should we do about this "silence?"

REACT AND RESPOND

Write a one-page testimony explaining why you are glad that God gave us His Word in writing.

REJOICE AND WORSHIP

David wrote many of his praises, so that I may use them in my worship. How is the Twenty-third Psalm an expression of my praise to God?

Study 3

IT IS A COMPLETE WORD

READ AND RESEARCH (Luke 24:25-32; 2 Peter 3:1, 2, 14-18; Revelation 22:18, 19)

The Bible is a complete library in one volume. It has 66 books, grouped as two testaments. It contains a variety of literary types, including prose, poetry, history, letters and much more.

In the Bible, God tells us everything we need to know for salvation and for productive Christian living. Scripture is the major method by which "His divine power has given to us all things that pertain to life and godliness" (2 Peter 1:3).

With the rise of true prophets, false prophets arose, preaching heresies. It became necessary to know who was speaking for God and who was not. It still is necessary.

We must have a standard--a rule--by which we can know for certain what is the Word of God. That standard is called a *Canon*, a list of books recognized as the inspired Word of God.

Under Ezra, about 400 years before Christ, Jewish leaders collected the books of the Old Testament and completed the Jewish Canon. It contained the same books that compose our Old Testament, but they were grouped differently. Also, the books of Samuel, Kings and Chronicles had not been divided into six books, as they are today.

Discipleship

The Torah, five books of the Law, written by Moses, is the first group in our Bible. The second group, called the Prophets, was written by men anointed to fill the office of prophet and included several that we list as historical. The third group, called the Writings, was penned by anointed writers who did not officially hold the office of prophet. The latter group included the Wisdom Literature and was headed by the Psalms. Sometimes the third group, while including all the Writings, was identified by the first book in the group and was called Psalms.

This is the Bible that Jesus used, and He often referred to these books and groupings. He spoke of "'the law,'" meaning instruction, not legislation (Matthew 5:18). He referred to "'the Law and the Prophets'" (Matthew 7:12); "'the Law of Moses and the Prophets and the Psalms'" (Luke 24:44); and "'the Scriptures'" (Mark 12:24; 14:49). In these declarations Jesus recognized the entire Jewish Canon as the inspired Word of God. These were all ways of referring to the Old Testament in its entirety.

The Roman Catholic Church added certain books written between the times of Malachi and Matthew to their Old Testament. These, called "The Apocrypha," are not accepted in the Jewish Bible, nor were they recognized by Jesus.

New Testament books began to be written about 20 years after the death and resurrection of Jesus. Most of them were in the form of letters, which began to be shared by the churches. They were read in church services along with the Old Testament and were accepted as having the authority of Scripture (1 Thessalonians 5:27; Colossians 4:16).

Of those books, 27 have been recognized as inspired writings and constitute the New Testament Canon.

The forming of the Canon is a matter of spiritual discernment. It is not a human decision. Although church councils dealt with questions about the Canon, to know which books are inspired by God can only be done with the help of the Holy Spirit.

The prophets of God did not rely on trances or spells to confirm their anointing. These practices usually came from false prophets (Deuteronomy 18:9-14; 1 Kings 18:26-29). The true prophet has a calm assurance that allows him to speak with divine authority (1 Kings 18:30-41). He knows that he is speaking for God, and the people of God also know it.

Jesus said that His sheep recognize and follow the voice of the Good Shepherd, "'Yet they will by no means follow a stranger, but will flee from him, for they do not know the voice of strangers'" (John 10:5).

God requires His people to know the difference between true and false prophets (Jeremiah 29:8, 9). He gives specific tests to show if a prophet is from God: (1) He proclaims true worship (Deuteronomy 13:1-3); (2) he preaches obedience (Deuteronomy 13:4, 5; 18:15-20; Matthew 5:19, 20); (3) his words are true (Deuteronomy 18:21, 22); (4) he lives right (Matthew 7:15-20); (5) he believes the truth about Jesus Christ (1 John 4:1-3); (6) he honors the lordship of Jesus Christ (1 Corinthians 12:3; 14:37); (7) he knows the way of salvation (Galatians 1:6-12); and (8) he is recognized by those who are spiritual (1 Corinthians 12:10; 14:29, 37).

In the early history of the church, Christian writers often mentioned books and letters which compose the New Testament. They quoted them as having divine authority--as Scripture. Some books had been circulated more widely and were better known than others. There were disagreements about some books. There is clear historical evidence, however, that the books of our New Testament were in use and were recognized as having spiritual authority from their earliest days. Church synods at Rome (A.D. 382) and Carthage (A.D. 397) gave the final, official endorsement to the New Testament Canon.

REFLECT AND MEDITATE

How do I recognize the will of God for my life?

REACT AND RESPOND

Discuss with spiritual friends:

1. If others had not discerned which books belong in the Bible, how would we recognize the inspired writings?

2. Are there any books we might have left out?

3. Why did God give the books we might not have chosen?

REJOICE AND WORSHIP

Name three ''exceedingly great and precious promises,'' and thank God for them (2 Peter 1:4).

Study 4

IT IS AN INSPIRED WORD

READ AND RESEARCH (2 Timothy 3:14-17; 2 Peter 1:12-21)

The Bible is inspired. Paul stated, ''All Scripture is given by inspiration of God'' (2 Timothy 3:16).

Inspiration means breath. In the Greek it is a compound of two words: God and breathe. The Bible holds that the breath of God is responsible for creating the universe (Psalm 33:6), for originating human life (Genesis 2:7) and for producing the Holy Scriptures.

Inspiration is the process by which the Holy Spirit supernaturally directed chosen men to record accurately and authoritatively the revelation of divine truth. Revelation is the disclosure of God's truth. Inspiration is the method by which His revelation is communicated and its accuracy preserved. Inspiration means that God gave the Holy Scriptures; therefore, they are His Word.

The Bible says it is the Word of God. In his dying words, David told of the inspiration he experienced: '''The Spirit of the Lord spoke by me, and His word was on my tongue''' (2 Samuel 23:2). God said to Jeremiah, ''Behold, I have put My words in your mouth'' (Jeremiah 1:9; see also Isaiah 59:21).

The Bible declares that God spoke through the prophets: ''God, who at various times and in different ways spoke in time past to the fathers by the prophets'' (Hebrews 1:1); '''Things which God foretold by the mouth of all His prophets. . . which God has spoken by the mouth of all His holy prophets since the world began''' (Acts 3:18, 21).

Jesus promised inspiration to His apostles,

pledging that the Holy Spirit would finish their instruction and perfect their memories (John 14:25, 26; 16:12, 13).

The apostles claim inspiration. Paul insisted that Christ was the source of his message: ''But I make known to you, brethren, that the gospel which was preached by me is not according to man. For I neither received it from man, nor was I taught it, but it came through the revelation of Jesus Christ'' (Galatians 1:11, 12).

Paul identified the Holy Spirit as the agent of revelation: ''Now we have received, not the spirit of the world, but the Spirit who is from God, that we might know the things that have been freely given to us by God. These things we also speak, not in words which man's wisdom teaches but which the Holy Spirit teaches, comparing spiritual things with spiritual'' (1 Corinthians 2:12, 13).

Paul commanded, ''If anyone thinks himself to be a prophet or spiritual, let him acknowledge that the things which I write to you are the commandments of the Lord'' (1 Corinthians 14:37). He rejoiced, ''For this reason we also thank God without ceasing, because when you received the word of God which you heard from us, you welcomed it not as the word of men, but as it is in truth, the word of God, which also effectively works in you who believe'' (1 Thessalonians 2:13).

Peter declared, ''Prophecy never came by the will of man, but holy men of God spoke as they were moved by the Holy Spirit'' (2 Peter 1:21).

It is important to know how much of the Bible is inspired. If some of it is not the Word of God, we must know. Some believe in *partial* inspiration--that some portions of the Bible are not inspired. We believe in full or *plenary* inspiration-- that the whole Bible is the inspired Word of God.

The apostle Paul wrote, "All Scripture is given by inspiration of God" (2 Timothy 3:16). Peter agreed, insisting that God had spoken "'By the mouth of all His holy prophets since the world began'" (Acts 3:21). He recognized the inspiration of the gospel: "The word of the Lord endures forever. Now this is the word which by the gospel was preached to you" (1 Peter 1:25). He considered the "holy prophets" and "the apostles of the Lord and Savior" as equally authoritative (2 Peter 3:2). He regarded the epistles of Paul as Scripture (2 Peter 3:15, 16).

It is important to know that the Bible is inspired. Some hold that only major redemptive themes are inspired. Some believe that inspiration is a matter of spiritual impact, when the Holy Spirit makes a biblical text to *become* the word of God at a particular time to a particular reader. We believe in *verbal* inspiration--that the very words of the Bible are inspired.

Solomon warned, "Every word of God is pure; He is a shield to those who put their trust in Him. Do not add to His words, lest He reprove you, and you be found a liar" (Proverbs 30:5, 6).

Jesus held a very strict view of verbal inspiration. He claimed that all Scripture would be fulfilled--even the smallest letter of the alphabet and the smallest stroke of the pen: "'For assuredly, I say to you, till heaven and earth pass away, one jot or one tittle will by no means pass from the law till all is fulfilled'" (Matthew 5:18; see also Luke 16:17). He based doctrine on the tense of one single verb in Exodus (Matthew 22:29-33; Mark 12:24-27; Luke 20:37-40).

From these Scriptures we conclude that every word (verbal inspiration) in the whole Bible (plenary inspiration) was given by God.

REFLECT AND MEDITATE

Has God ever tried to speak through me? How did I feel? What did I do?

REACT AND RESPOND

Discuss with spiritual friends what you should do if someone claims to give you a word from God.

REJOICE AND WORSHIP

In 2 Timothy 3:14-17, find reasons to thank God for His Word.

Study 5

IT IS A DEPENDABLE WORD

READ AND RESEARCH (Matthew 5:17, 18; John 10:35; Psalm 19:7-14)

God has given us a revelation we can trust. The faithfulness of God is seen in the trustworthiness of His Word. When we speak of the Bible as being *infallible*, we mean that it cannot fail. When we say it is *inerrant*, we mean that it contains no errors. The Word of God is true. You can count on it. You can trust your life to it.

The Bible has been thoroughly tested. It is not a book of science, geography, history or psychology, but when it speaks about these things, it speaks accurately.

Unbelieving scholars have tried to discredit the Bible by saying that it conflicts with science. Many supposed conflicts have been resolved over the years. The Bible did not change--science did. New discoveries proved that the Bible had been right all along.

It is the Bible which first recognized the earth to be circular (Isaiah 40:22). It was the Bible which first declared the blood of all human races to be the same (Acts 17:26). It was the Bible that first compared the number of stars in outer space to the number of grains of sand on the seashore (Genesis 22:17).

The entire Hittite nation disappeared from human history. Secular historians said the Bible was wrong, for it spoke of them as having a major role in history. How could a major nation disappear from history without a trace? Archaeologists later found the ruins of Hittite cities and learned that in their day the Hittites had been a powerful nation.

Historians found no evidence of King Belshazzar in Babylon in the list of kings who had ruled there. Later they found that the last king had made Belshazzar his coregent--setting him on the throne as second in command. The Bible said that in his panic Belshazzar had offered to make Daniel the '''third ruler''' in the kingdom (Daniel 5:7, 16, 29). Now we know why he could not offer to make him second ruler as Pharoah had done for Joseph (Genesis 41:40).

The Bible has recovered lost kingdoms and missing kings. It has filled in major gaps in the historical record. Archaeology and history continue to show that the Bible is accurate in its recording of human events. It is a book that is true and dependable.

The Bible has predicted the future with amazing accuracy. It does not use generalities like astrologers, sorcerers and fortune-tellers do. It speaks precisely and often writes history far in advance.

Before the Babylonian captivity, Jeremiah predicted the duration of the Jewish exile to be 70 years (Jeremiah 25:11, 12; 29:10). Isaiah named the unborn king who would release Israel from their captivity and told of rebuilding the temple before it was destroyed (Isaiah 44:28; 45:1). Ezekiel described the destruction of Tyre exactly, clearly distinguishing the separate attacks by Nebuchadnezzar and Alexander the Great (Ezekiel 26:3-14, 21). Daniel described the characteristics and events of four successive empires, detailing events which are still being fulfilled in our day (Daniel 2, 7).

When the Old Testament was completed, more than 400 years before Christ, it held 332 specific prophecies about the first coming of Jesus. They dealt with His birth, His life, His death and His burial in detail, and they were fulfilled perfectly (Psalm 22; Isaiah 53: Micah 5:2).

Such accuracy can only come from an eternal God who knows everything.

The Bible makes a difference in human lives. Its message works, because it brings forgiveness from sin, deliverance from bondage and entrance into life everlasting. In every congregation of believers there are many who can give convincing testimony of the change the Holy Scriptures brought into their lives. It is a miracle which happens again every day.

The most important principles to guide our relationships are found in the Word of God. The Bible tells us how to build better marriages, raise better children and live better lives.

REFLECT AND MEDITATE

How have I discovered for myself that the Bible is true?

REACT AND RESPOND

Write one paragraph explaining how it would affect you if it were proven that there are historical or scientific errors in the Bible.

REJOICE AND WORSHIP

In your worship today, sing the old gospel song ''Standing on the Promises.''

DISCIPLESHIP COMMITMENT

Since God has spoken to me by His Word, I will seek each day to obey His Will and to trust His promises.

CHAPTER 6

How Can I Understand the Word of God?

INTRODUCTION

God gave us His Word to instruct us--not to confuse us. He wants us to know what it means. He wants the message to be clear. He wants us to know how much He loves us--and how well.

Many have read the Bible without understanding it. Skeptics think that anything can be proved by the Bible, that the Bible, therefore, loses its validity. False doctrines are taught by people who claim to be students of Scripture. Dangerous cults lead their victims to destruction while pretending to teach the Word of God. Many have stopped trying to understand Scripture--they don't even read it anymore.

How can there be so much confusion about a book that is supposed to be so clear? If God gave His Word to instruct us, why is it so difficult to understand what it means?

One barrier is the content. The Bible speaks heavenly things to earthly minds. It brings the infinite to the finite. The greatness of God will not fit into the smallness of our understanding. Some things will not be perfectly clear until we get to heaven.

Paul explained, ''For now we see in a mirror, dimly, but then face to face. Now I know in part, but then I shall know just as I also am known'' (1 Corinthians 13:12).

A second barrier is the flow of history. God spoke through human writers at specific moments in history, but the message is for all the ages. He spoke at specific times and places for all times and places. Times change . . . situations change . . . languages change, but the message does not change. Changing conditions make it difficult to understand the unchanging Word.

A third barrier is careless study through (1) random reading--choosing portions here and there, with no systematic approach to Bible reading; (2) academic reading--learning about Scripture but not studying the Bible itself; (3) biased reading--approaching Scripture with minds prejudiced by human traditions and doctrines; (4) proud reading--refusing instruction from anointed teachers; (5) carnal reading--coming to Scripture with a wrong spirit and without the Holy Spirit.

Jesus told the scholars of His day that they had missed the whole point of Scripture; as a result, they had missed Him (John 5:37-40). That is the danger--to miss the Word of God is to miss God.

There are ways of dealing with the barriers. Bible scholars have rules by which the message of Scripture can be made more clear. The art and science of accurately interpreting Scripture is called *hermeneutics*. It can help guide all of us to a better understanding of the Bible.

We will understand Scripture more clearly when we

1. Understand Its Unity
2. Understand Its Language
3. Understand Its Setting
4. Understand Its Literature
5. Understand Its Spirit

DISCIPLESHIP GOAL

1. To believe that the Word of God can be understood

2. To learn the ways by which to understand the Bible

READING ASSIGNMENT
The Living Book, pp. 61 - 71

Study 1

UNDERSTAND ITS UNITY

READ AND RESEARCH (2 Peter 1:20, 21; Galatians 3:15-25)

The whole Bible is the Word of God--including both Old and New Testaments. It was given through some 40 writers, with varying education, of diverse occupations, on three continents, in three languages, over a period of 1,600 years. Generally, they did not know each other, were not aware of each other's writings and had no opportunity to compare notes. Yet the Bible presents a harmonious message.

Imagine what would happen if 10 writers--about the same age, with the same education, speaking the same language, living at the same time, from the same community--were asked to write articles about just one of the controversial subjects discussed in Scripture. There would be no unity. Their work would be a mass of conflicts and contradictions.

The unity of Scripture was not forced by an editor or compiler, trying to make sense of conflicting views. Its unity is proof that God was in control of the whole process.

The first rule for understanding the Bible is to recognize that it is one harmonious revelation. This is called *unity of Scripture.*

To believe in the disunity of Scripture would make you expect contradictions. It would mean discarding part of the Bible as untrue. You would have to choose sides in the conflicts, and you could not be sure you had chosen the right side. You might like portions, but you would not be sure of their accuracy. You could not take the Bible seriously. Eventually, you would lose faith altogether.

When you believe in the unity of Scripture, you know there is an answer for apparent contradictions. You realize that ''conflicts'' are just different facets of the same truth. You keep looking for the key that unlocks the whole truth and helps understand both statements better.

The second rule for understanding the Bible is to recognize that Scripture is its own interpreter. This is called *analogy of faith.*

The best explanation of a Bible truth will be found in the Bible itself. The best test of an interpretation is to compare it with other Scriptures on the same subject. To find what a text really means, find what the rest of Scripture says.

The more you study the Bible, the more you will understand it. The more you understand the whole Bible, the more you will gain from portions of it. Over the years your Bible study will become clearer, richer, deeper and more exciting.

The third rule for understanding the Bible is to recognize that truth was disclosed gradually, over a long period of time. This is called *progressive revelation.*

The process of revelation did not happen all at once. It required 16 centuries. God did not tell everything about a topic the first time it was mentioned. Sometimes man was not ready to receive the whole truth. Sometimes God had to build understanding in small steps.

Through progressive revelation, the fuller expression was given later. It is wise to look for the later and fuller explanations in order to properly understand a particular truth.

REFLECT AND MEDITATE

When has one scripture explained another scripture to me?

REACT AND RESPOND

Write three questions about the Bible which trouble you and/or three conflicts which you have not yet resolved, record today's date, and save them in your study Bible for future reference. As you discover the answers, write them on the same paper, recording the dates.

REJOICE AND WORSHIP

In prayer, give three things you are thankful for (Psalm 119:89).

Discipleship

UNDERSTAND ITS LANGUAGE

READ AND RESEARCH (Nehemiah 8:8; Matthew 22:23-33)

Language is a special gift from God. It makes man different from all the other earthly creatures.

We listen, speak, read, study and learn with language. We even think and dream with language. Language allows us to communicate. It permits us to enter into the experience of others and mentally escape the limitations of time and place. It is a precise instrument with which to receive and convey truth.

We will understand the Word of God better if we understand the use of language in the Bible. Priority of the Original Languages

The Bible came to us in human languages. The Old Testament was written mostly in Hebrew, with some portions of Daniel in Aramaic. The New Testament was written mostly in Greek, with at least one book in Hebrew.

God did not create a special language for His revelation. He gave the Scriptures in the language of the people. The New Testament could have been written in classical Greek--the formal language of the scholars. Instead, God chose *Koine* Greek--the everyday language of common people.

The process of inspiration guided the human writers, so their writings are truly the Word of God. The words which they used were rich and full of meaning. Jesus attested to their accuracy to the smallest letter of the alphabet, to the smallest stroke of the pen and to the very tenses of the verbs (Matthew 5:18; 22:29-33).

When words are translated from one language to another, some meaning may be lost. Some thoughts and suggestions which attach to a statement in one language might not in another language.

The Scriptures are understood best and their fullest meanings can be realized when they are studied in their original languages. This is called the *priority of the original languages*.

Most of us cannot read Hebrew, Aramaic and Greek. It would not be possible for us to know the Word of God if it were available only in the original languages. The entire Bible has been translated into all the major languages of the world and is now being translated into minor languages and dialects.

God gave His Word in the language of the common people, showing that He wants all of us to understand it in our everyday languages. New Testament writers and teachers quoted from the *Septuagint Version*, a Greek translation of the Old Testament, showing that it is proper for us to use translations.

The King James Version, translated nearly 400 years ago, is one of the most beautiful pieces of literature in our language. It is the most popular English version and is excellent for public reading and for the memorization of Scripture. However, because our language has changed so much in these four centuries, the King James Version is very difficult for many modern readers to understand.

Outstanding Christians scholars, using ancient Bible manuscripts, have produced two excellent translations in modern English: *New American Standard Bible* and *New International Version*. These and other translations are good for Bible study. They convey truth without distortion. Every major Christian doctrine is taught well in their pages. This is what we mean by the *adequacy of Bible translations*.

Just as God adapted revelation to human language, He adapted it to the limitations of the human mind. He speaks truth in forms and concepts that humans can understand. Sometimes He compares heavenly things with earthly things. Sometimes He gives us a small measure of an infinite truth. This is called *accommodation of revelation*.

The Bible speaks to us in normal, everyday language--the language we read in the newspaper and use in conversations with our friends. Our words have commonly understood meanings.

In a particular setting, a word usually has only

one meaning. To understand that word as having its usual meaning in that setting is *literal interpretation*. Literal interpretation is an effort to find the real, true and plain meaning of the text, so that it makes good sense.

Normal, everyday language will often include idioms and figures of speech. In that particular setting, those words are clear, having commonly understood meanings. Literal interpretation requires us to recognize that true and plain meaning.

The Bible uses many figures of speech: (1) *metaphor*: describing something or someone by identifying one as the other--'"You are the *salt of the earth*.... This [bread] is *My body*'" (Matthew 5:13; Luke 22:19); (2) *simile*: comparing two things, using "as, like, and so forth"--'"I send you out *as sheep* in the midst of wolves. Therefore be wise *as serpents* and harmless *as doves*'" (Matthew 10:16); (3) *analogy:* comparing two things, one explaining the other--"The *message of the cross is foolishness* to those who are perishing, but to us who are being saved *it is the power of God*" (1 Corinthians 1:18); (4) *hyperbole*: deliberate and obvious exaggerations to make a point--'"And

why do you look at the speck in your brother's eye, but do not consider *the plank in your own eye?*'" (Matthew 7:3); (5) *anthropomorphism:* using human, physical features to describe God, who is spirit--'"Behold, *the Lord's hand* is not shortened, that it cannot save; nor *His ear* heavy, that it cannot hear'" (Isaiah 59:1).

REFLECT AND MEDITATE

What biblical words or expressions describing God are the most precious to me?

REACT AND RESPOND

Discuss with spiritual friends:

1. What is the most difficult thing to understand about God?

2. How does God make it easier for me to understand this?

REJOICE AND WORSHIP

Choose three separate words that reflect your appreciation of God, and explain to Him in worship what those words say about your love for Him.

Study 3

UNDERSTAND ITS SETTING

READ AND RESEARCH (Luke 24:25-27; John 5:46, 47)

Every scripture can be understood best in its setting. Taken out of that setting, the statement can mean something entirely different. To understand a scripture, we must know its setting. The setting of a text is called its *context*. Often an author will make his meaning clear by the way his words are used in their context.
Immediate Context

The verses which surround a text are its *immediate context*. Often they complete the paragraph. Usually they will help to clarify the thought.

It is helpful to look for paragraph markings when you examine the immediate context of a scripture. Some of the modern translations set the

text in paragraphs to make it easier to study the context.

If the text is part of a parable, read the whole story. If it is part of a narrative, read it from beginning to end.

Often the Bible builds truth on truth. You must know the preceding statement to understand the present one. Studying the context is one of the most important steps in the proper interpretation of a scripture.

After becoming acquainted with the immediate context, expand your study to more of the surrounding scriptures. You may find that the immediate text is part of a larger section that must be seen in its entirety.

You will soon want to see how the section fits into the whole book in which it appears. Learn who wrote the book, when and why. Outline the whole book to see how your chosen text fits into its total message. This is the *book context*.

At this point you can learn how your chosen scripture, its surrounding texts and the entire book fit into the whole message of the Bible.

Jesus taught that the whole Bible focused on His mission. Without understanding His central role, it is impossible to fully understand the Word of God. Each book has a special purpose in the Canon of Scripture. Each book gives an important piece of the redemptive message.

Good interpretation requires that you view the scripture in its *Biblical context*, seeing how it fits into the message of the whole Bible.

What is your chosen scripture trying to prove? What doctrine is it clarifying? Texts that touch on doctrinal themes should be studied in comparison to other scriptures that deal with that same doctrine--in the surrounding verses and in the rest of the Bible. This is the *theological context*.

Customs and practices change over the years. Everyday activities often are very different from generation to generation. Historical events change priorities, attitudes and relationships.

We cannot fully understand a scripture unless we have some knowledge of the historical events, issues and customs that influenced thinking at that time. We must try to understand the social conditions which were present when the text was written. This is the *cultural context*.

We probably have the best understanding of a scripture when we understand what it meant to the writer and his original readers. The text probably does not mean something today that it did not mean to them.

When we share common situations with them, or understand their life situations, the scripture will mean the same to us as it did to them.

REFLECT AND MEDITATE

When has the setting (the context) helped me to understand a scripture better?

REACT AND RESPOND

Have your words ever been taken out of context? What would that experience teach you about understanding the Word of God?

REJOICE AND WORSHIP

''A word fitly spoken is like apples of gold in settings of silver'' (Proverbs 25:11). Pray that the Word of God might always fit so beautifully in your life.

Study 4

UNDERSTAND ITS LITERATURE

READ AND RESEARCH (Daniel 2:24-45)

The Bible contains several kinds of literature, including prose, poetry, history, legal codes and letters. Each form of literature must be understood according to its own style.

The Old Testament was a covenant, binding on two parties: God and Israel. It is not the same as the New Testament, and it is not our covenant. The New Testament is a covenant between God and the church. Some Old Testament principles are retained for us and are clearly stated in the New Testament. Much of the Old Testament was fulfilled in Christ. Epistles to the Galatians, Romans and Hebrews tell about this fulfillment and our new standing in Christ.

The Old Testament is still God's Word to us, even though it may not be His command for us. To properly interpret any legal code, it is necessary to answer the following questions: (1) Is this command applied to Christians in the New Testament? (2) Is this command exclusively identified with Israel, either in the Old or the New Testament? (3) Is this command fulfilled for us by Christ?

Both Testaments contain historical and biographical narratives. These are actual reports of true human events, told at three levels. First, they are the story of God, overseeing the affairs of men and ruling in history. Second, they are the story of a people--Israel in the Old Testament and the church in the New--God's people, experiencing His guidance, suffering His judgment and enjoying His loving care. Third, they are stories of individuals, experiencing the joys, sorrows and foibles of earthly life.

Narratives do not usually teach a doctrine, but they may illustrate doctrines taught elsewhere. They tell what happened but not always how or why. What is recorded is true, whether good or bad, but the moral is not always evident. Usually, they do not establish a precedent to be followed, unless one is declared specifically.

Hebrew poetry is not identified by rhyme and rhythm but by figurative language and parallel thoughts. Three types of parallel statements are found in Scripture.

Synonymous parallels are two statements making the same point with different words or figures:

"The Lord is my light and my salvation; whom shall I fear? The Lord is the strength of my life; of whom shall I be afraid?" (Psalm 27:1).

Antithetical parallels are contrasting statements:

"They did not cry out to Me with their heart when they wailed upon their beds" (Hosea 7:14).

Synthetic parallels produce a new thought from the preceding one:

"Then saviors shall come to Mount Zion to judge the mountains of Esau, and the kingdom shall be the Lord's" (Obadiah 21).

It is important in the interpretation of poetry to understand its use of figurative language. The psalmist was rejoicing in the tender care of divine protection and not giving God's physical description when he sang: "He shall cover you with His feathers, and under His wings you shall take refuge" (Psalm 91:4).

Wisdom Literature examines major principles that affect human life. Sometimes it is written as poetry; sometimes as drama.

For proper interpretation of this literature, identify the speaker, and determine his credibility. In the book of Job, believe God but not the devil; give more credence to Job than to Eliphaz the Temanite, Bildad the Shuhite or Zophar the Naamathite.

Determine whether a statement is presented as truth or as a rhetorical argument which will be disproved or rejected later.

Prophets are people who speak for God, not necessarily predictors of the future. They proclaim the will of God and call men to obedience.

Their speeches are oracles given at different times. Often several speeches are recorded in run-on fashion, and the time gaps are not made clear. Each speech should be studied as a unit.

Predictive prophecies may have more than one fulfillment, but they are usually evident in Scripture. Hidden meanings must not be forced on them to suit the fancy of the reader. They may use symbolism and dramatic visions to give insights concerning the future. The meaning of a vision often may be found in the immediate context or in other scriptures that deal more clearly with the same future events.

Jesus used parables as His main form of instruction. They are realistic stories drawn from common situations and used to illustrate truth. Often they make a sharp point, with a touch of sarcasm. Always look for the main point that is being made. Focus on the main point and not on minor details.

Most of the books in the New Testament are epistles--letters written to churches or individuals. They were read in the churches to which they were sent and later were shared with other churches. The letters conveyed apostolic authority and were read as Scripture.

Often the letters had limited purposes or dealt with specific problems in specific places. They usually give the solution without stating the problem or give the answer without repeating the question. The epistles can resemble one side of a telephone conversation. It is easier to understand what you are hearing if you have some idea of what is being said at the other end of the line.

To understand an epistle, try to discover the basic outline--the main sections and the subtopics. Study it in paragraphs, and examine the context. A study of the cultural context may help to uncover the background and purpose of the epistle. The immediate context may provide important clues concerning the problem being addressed.

Discipleship

REFLECT AND MEDITATE

What do I like most about each type of literature in the Bible?

REACT AND RESPOND

How does the type of literature help me to answer these questions?

1. Does Genesis 12:10-20 teach us to lie?

2. Does Job 2:4 prove that "every man has his price?"

3. Does Psalm 91:4 mean that God has feathers?

REJOICE AND WORSHIP

God speaks with great variety, but His Word never varies--it is always true!

Study 5

UNDERSTAND ITS SPIRIT

READ AND RESEARCH (Matthew 16:17; 1 Corinthians 2:9-16)

Helpful rules come to us from biblical hermeneutics, the art and science of accurately interpreting Scripture. They give assurance that in our study of the Bible, we can understand what God has said to us.

Assurance is appropriate; pride is not. Our assurance should be paired with genuine humility. The Bible is not a human production. It is the Word of God. His ways are high above our ways; His thoughts are far beyond our thoughts.

The Word of infinite God is far beyond the understanding of finite man. We have no reason for arrogance and dogmatism. The Bible does not encourage us to argue and fight over Scripture. When we do, our attitudes deny our words.

When God speaks clearly to us, we must not compromise or deny His Word. We must love His truth and stand ready to die for it. His Word is our sword against the Enemy, but we must remember who the enemy is.

God is never wrong. We often are. Our conclusions may be convincing to us, but we may have missed something. Even when we have done our best and learned the most, we still have much to be humble about--we still have much to learn by more study.

Pride can cause us to adulterate the truth. In the time of Jesus, the Pharisees wanted to improve Scripture by adding their traditions to it. Jesus said they made it void by their additions (Matthew 15:6; Mark 7:13).

The Saduccees sought to improve Scripture by removing what they found hard to believe. They subtracted the supernatural from the Word of God, displaying their ignorance (Mark 12:18-27). It is the fool who denies the supernatural (Psalm 14). Unfortunately, one characteristic of a fool is that he does not know himself to be one.

To protect ourselves from pride, error and self-deception, we should compare the results of our study with the conclusions of others who have studied the same scriptures. If we have learned something that has never been known before, we are probably mistaken. The faith of our fathers is a good signpost for eternal truth.

The source of Scripture is the Holy Spirit. The revelation far exceeds the beauty of words and defies the understanding of man.

Paul testified that the message "did not come with excellence of speech or of wisdom. . . . And my speech and my preaching were not with persuasive words of human wisdom" (1 Corinthians 2:1, 4).

Yet, the message is wisdom--"the wisdom of God" (1 Corinthians 2:7). That which was not visible to the eye or evident to the heart, God has revealed by His Spirit (1 Corinthians 2:8-10).

The revelation comes from the Holy Spirit, and it is spiritual. Natural man cannot understand it because it is foolishness to him, and he cannot discern it (1 Corinthians 2:14). Jesus said the new birth is required for a person to see the things of God (John 3:3). This is the minimum requirement. Paul said we need--and have--the mind of Christ, which is the Holy Spirit.

Jesus promised the Holy Spirit as our teacher:

"He will teach you all things, and bring to your remembrance all things that I said to you. . . . I still have many things to say to you, but you cannot bear them now. However, when He, the Spirit of truth, has come, He will guide you into all truth . . . and He will tell you things to come" (John 14:26; 16:12, 13).

Rules alone will not be enough to show us what God wants us to see in His Word. We need someone to help us . . . to enlighten us . . . to show us the wisdom of God (Matthew 16:17; Luke 24:31; Psalm 119:18). We need the Holy Spirit, and He has come to us.

Always respect the authority of Scripture. Always receive the message of Holy Scripture. Always depend on the instruction of the Holy Spirit. Rely humbly on the Holy Spirit.

REFLECT AND MEDITATE

Is there anything from God that I am slow in learning because my spirit is not right?

REACT AND RESPOND

Discuss with spiritual friends: If "eye has not seen, nor ear heard," can we know it at all? (See 1 Corinthians 2:9, 10.)

REJOICE AND WORSHIP

Invite the Holy Spirit to lead you and speak to you. Wait quietly after prayer to see if He impresses anything in your spirit.

DISCIPLESHIP COMMITMENT
Since the Bible was given for my understanding, I will seek to learn its message and apply its principles in my daily life.

CHAPTER 7

How Shall I Respond to the Word of God?

INTRODUCTION

The Word of God requires a response. It is not entertainment. It is not for warm feelings at bedtime nor for ecstatic feelings at camp meeting time. It is given to produce action. It demands a decision. It pronounces a verdict.

When Moses delivered the Word of God to Israel, their response was spontaneous: "So Moses came and told the people all the words of the Lord and all the judgments. And all the people answered with one voice and said, 'All the words which the Lord has said we will do'" (Exodus 24:3). It is the function of the Word to require a response.

At the end of his life, when he gave Israel his final challenge, Moses made it painfully clear that the Word of God demands a decision. He cried, "'For this commandment which I command you today, it is not too mysterious for you, nor is it far off. . . . But the word is very near you, in your mouth and in your heart, that you may do it. See, I have set before you today life and good, death and evil'" (Deuteronomy 30:11, 14, 15).

Moses emphasized three vital points: (1) You have the Word, (2) you can obey the Word, and (3) your destiny depends on what you do with the Word. That message applies to us today.

Joshua climaxed his ministry with a powerful challenge to Israel: "'Choose for yourselves this day whom you will serve.'" He chided them for the weakness of their moral resolve and warned that the holiness of God would consume them in judgment if they disobeyed. He set the example: "'But as for me and my house, we will serve the Lord.'" Israel pledged, "'We also will serve the Lord, for He is our God. . . . The Lord our God we will serve, and His voice we will obey'" (Joshua 24:14-25).

The Word of God forces that kind of decision. It offers two choices--obedience or disobedience. It brings two results--blessings or cursings. It executes two verdicts--life or death.

God promises: "'So shall My word be that goes forth from My mouth; it shall not return to Me void, but it shall accomplish what I please, and it shall prosper in the thing for which I sent it'" (Isaiah 55:11).

When His Word goes forth, it requires a decision, it pronounces a verdict, and it glorifies God. Either His love is vindicated by His grace toward the penitent, or His holiness is vindicated by His justice toward the unrepentant. His Word does its work. It never fails.

The impact of the Word depends totally on the response. To those who reject it, the message is "foolishness"; to those who believe, it is "the power of God" (1 Corinthians 1:18). Paul claimed that the gospel messenger is "the fragrance of Christ": to some, the stench of death; to others, the perfume of life (2 Corinthians 2:14-16). It all depends on the response.

In the following lessons we will learn how to receive the Word of God so that in us it might produce life and blessing. We will learn how to

1. Listen for It
2. Read Through It
3. Meditate on It
4. Study in It
5. Live by It

DISCIPLESHIP GOAL

1. To listen for the Word of God with heart and with ear

2. To learn the Word of God daily through careful study

3. To live the Word of God convincingly for others to believe

READING ASSIGNMENT: pp. 72 - 87

Study 1

LISTEN FOR IT

READ AND RESEARCH (Romans 1:14-16; 10:8-17; 1 Corinthians 1:17-24; Hebrews 2:1-4; 12:23-25)

Hearing came before reading; listening, before obeying.

Before the printing press, books were laborious to copy and expensive to own. Many Christians could not afford scrolls of their own, so they copied scriptures by scratching them on potsherds (broken pieces of pottery). The Word of God was precious to them.

In the days of the apostles, the message was received mostly by hearing and not by reading. Paul expected his epistles to be read in the churches--publicly (Colossians 4:16). John expected public reading when he pronounced his blessing: "Blessed is he who reads and those who hear the words of this prophecy, and keep those things which are written in it; for the time is near" (Revelation 1:3).

Paul asked, "How then shall they call on Him in whom they have not believed? And how shall they believe in Him of whom they have not heard? And how shall they hear without a preacher?" He concludes, "So then faith comes by hearing, and hearing by the word of God" (Romans 10:14, 17).

People usually don't read the Word unless they have heard it. They don't desire it for strength until they have received it for eternal life.

Hearing brings us to salvation. Hearing is the most frequent way we continue to receive the Word of God.

With a tone of sadness, the Bible assesses the time of Eli: "And the word of the Lord was rare in those days; there was no widespread revelation" (1 Samuel 3:1).

The Word of God was so rare that Samuel did not recognize it when he heard it. After he had three times mistaken the voice of God for that of Eli, Samuel was instructed to answer, "Speak, Lord, for Your servant hears" (1 Samuel 3:2-10).

We suffer from the same problem today. Many of us do not know how eager God is to speak to us. He promises that the Holy Spirit will teach us "all things," guide us into "all truth," and tell us "things to come" (John 14:26; 16:13).

The Holy Spirit is offered to us as "the spirit of wisdom and revelation" (Ephesians 1:17). We are to live in Him, walk in Him and be led by Him (Galatians 5:16, 18, 25; Romans 8:1, 4, 5). He reveals the things of God; He is "the mind of Christ" (1 Corinthians 2:14, 16).

Many of us do not know how to listen to the Spirit. We do not recognize His voice. We do not have listening hearts. We may never hear the voice of God from the pulpit or from the printed page unless we learn to listen with our hearts.

Warmth . . . peace . . . assurance comes to our hearts when He speaks and when we do His will. The disciples on the road to Emmaus belatedly recognized the touch of the Holy Spirit when they said, "'Did not our heart burn within us while He talked with us on the road, and while He opened the Scriptures to us?'" (Luke 24:32).

He speaks with such a "still small voice" that we often mistake it for our own thoughts. His words come with special assurance--with an added measure of faith. Even when our minds are questioning, there is a spiritual sense of certainty. What He speaks to us is holy and good. His voice speaks wisdom beyond ours.

We must learn to hear His voice, for He has much to say. He wants to lead us, perfect us and flow through us in ministry to others.

The Bible charges, "'He who has an ear, let him hear what the Spirit says to the churches'" (Revelation 2:7). Jesus lamented, "'Seeing they do not see, and hearing they do not hear, nor do they understand'" (Matthew 13:13).

God still speaks from the pulpit and the lectern. He anoints preachers and teachers to declare His Word. He convicts and saves through preaching (Romans 1:16; 1 Corinthians 1:17-25). Most of the spiritual gifts are manifestations of God through the spoken word (1 Corinthians 12:7-10). If we don't listen, we will miss God!

Seven steps will help train our ears to listen: (1)

Discipleship

Expect God to speak--in preaching, in teaching, in class discussions, in private conversations, in reproof, in correction and in His still small voice; (2) live in His presence--be conscious of His presence with you everywhere; (3) avoid agitated emotions--anger, worry, fear, anxiety and stress are "static" which prevent us from hearing His voice; (4) come to church worshiping--"Enter into His gates with thanksgiving, and into His courts with praise" (Psalm 100:4); (5) carry tools to retain what you hear--Bible, pen, notepad and cassette recorder; (6) ask God to apply His Word--"'Lord, what do You want me to do?'" (Acts 9:6); (7) Do what He says--He will not continue speaking to a disobedient heart.

REFLECT AND MEDITATE

What can I do to get more out of the sermons I hear?

REACT AND RESPOND

Tell someone about an occasion when you knew God was speaking directly to you through a sermon or lesson you heard.

REJOICE AND WORSHIP

Pray for your pastor, that God will speak through his preaching.

Study 2

READ THROUGH IT

READ AND RESEARCH (Nehemiah 8:1-8; Revelation 1:3)

Everything we need to know about God, salvation and spiritual living is in the Bible, but how do we find it? Where should we start? We will discover the treasures of Scripture by reading it. Every Christian should make a lifelong commitment to daily Bible reading.

It is an act of worship to read the Bible publicly--an act which shows reverence for the sacredness of Holy Scripture. Worship in the Bible gave prominence to the public reading of Scripture.

Those who have not accepted Christ as savior, probably do not read the Bible for themselves. Public reading exposes them to the Word, which convicts and saves.

Public reading focuses attention on a particular text, bringing the congregation into mental and spiritual agreement on one great spiritual theme. The Bible is clear enough to be understood and powerful enough to do its work without explanation.

Scriptures for public reading should be chosen prayerfully. The readers should have good voices and the ability to read well in public. Above all, their personal lives should demonstrate a daily walk with the God of the Word.

The congregation should listen carefully, following the reading in their own Bibles. They should not converse or move around. This is a sacred time when God is speaking from the Holy Scriptures.

The value of Scripture is recognized best by young minds when children see their parents reading the Bible. The Bible should be prominent in the home--and in the daily schedule. Children should know that their parents read the Bible daily in private devotions. They also should participate in times of family devotions, when the Bible is the focus of family attention.

When children are young, keep the readings short and read portions they can understand. As they grow, allow them to take turns reading--and leading in prayer. Keep devotional times warm, friendly, exciting, interesting and no longer than their attention span. Make it an honor to read and to pray in the family devotional times.

Get serious about personal Bible reading. It takes time, and it takes effort, but it makes an eternal difference. Personal Bible reading is a time of spiritual growth, a time when God speaks to you and changes you. Your understanding will increase, your faith will grow, and you will blossom into fruitfulness.

First, establish a regular time for prayer and Bible reading every day. Reserve at least 15 minutes just for reading. Early-morning devotion times are usually best; they give you a good start for the day. There are too many interruptions during the day, and you may feel too tired at night. You can train yourself to get up half an hour earlier and give the Lord your best time, before your mind is cluttered with other things.

Second, choose a regular place where you will not be distracted or disturbed.

Third, read a solid portion of Scripture every day--at least 15 minutes per day. Read enough to immerse yourself in the Word of God.

Fourth, read with a pencil in hand. Make notes in your Bible. Keep a notepad handy to write down impressions, outlines and questions for further study.

Fifth, read devotionally, always listening to the voice of the Holy Spirit. This private time with the Lord is a time of blessing. Enjoy it. Grow with it.

Sixth, read systematically. Plan a reading schedule that will allow you to complete the entire Bible on a regular basis. If you are a new Christian, you may want to start with 1 John, followed by the gospel of Mark, the gospel of John and the short epistles of Paul (Galatians through Philemon).

The easiest way to read the Bible in one year is to read three chapters each day, Monday through Saturday, and five chapters on Sunday. By varying the order of the books, you will not be faced with all the Jewish laws and genealogies at one time. You may want to intersperse books from the New Testament with those in the Old. Reading straight through may help place Bible events in their historical order and clarify the relationships between the books.

With *The One Year Bible*, each day you read about two chapters from the Old Testament, one from the New Testament, a portion from Psalms and a short verse from Proverbs. This gives more variety, but it can be confusing, since you read from four different books of the Bible every day.

Seventh, read analytically. Ask yourself: (1) What does the text say? (2) What does it mean? (3) What is God's message for me today? (4) Is there a promise for me? (5) Is there a commandment for me? (6) Is there a guiding principle for me to follow? (7) What am I going to do about it?

Read the Bible by books. Read it repeatedly. Read it entirely. Read it to find help for your needs. Read it when you feel like it, and read it when you don't. Read it as a personal visit with God. Read it obediently and expectantly. Read it every day, and don't make any exceptions.

REFLECT AND MEDITATE

How can I get more out of my daily Bible reading?

REACT AND RESPOND

Write one page about a time when you knew God was speaking directly to you from your daily Bible reading. What did He say to you? What have you done about it?

REJOICE AND WORSHIP

In your worship, thank God for three specific times when He gave you "the victory through our Lord Jesus Christ" (1 Corinthians 15:57).

Study 3

MEDITATE ON IT

READ AND RESEARCH (Psalm 1; 119:11)

To fill yourself with the Word of God and immerse yourself in it, you must meditate on it. Pagan forms of meditation have invaded our society, and we must avoid them. We must not neglect to meditate the way God commands us to do it.

God reserves special blessings for those who meditate on His Word. He commanded Joshua to meditate in His Word "day and night," promising two results: (1) the ability to do what it says and (2) prosperous ways and good success (Joshua 1:8).

The Bible promises the man who delights in the

law of the Lord and meditates on it day and night that "whatever he does shall prosper" (Psalm 1:3).

Meditation is thinking . . . deep thinking. It reviews a matter, looks from different perspectives, considers the possibilities and seeks new applications. Great inventions have resulted from this type of contemplation.

True character is found in the thought life. The wickedness of this generation is evident by what occupies its thoughts. Their secret thoughts often are filled with greed, revenge and immorality. The most common form of meditation in our society is called *fantasizing*. The lingering, contemplative thoughts are called *fantasies*. The very words, in our day, have become synonymous with lust and perversion.

God will judge men for their secret thoughts. Jesus warned against the murderous and adulterous thoughts of the heart (Matthew 5:21-30). Paul reminded that "God will judge the secrets of men" (Romans 2:16). The thought life can be dangerous to our eternal future.

The thought life of a Christian may become polluted with all kinds of negative thoughts, such as unbelief, worry, fear, anger and criticalness. These destroy faith and harmony. They drag the Christian into defeat and failure. These thoughts are not pleasing to the Lord.

The psalmist pleaded, "Let the words of my mouth and the meditation of my heart be acceptable in Your sight, O Lord, my strength and my redeemer" (Psalm 19:14).

Paul indicated in 2 Corinthians 10:3-6 that our thoughts can be made acceptable to God. We have spiritual weapons powerful enough to conquer the strongholds of the thought life, "bringing every thought into captivity to the obedience of Christ."

He recommended that we take control of our thoughts by filling our minds with good things: "Finally, brethren, whatever things are true, whatever things are noble, whatever things are just, whatever things are pure, whatever things are lovely, whatever things are of good report, if there is any virtue and if there is anything praisewor-thy--meditate on these things" (Philippians 4:8).

There is nothing more true, noble, just, pure, lovely, good, virtuous and praiseworthy than the Word of God. We can fill our minds with good things by filling them with Holy Scripture.

God wants us to think deeply about His Word . . . to review it until we gain new understanding . . . to look at it from various angles . . . to consider its possibilities . . . and to find new ways of applying it.

His Word is far richer than we ever imagined. The better we know it, the more we find in it. It is a treasure chest of great riches, and there are new delights to be discovered every day (Matthew 13:52).

In biblical language, the word for *meditation* is also used for the satisfied lion growling over his prey. It is a sound of pleasure and fulfillment (Isaiah 31:4).

True meditation goes beyond thinking about the Word of God. It is also enjoying the Word. The blessed man finds "his delight" in the law of the Lord (Psalm 1:2). Hear the passion of the seeker who says, "I opened my mouth and panted, for I longed for Your commandments. . . . I rejoice at Your word as one who finds great treasure" (Psalm 119:131, 162).

Jeremiah rejoiced, "Your words were found, and I ate them, and Your word was to me the joy and rejoicing of my heart" (Jeremiah 15:16).

When we feast on His Word, our love for God grows. The more we love Him, the more we love His Word. Meditate on His Word, and you will develop a taste for it--you will develop a voracious appetite for it.

In His ministry on earth, Jesus was always ready with an answer from Scripture. He thought on the Word, enjoyed the Word and retained the Word. He had memorized it, so that it was always available when He needed it.

Memorizing Scripture provides many benefits: (1) resistance to temptation, (2) victory over worry, (3) confidence in witnessing, (4) direction for decisions, (5) tools for effective service and (6) nurture for spiritual growth.

Memorization should become a daily pleasure: (1) Write the verses on cards; (2) learn verses by topics; (3) learn the references; (4) memorize three verses each week; (5) read the verse aloud, and picture it in your mind; (6) memorize the words exactly; (7) review new verses daily; and (8) review the more familiar verses frequently.

REFLECT AND MEDITATE

How can I get more from meditating on the Word of God?

REACT AND RESPOND

After meditating on Psalm 119:11 for five minutes, write an outline or summary of the thoughts that came to you.

REJOICE AND WORSHIP

When I meditate on His Word, He speaks more personally to me. Hallelujah!

Study 4

STUDY IN IT

READ AND RESEARCH (Proverbs 2:1-5; John 5:38, 39; 2 Timothy 2:15)

Study seeks to discover the actual intent of a scripture rather than attempting to impose a meaning on it.

Bible study has four objectives: (1) Observation--what does it say? (2) Interpretation--what does it mean? (3) Application-- how does it relate to me? (4) Communication--how do I give it to others?

As the years go by, you will discover many tools to help your Bible study. Some are expensive. Many are designed for scholars, not laymen. If you love the Word of God, your study library will grow.

If you are just starting and lack a large library, do not be discouraged. A great adventure awaits the rest of your life. A few simple tools will give you a good start.

First, you need at least one good Bible. The King James Version, in Elizabethan English, is the standard. The *New International Version* and the *New American Standard Version* are two excellent translations in modern English.

Second, get a good concordance. It is an index which lists the Bible words and tells the texts where they are found. If you can use a telephone book, you should be able to use a concordance.

Strong's Exhaustive Concordance of the Bible is the most complete and easiest to use.

Third, you can learn much from a Bible handbook, Bible dictionary and/or Bible encyclopedia. Any of these will define terms and give background information which will clarify Scripture. Bible encyclopedias have everything found in the handbooks and dictionaries, and they are more complete, but they cost more.

Fourth, consider a good dictionary of Bible words. Remember that the Bible was not written in English--Webster will not be a big help. Choose a dictionary that gives the original meanings of Bible words. W.E. Vine's *Expository Dictionary of New Testament Words* is one of the easiest to use, and it is now available in combined editions with dictionaries of Old Testament words.

You need a way to select a portion of Scripture to study. Many methods have been used. We will examine three common approaches.

An easy method is the biographical study. Many Bible narratives focus on individuals, such as Abraham, Moses, David, Paul, and so forth. A concordance will show every verse naming the chosen character. A Bible encyclopedia will provide historic information. After completing the study of one character, you may want to proceed to another character or to another Bible-study method.

A topical study compares several scriptures that deal with one particular doctrine or theme. A concordance will be helpful in finding verses that contain key words related to the chosen topic. Topical Bibles and cross-references in the margins of your study Bible may lead you to other verses dealing with the same topic.

A sequential study of consecutive scriptures is one of the most satisfying methods of Bible study. If you are ambitious and patient, you may want to pursue a sequential study of the whole Bible, beginning at Genesis. Or you may want to consider a sequential book study, beginning at the first verse and proceeding with an analysis of the entire book. One of the smaller epistles, such as Ephesians or Philippians, might be a good book with which to start. A sequential study may be limited to one chapter or one paragraph, studied very thoroughly from beginning to end.

Study should be a daily habit at a regular time, in a regular place with no distractions. Your study materials should be handy. You should begin your study with prayer.

The study process begins with the reading and rereading of the text. It is often helpful to reread the text, along with its immediate context, several times and to reread the whole book.

The second step is the full examination of the context: immediate, book, theological and cultural. Learning the historic background of the text can be most helpful.

Third, study the words, find their definitions, and note how they are used in this text. Fourth, analyze the sentence structure and grammar. Fifth, compare this scripture with others on the same subject. Sixth, find the main point(s) in this portion of Scripture, and develop an outline. Seventh, check your references and commentaries to gain additional insights and to verify the accuracy of your conclusions. Eighth, find the application--how this scripture applies to daily life. Ninth, add illustrative material. Tenth, file your notes so that you will be able to find them when you need them.

REFLECT AND MEDITATE

How can I get more out of studying the Bible?

REACT AND RESPOND

Select a scripture or a topic with which you would like to begin your daily Bible study, and begin.

REJOICE AND WORSHIP

Thank God for one thing you have learned through Bible study.

Study 5

LIVE BY IT

READ AND RESEARCH (Matthew 7:24-29; 28:19, 20; James 1:22-27)

God requires a response to His Word. We have seen the benefits to be gained from listening for it, reading through it, meditating on it and studying in it. All this must lead to the final step of living by it. What really matters is not what we think about the Bible or how well we can recite it, but whether we are living by its precepts.

The first step in living the Word of God is to believe it. His Word gives life only to those who believe it (John 3:16-18, 36). Paul said, ''The gospel of Christ . . . is the power of God to salvation for everyone who believes'' (Romans 1:16). Faith is the foundation of relationship with God: ''Without faith it is impossible to please Him'' (Hebrews 11:6).

The Bible does not teach an ''easy believism.'' Faith is not something we do with our heads. It is something we do with our hearts and with our lives. James insisted that ''easy believism'' is not enough. He said, ''You believe that there is one God. You do well. Even the demons believe--and tremble!'' (James 2:19).

Saving faith must meet three qualifications. First, it must have *content*. It believes very specific facts about Jesus Christ: His incarnation--''that Jesus Christ has come in the flesh'' (1 John 4:3; 2 John 7); His death, burial and resurrection--''that Christ died for our sins according to the Scriptures, and that He was buried, and that He rose again the third day according to the Scriptures'' (1 Corinthians 15:3, 4).

Second, faith must declare *assent*. This is a confessional requirement. It is not enough to know the *content* of the faith. We must embrace it and confess it. Paul wrote, ''If you confess with your mouth the Lord Jesus and believe in your heart that God has raised Him from the dead, you will be saved. For with the heart one believes to righteousness, and with the mouth confession is made to salvation'' (Romans 10:9, 10).

Third, faith must give *consent*. There must be acceptance of God's gift. Eternal life is ''the gift of God'' (Romans 6:23), but it is not given unless it is received. John explained, ''He came to His own, and His own did not receive Him. But as many as received Him, to them He gave the right to become children of God, even to those who believe in His name'' (John 1:11, 12).

True faith in the Word of God is (1) knowing it, (2) affirming it and (3) submitting to it.

Faith is not complete until it produces obedience. We do not really trust God unless we are willing to do what He says. Disobedience is rebellion. Inaction is unbelief.

Jesus taught that neither verbal claims (''Lord, Lord'') nor miraculous results are adequate evidence of citizenship in His kingdom. He welcomes the one '''who does the will of My Father in heaven,''' but to the disobedient He will respond, '''I never knew you; depart from Me, you who practice lawlessness!''' (Matthew 7:21-23).

Jesus takes obedience very seriously. He insisted, '''If anyone loves Me, he will keep My word; and My Father will love him, and We will come to him and make Our home with him''' (John 14:23).

We must take His Word very seriously, and we must respond with obedience. The alternative is too drastic!

God expects us to share His Word with others. First, it is an urgent mission. Second, it is a major sign of spiritual maturity.

We have a life-saving message which belongs to all the world. Jesus gave the message and the command to proclaim it. We are His messengers and His witnesses (Matthew 28:18-20; Mark 16:15-20; Luke 24:44-48; Acts 1:8). We are accountable to Him for our faithfulness in proclaiming the message (Matthew 10:32, 33).

To witness is an urgent obligation of the redeemed. To teach is the high privilege of the mature. God expects those who know His Word to share it with others.

The writer to the Hebrews complained, ''For though by this time you ought to be teachers, you need someone to teach you again the first principles of the oracles of God; and you have come to need milk and not solid food'' (Hebrews 5:12). As growing Christians attain maturity, they are expected to teach others. One qualified by his maturity for a position of leadership should be ''able to teach, . . . holding fast the faithful word as he has been taught, that he may be able, by sound doctrine, both to exhort and convict those who contradict'' (1 Timothy 3:2; Titus 1:9).

Be encouraged, young Christian, if you lack maturity or confidence for witnessing and teaching. Maturity comes through experience with the Word of God: ''But solid food belongs to those who are of full age, that is, those who by reason of use have their senses exercised to discern both good and evil'' (Hebrews 5:14).

''But . . . continue in the things which you have learned. . . . All Scripture is given by inspiration of God, and is profitable for doctrine, for reproof, for correction, for instruction in righteousness, that the man of God may be complete, thoroughly equipped for every good work'' (2 Timothy 3:14, 16, 17).

Stay in the Word, and you will learn to share it well; but begin sharing it now.

In truth thou canst not read the Scriptures too much;

And what thou readest, thou canst not read too well;

And what thou readest well, thou canst not too well understand;

And what thou understandest well, thou canst

Discipleship

not too well teach;
And what thou teachest well, thou canst not too
well live.--Martin Luther

REFLECT AND MEDITATE

How can I share the Word of God more effectively?

REACT AND RESPOND

Write your answers to the following questions:
1. What scripture do I need to begin applying in my life?
2. How shall I begin?

REJOICE AND WORSHIP

Let Deuteronomy 30:14 be your reason for praise!

DISCIPLESHIP COMMITMENT
I will listen to the Word of God, I will study that I may understand it, and I will share with others that they may know the riches of His Word.

CHAPTER 8

What Is a Family?

INTRODUCTION

The saga of God and His love for the human family begins in the first chapter of Genesis, where we read, "Then God said, 'Let Us make man in Our image, according to Our likeness; let them have dominion over the fish of the sea, over the birds of the air, and over the cattle, over all the earth and over every creeping thing that creeps on the earth.' So God created man in His own image; in the image of God He created him; male and female He created them. Then God blessed them, and God said to them, 'Be fruitful and multiply; fill the earth and subdue it'" (1:26-28).

And that strand of "family" continues throughout the Old Testament and closes with the very last verse, which says, "And he will turn the hearts of the fathers to the children, and the hearts of the children to their fathers, lest I come and strike the earth with a curse" (Malachi 4:6).

The New Testament assumes the established family and gives admonition concerning relationships within the home. Large portions of Scripture are devoted to genealogies or family histories. In the course of Scripture, God made eight great covenants with humankind, and each of these was dependent to some extent on *family*.

In the Bible as well as in the world today, the composition of families varies widely. There are large extended families, nuclear families and households of single individuals. God works in and through each of these family patterns.

During the next five sessions, we will explore the following answers to the question "What is a family?"

1. The Family--Instituted by God
2. The Family--Named After God
3. The Family--In Covenant With God
4. The Family--A Covenant With Each Other
5. The Family--Composition May Vary

Throughout each of these sessions, the disciple should be involved in soul-searching and definite planning in order to take steps as an individual to make his or her household and his or her church the kind of family that God intended it to be.

DISCIPLESHIP GOAL

After considering the question "What is a family?" during the next five sessions, the disciple will realize that the family was instituted by God and can and should flourish in covenant with Him and in covenant between family members. As evidence of this realization, the disciple will renew covenants verbally and will express appreciation to both God and his or her family members.

READING ASSIGNMENT
The Living Book, pp. 87 -99

Discipleship

THE FAMILY--INSTITUTED BY GOD

READ AND RESEARCH (Genesis 1, 2; Matthew 19:4-6)

Genesis 1 and 2 give the story of Creation and provide the basic ideal for marriage. Humankind was created male and female. The first man, Adam, was portrayed as being alone. God judged that aloneness was "''not good'''" and determined to "''make him a helper'''" (2:18). When Eve was created and brought to Adam, his response was overwhelmingly positive: "''This is now bone of my bones and flesh of my flesh'....Therefore a man shall leave his father and mother, and be joined to his wife, and they shall become one flesh'' (2:23, 24).

The first family was established in the Garden of Eden by God's own hand. Adam and Eve accepted the marriage goal that was set--that of being joined and of becoming ''one flesh.'' God gave them His blessing and set their tasks: "''Be fruitful and multiply; fill the earth and subdue it'''" (1:28).

Adam and Eve were to be one in their flesh and in their commitment to each other. They were equally blessed and were jointly commissioned to ''subdue'' the earth and to ''have dominion over'' the earth. Just as neither the male nor the female could multiply and fill the earth alone, neither could he or she subdue it and have dominion over it alone.

The first family was established as an idyllic relationship without superiority or subservience. They were complete in each other. Had it not been for sin, their relationship would have continued in that manner--egalitarian and orderly.

But sin did occur within the first family, and the woman and the man were cursed along with the serpent and the earth itself (3:14-19). Families have suffered from the effects of sin and the curse from that time forward. Historical records and the Bible itself give accounts of the effects of sin on the family--fratricide, polygamy, incest, adultery, dissolution, and so forth.

Then Jesus came. And He attempted to restore the pattern for marriage that was established in the Garden of Eden. ''And He answered and said to them, 'Have you not read that He who made them at the beginning made them male and female.' and said, 'For this reason a man shall leave his father and mother and be joined to his wife, and the two shall become one flesh'? So then, they are no longer two but one flesh. Therefore what God has joined together, let not man separate''' (Matthew 19:4-6).

The triune God established the family, and Jesus reaffirmed it. The family was an important channel through which God worked in Scripture. It can and should be an important channel through which He works today.

REFLECT AND MEDITATE

1. Think about the state of the family and life in your community. Do those families reflect the goals of cherishing and supporting one another? Do most of the families provide the cure for human aloneness that God intended when Eve and Adam were brought together?

2. Jesus stated His affirmation of God's original intent for marriage in Matthew 19:4-6. Meditate upon the ways that your relationship to Jesus Christ has enriched your marriage and/or family relationships. How could a deepening of your relationship with Him affect your family in an even more positive manner?

REACT AND RESPOND

Draw a triangle and write ''God'' at the apex. On one of the angles at the base of the triangle, write your name. On the other base angle, write the name of your spouse or, if you are single, the name of another family member or friend with whom you would like a closer relationship.

Place your two index fingers on the names at the base, and move them up the sides toward God. Notice how you move closer to each other as each of you moves closer to God.

Now make a list of ways that you can move

toward God and your family simultaneously.

REJOICE AND WORSHIP

Bow in a prayer of thanksgiving for your family. Call the names of family members who have impacted your life positively. Thank God for each one individually and for specific reasons. Pray for unity and love within the nuclear family, the extended family and the church family.

After prayer, write an affectionate note of appreciation to a family member who has been helpful to or supportive of you. Deliver or mail your note with a determination to express freely your appreciation for family to both God and to family members.

Study 2

THE FAMILY--NAMED AFTER GOD

READ AND RESEARCH (Psalms 127, 128; 1 Corinthians 13; Ephesians 3:14, 15; 1 John 4)

All that is positive on this earth is patterned after heaven. To fully understand what earthly institutions should be, we must examine the heavenly example. The family is an earthly institution with a heavenly origin and a heavenly plan. Successful homes are the building blocks of successful churches and nations.

Paul wrote these words to the Ephesians: "For this reason I bow my knees to the Father of our Lord Jesus Christ, from whom the whole family in heaven and earth is named" (3:14, 15). This verse being true, it follows that we must try to understand the attributes of God and His Son in order to understand what God intends the earthly family to be.

The underlying attribute of God and family is love (1 John 4). A family built on anything else lacks proper foundation. That foundation is perfectly described in 1 Corinthians 13.

The famous preacher G. Campbell Morgan in his sermon "The Home" made the following observation about God and family:

"The Bible reveals Him in His fatherhood, the Bible reveals Him in His motherhood. In fatherhood as truth, strength for ever caring; in motherhood as grace, essential comfort for ever strengthening. Further, the Bible reveals Him as trinity in unity, the duality completed in the Son, who in the fullness of time appeared in human history, and men beheld Him, and this selfsame apostle wrote of Him, 'We beheld his glory, the glory as of the only begotten of the Father, full of grace and truth.' Thus He was the revealer of fatherhood and motherhood.

"All these things are eternal in God, without beginning and without end: fatherhood, motherhood, and sonship. We never begin to understand fatherhood or motherhood or childhood on earth until we see that these things are all the image and the likeness of that which is essential and eternal in God."

The Christian family, then, begins to live up to its name the more godlike it becomes in its relationships. And since "God is love," love must be the essence of family. Within the triune Godhead the Father eternally loves the Son, the Son eternally receives and returns that love, and the Holy Spirit is the eternal medium of that love. That love is our example.

A deep trust is another necessary element of the godly family. God the Father trusted Jesus the Son with the entire plan of salvation. Jesus in the flesh executed the plan perfectly. Jesus trusted the Father enough to pray in Gethsemane: "'O My Father, if it is possible, let this cup pass from Me; nevertheless, not as I will, but as You will'" (Matthew 26:39). And then when salvation was complete, Jesus trusted the work of the Spirit enough to say to His disciples: "'It is to your advantage that I go away; for if I do not go away, the Helper will not come to you; but if I depart, I will send Him to you'" (John 16:7). Mutual trust between spouses and between parents and children is necessary.

Another task of the home that is godlike is the birth of hope and definite plans and progress toward the realization of that hope. The potential for the development of each individual family member should be recognized, planned for and accomplished. And that hope should encompass eternity, not just the earthly life span.

In addition to love, hope, trustworthiness and much more, God is identified as a source of rest, comfort, refuge and solace. And the family that is named after Him should provide the same. No matter what negative experiences may occur outside the walls of the home, the family should always provide a refuge.

The family is named after God. As disciples, we must do everything possible to influence our families to follow after God.

REFLECT AND MEDITATE

Review 1 Corinthians 13. Ask yourself whether or not you live out the attributes of love that are described in that chapter in your everyday relationships within your own family. Be honest with yourself and with God.

REACT AND RESPOND

Write a short letter or note to each person who lives with you. Express your love, your trust and your hope for that person. Pledge yourself to improve in ways that were impressed upon you in your meditation. If you live alone, write to a family member outside your home or in your church.

REJOICE AND WORSHIP

Pray a prayer of thanksgiving to God for what He is, for His attributes. Sing a chorus of praise directly to Him. Now pray a sincere prayer that you may show forth those same attributes within your family.

Study 3

THE FAMILY--IN COVENANT WITH GOD

READ AND RESEARCH (Genesis 1:28-30; 3:15; 9:8-17; 12:1-7; 17:1-19; 22:9-18; Exodus 12:24-28; Deuteronomy 30:11-20; 31:10-13; 2 Samuel 7:12-17; Hebrews 8:7-13)

Through the course of Scripture, God made eight great covenants with man, and each of these covenants was dependent upon the family.

The first covenant was the Edenic covenant of Genesis 1:28-30. Man and woman were to be fruitful and multiply and subdue and rule over. In return, God would feed them. The covenant was with man and wife, and the command to multiply indicated children.

The second covenant was the Adamic covenant after the Fall. This covenant was stated in Genesis 3:15. "'And I will put enmity between you and the woman, and between your seed and her Seed; He shall bruise your head, and you shall bruise His heel.'" Once again the descendants, the future family members, were involved as God promised that the progeny of Adam and Eve would bruise the head of the serpent.

In Genesis 9:8-17, God gave the third covenant to Noah and to his sons. "'And as for Me, behold I establish My covenant with you and with your descendants after you'" (v. 9). And He reminds us all of that covenant each time that we, the descendants of Noah, see God's rainbow in the clouds.

The fourth covenant was the great Abrahamic covenant in which God promised Abraham, "'I will make you a great nation'....'To your descendants I will give this land'....'One who will come from your own body shall be your heir'" (Genesis 12:2, 7; 15:4). And on and on God spoke promises to Abraham for his seed. He stated and restated His covenant.

Finally, in Genesis 22:16-18 God told Abraham, "'By Myself I have sworn, says the Lord, because you have done this thing, and have not withheld your son, your only son, in blessing I will bless you, and in multiplying I will multiply your descendants as the stars of the heaven and as the sand which is on the seashore; and your descendants shall possess the gate of their enemies. In your seed all the nations of the earth shall be blessed, because you have obeyed My voice.'"

The Mosaic covenant rescued not just Moses but everyone who dwelt inside the houses with the blood of the Passover lamb on the doorposts. In it God demanded the sacrifice of the firstborn. In the Ten Commandments He dealt with marital fidelity and parental respect. And over and over again, the Israelites were admonished to teach the provisions of this covenant to their children.

In the Palestinian covenant of Deuteronomy 30 and 31, the choice of life or death was for the entire family.

In the Davidic covenant of 2 Samuel 7:16, God promised David, "'And your house and your kingdom shall be established forever before you. Your throne shall be established forever.'" And of course we know that David's eventual heir was the Messiah--Jesus Christ. This covenant too was dependent on the family.

Now we have a new covenant found in Hebrews 8:7-13. Once again this covenant is with the "house" of Israel and the "house" of Judah. "'For this is the covenant that I will make with the house of Israel: After those days,' says the Lord, 'I will put My laws in their mind and write them on their hearts; and I will be their God, and they shall be My people'" (v. 10). Now the covenant is written on each individual heart. But all the promises of God are written to the family as a group and to each member of it as an individual.

God still has a covenant with the family!

REFLECT AND MEDITATE

1. Review each of the eight covenants in your mind. Think about God's faithfulness in keeping His part of those covenants. Each one has been and currently is being carefully fulfilled. How is the family important to each one?

2. Jesus shed His blood and sent His Spirit in order to establish the new covenant, which is described in Hebrews 8:7-13. Are you keeping your end of the bargain? Read Hebrews 9 and 10.

REACT AND RESPOND

Look again at Hebrews 10:19-25. Make a list of the responsibilities we as believers and disciples have as our part of the new covenant. Can you fulfill these as an individual and as a family? Make specific plans.

REJOICE AND WORSHIP

Celebrate the new covenant by singing (first alone and later in family worship) one or more of the following spiritual songs:

"Nothing but the Blood"

"Power in the Blood"

"The Blood Will Never Lose Its Power."

Offer a prayer of thanksgiving for the privilege of going directly to the throne of God through Jesus Christ our High Priest.

Study 4

THE FAMILY--A COVENANT WITH EACH OTHER

READ AND RESEARCH (Matthew 19:4-6; 1 Timothy 5:1-8; Malachi 2:14, 15; Proverbs 31:10-31; Ecclesiastes 9:9)

Yes, God still has a covenant with the family. Furthermore, family members have a covenant with one another. The covenant with husband and wife and between other family members is binding and includes all aspects of a human being. The family covenant is not limited to the physical responsibilities.

A family begins with the marriage of a man and a woman. Study 1 set the basis for the marriage covenant established in the Garden of Eden (Genesis 1 and 2) and reaffirmed by Jesus (Matthew 19:4-6). The words *leave* and *cleave* suggest both physical-sexual union and a spiritual-emotional union. Charles M. Sell in his book *Family Ministry: The Enrichment of Family Life Through the Church* says: "Marital fidelity includes more than avoiding an affair; it demands that there be a growing, satisfying relationship between marriage partners."

It is true that marriage serves a sexual, a social

and an economic purpose. However, it is intended by God to be much, much more. After all, marriage is presented throughout Scripture as an analogy of the love of God for Israel and the love of Christ for the church (Isaiah 54:1-10; Ephesians 5:22, 25).

Husbands and wives are helpers (Genesis 2:18); they are companions (Malachi 2:14); they are providers (Proverbs 31:10-31; 1 Timothy 5:1-8); and they are givers of themselves for the development of each other (Ephesians 5:25-33). This covenant is modeled by God and is sanctioned by Him. Jesus said, "'Therefore what God has joined together, let not man separate'"(Matthew 19:6).

The covenant of family is not limited to husband and wife. Parents have a covenant responsibility to children to teach them (Deuteronomy 6:7; Proverbs 22:6), to provide for them (2 Corinthians 12:14), to nurture them (Ephesians 6:4), to discipline them (1 Timothy 3:4) and to love them (Titus 2:4). Parents must never break covenant with their children. In the parable of the prodigal son, the father remained faithful to both the sinful son and the son that was always with him (Luke 15:11-32).

Children, in turn, have a covenant to keep with parents. They are to honor them (Exodus 20:12), respect them (Proverbs 23:22) and obey them (Ephesians 6:1-3).

The extended family has mutual responsibilities as well. Children and nephews are mentioned as having primary responsibilities for widows (1 Timothy 5:4). Responsibility of other extended family members one for another may be inferred. And where the extended family leaves off, the church family takes over.

The covenant of family is one of mutual love, mutual support and mutual commitment. Changes in societal views of marriage and the family must not let Spirit-filled believers feel free to break any part of the family covenant.

REFLECT AND MEDITATE

We often hear male and female referred to as "opposite" sexes. Perhaps a better term would be "complementary" sexes. Think about the ways that males and females complete each other rather than oppose each other. How might thinking in terms of complementary sexes rather than opposite sexes be beneficial to our relationships since language shapes thought and action?

REACT AND RESPOND

1. If you are married, select a portion of the Song of Solomon to read aloud to your spouse with feeling and sincerity.

2. Choose a widow or widower in your extended family or your church family. Do something specific this week to meet her or his material or emotional needs.

3. Plan an activity with your own child(ren) or a child(ren) in your extended family or church that will be a memorable experience for him or her (or them). Remember that positive emotional experiences are more memorable than expensive experiences. Time and attention are worth more than money. Carry out your plan this week.

REJOICE AND WORSHIP

Approach God in prayer as a child approaches a kind and loving father. Call Him "Abba, Father" which is similar to our familiar appellations, "Dad," "Daddy" or "Papa." Talk to Him in the spirit of Mark 14:36, Romans 8:14-17 and Galatians 4:1-7. Remember to thank Him as well as bring Him your requests. Remember to be thankful for your nuclear family, your extended family and your church family. Include family in your intercessory prayer.

Study 5

THE FAMILY--COMPOSITION MAY VARY

READ AND RESEARCH (Matthew 19:3-12; 1 Corinthians 7:1-40; 1 Timothy 5:1-8)

The mental image that most people have of a "family" is a husband, a wife, and one or more children. That kind of family is referred to as a nuclear family. There is no doubt that the nuclear family is very important to us socially, culturally, economically and biologically. Much of Studys 1-4 has dealt with the nuclear family. As important as this pattern is, it certainly is not the only type of household that may function effectively.

In the United States, fewer than one-half of the population live in a nuclear family. Fewer than one-fourth of the population live in a traditional family in which there is a husband who is the wage earner, a wife who is not employed outside the home, and one or more children who live with both of those parents. The remainder of the population is composed of adults who are single-- never married, divorced, widowed and married with children who do not live with both parents. Demographic changes in recent years show a trend toward more households headed by single adults, with increases especially among young males and older females. So there are many different patterns among households.

The percentages of various types of household compositions may change from one era to another. But throughout history these differing patterns have existed.

Sarah and Abraham were childless for many years and brought nephew Lot and servant Eliezer into their family in roles similar to those of sons (Genesis 12:4, 5; 15:2). The prophets Elijah and Elisha seem to have been single men dedicated to the work of God (1 and 2 Kings). There are many more Old Testament examples of households other than nuclear families.

In the New Testament we again find a variety of patterns among Christian families. The apostle Paul was a single man who seemed to believe that singleness was the best status for a person who really wanted to work for the Lord (1 Corinthians 7:32-36). He did not condemn marriage, but he seemed to encourage singleness for those Christians who were able to remain celibate. Paul channeled his fatherly instincts toward young men who were his spiritual sons in the faith. He trained young men such as Timothy, John Mark and Titus by example as well as by his written words (1 and 2 Timothy and Titus).

The greatest model for ministry and for living is, of course, Jesus himself. He began His earthly life as a very special child in a nuclear family. As an adult, however, Jesus was a "single." Traditionalists sometimes belittle a role that was modeled so perfectly by the Lord himself.

It would be inappropriate to say that Jesus, because He was single, had no family. Matthew quotes Jesus as saying, "'Who is My mother and who are My brothers?' And He stretched out His hand toward His disciples and said, 'Here are My mother and My brothers! For whoever does the will of My Father in heaven is My brother and sister and mother'" (Matthew 12:48-50).

Therefore, Jesus modeled for us a "family of one." His own oneness with the heavenly Father brought Him into a family relationship with everyone who does the will of the heavenly Father. It is a relationship Jesus said can be truly a parent-child and a brother-sister relationship.

REFLECT AND MEDITATE

Every individual whether married or single is as much a part of the human family as every other individual, and every believer whether married or single is as much a part of the heavenly family as every other Christian. Think about ways that believers from many different types of households can be more fully integrated into the life of your church. Are marrieds, singles, widows, single parents, and children with and without both parents appropriately ministered to? Are each of these involved in ministry to others?

Discipleship

READ AND RESPOND

Make a list of single Christians in the historical church and the contemporary church who have made great contributions.

Example: Corrie ten Boom, Pearl Starke, Dora P. Myers

REJOICE AND WORSHIP

Read John 19:25-27. In this passage Jesus transferred His earthly mother from His physical family to the physical family of John the Beloved. Moments later He cried, "'It is finished!'" He referred to the accomplishment of His redemptive death whereby we all may be transferred into the heavenly family.

Close your eyes. Picture Him on the cross as His mother looks on. Praise Him in your own way.

DISCIPLESHIP COMMITMENT

Abba, Father, I praise You for the redemptive work of Jesus Christ and for the spirit of adoption whereby I can come to You as a son and an heir--a joint heir with Jesus Christ himself. I commit to the task of being a responsible member of my earthly family and of the heavenly family.
Amen.

CHAPTER 9

What Are the Problems of the Family?

INTRODUCTION

The institution of the family by God in the Garden of Eden was followed closely by humankind's fall into sin. The family God had created in order fell into disarray. The first sin of disobedience was followed by murder when brother killed brother. The first murder was a family murder and was succeeded by a myriad of family sins--polygamy, lusts, drunkenness, nudity, cursings, pride, lying, jealousy, greed, sodomy, gang rape, incest and desertion--all in the first 21 chapters of Genesis.

Families have been fraught by problems ever since the Fall. But that is no reason to give up on the family. Families also have been blessed from the beginning, and God has protected and preserved His remnant throughout the history of humankind.

Of course, there are troubled families, but there are also strong families. Dr. Nick Stinnett in his article ''Six Qualities That Make Families Strong'' in the book *Family Building*, edited by George Rekers, has identified the following characteristics of strong families:

1. They are committed to the family.
2. They spend time together.
3. They have good family communication.
4. They express appreciation to each other.
5. They have a spiritual commitment.
6. They are able to solve problems in a crisis.

During the next five sessions we will be looking at problems that the contemporary family may face. The broad categories of problems that will be examined are

1. Disorder
2. Poor Communication
3. Outside Pressures
4. Lovelessness
5. Sin

These potential problems will be looked at in the positive light of Scripture and with the goal in mind of combating these five potential weaknesses with the six family strengths identified by Dr. Stinnett.

DISCIPLESHIP GOAL

After considering the question, ''What are the problems of the family?'' during the next five sessions, the disciple will be aware of some common family problems. The disciple will think of these problems in light of characteristics of strong families as well as his or her scriptural role in trying to solve them.

READING ASSIGNMENT
The Living Book, pp. 100 - 105

Discipleship

PROBLEMS OF THE FAMILY--DISORDER

READ AND RESEARCH (Genesis 21:9-21; Ephesians 5)

One of the strengths of strong families is a sense of commitment to the family by its members. Disorder in various forms disrupts a family when there is little or no commitment among its members. Very often the lack of commitment manifests itself in the form of broken covenants, an unwillingness to submit to one another and failure to accept responsibility. The eventual result is disorder in varying degrees from dissatisfaction to quarreling to separation--first emotional and later physical--to abandonment and divorce or dissolution in some form.

Marriage is a relationship. So are all family bonds. Those relationships may develop in either a positive or a negative manner. If the relationships are to continue, they must be respected, and they require considerable investment by all parties involved. Successful family relationships require commitment, the keeping of covenants.

Margaret D. Campolo wrote: "In a marriage as in so much of life, those who do what they ought to do are rewarded. It is one of God's ironies that when happiness becomes an end in itself, it is never realized. Happiness is a by-product of living out one's obligations."

Genesis 21:9-21 tells the story of the dissolution of one part of a polygamous marriage. It was not God's idea for Abraham to have a child by Hagar. Neither was the jealousy that developed in Abraham's home God's idea. Sarah and Abraham had entered into a commitment without God's direction, and as a result, Abraham was having to send away his own son. It was, no doubt, a wrenching experience for Hagar, Ishmael and Abraham. The comforting part of this sad story is that while God did not create the situation, He did still care for the people who were involved. He met the needs of each individual.

Successful family relationships require com-mitment. But the innocent victims of broken covenants can still rely on God for help. Many victims of divorce and abandonment are totally dependent on Him.

Another source of disorder is lack of submission to one another. Certain verses of Ephesians 5 are often used to teach submission of wives to husbands, and such submission is indicated. However, the message of the entire chapter is that all Christians should be in submission one to another. This mutual submission includes, but is not limited to, that of wife to husband. When this mutual submission is not in operation among church members, disorder in the church results. When mutual submission is not in operation among family members, disorder in the family results.

A third source of disorder in the family is a failure to accept responsibility. Paul wrote to Timothy that families should feel responsible for one another. He went so far as to say: "But if anyone does not provide for his own, and especially for those of his household, he has denied the faith and is worse than an unbeliever" (1 Timothy 5:8). Was he talking about material provisions only?

The disorder that may arise in a home is a problem that each family member should work to solve. And a happy home is well worth working for!

REFLECT AND MEDITATE

Does your household operate in a reasonably smooth manner both physically and emotionally? Are you keeping your covenants? Are you submitting yourself to other family members? Are you fulfilling your responsibilities? How can you improve your own behavior in order to enhance your home life?

REACT AND RESPOND

Grade yourself on the fulfillment of your responsibilities. E = Excellent. S = Satisfactory. N = Needs to improve. U = Unsatisfactory.

Affection ____ Time ____ Chores ____

Fulfilled Promises

To my spouse ———
To my children ———
To my extended family ———
To others ———

As a follow-up, take specific steps to raise your "grades."

REJOICE AND WORSHIP

If your home is a home of peace, pause now and praise the Lord. Pray for a family that you know is experiencing disorder and strife.

If you feel betrayed by family members, praise God for His faithfulness, resting on these words: "When my father and my mother forsake me, Then the Lord will take care of me" (Psalm 27:10).

Ask the Lord to show you your faults in the disarray. "Search me, O God, and know my heart; Try me, and know my anxieties; And see if there is any wicked way in me, And lead me in the way everlasting" (Psalm 139:23, 24).

Study 2

PROBLEMS OF THE FAMILY--POOR COMMUNICATION

READ AND RESEARCH (Ephesians 4:21-32; Proverbs 19:13, 14; 25:24; 27:15; 1 Peter 3:7)

Good communication is absolutely essential to any successful relationship. God prepared 39 books in order to speak to humankind. He followed those books by sending the Word in the flesh (Jesus) to live with humans. He followed that by preparing 27 more books. God has always gone to great lengths to communicate with humankind.

Communication occurs whether or not it is deliberate. But it takes effort to make sure that it is positive rather than negative. Three of the six characteristics of strong families involve communication directly--spending time together, having good family communication and expressing appreciation to each other. It is worth the effort!

It is important to remember that communication is both verbal and nonverbal. Research suggests that only 7 percent of spousal communication is by words alone, 38 percent is by tone of voice, and 55 percent of what is heard from spouses is nonverbal (body posture, facial expressions, etc.). Those statistics seem to confirm the adage "Actions speak louder than words."

An obvious truth that nevertheless needs to be reemphasized is that even family members cannot read one another's minds. So the channels of communication must be open, and people must talk in a frank and honest manner. Counselor Luis Palau suggests opening blocked communication channels by kneeling together, reading an appropriate Scripture passage, sharing prayer requests, and with arms around each other praying together for God's help. Blocked communication can be slow death to a family.

Time is another factor. Some research studies report an average of 27.5 minutes a week spent in actual communication between American husbands and wives. Many factors can intrude on family "talk" time--work, tiredness, chores, fear of disagreement, church and TV. One writer observed that watching TV together is not communication and that many American families know more about Cliff and Clair Huxtable's marriage and children than they know about their own.

There are some principles of communication to remember as you try to open up to your family.

1. Avoid negative communication. In Ephesians 4:29, Paul said, "Let no corrupt communication proceed out of your mouth, but what is good for necessary edification, that it may impart grace to the hearers."

The adage "Sticks and stones may break my bones, but words can never hurt me" just is not true. Criticism, put-downs, sarcasm, rejection and demanding language are not part of positive communication. They destroy rather than edify.

2. Maximize positive communication. Compliment and affirm one another every time it can be done sincerely. The self-esteem of your family member is at stake. Self-esteem is learned from the feedback received from those who are the closest and most important. If relatives give positive feedback, the self-image is likely to be positive. The converse is also true. Be careful that "constructive criticism" is given in a positive and sensitive manner.

3. Choose the appropriate response in terms of the situation and the timing. Try to perceive the other person's frame of mind and emotional need. Do not blurt out an insensitive response. Wisdom says: "A man has joy by the answer of his mouth. And a word spoken in due season, how good it is!" (Proverbs 15:23).

4. Speak honestly, but accept ownership of our own feelings. We must be honest with others but not cruelly so. We must communicate our feelings but not in an accusatory manner. For example, to say, "You make me feel like a failure," is to elicit anger and defensiveness. When you take ownership of your own feelings by saying, "I am beginning to feel like a failure," the communication channels remain open. You have not blamed your feelings on the other party. It is possible to be assertive without being aggressive or hostile. Timing and methods of sharing feelings are important. Saying, "You never talk to me," is aggressive and accusatory. Saying, "Honey, when I try to talk to you, I am able to get very little response. I feel frustrated and wonder what I am doing wrong" is assertive but sensitive.

5. Practice listening from the other person's perspective. Listen without interrupting or correcting. Ask silently, "How does this situation look from his or her perspective?" Observe nonverbal cues as well as words. Try to understand what the other person has to gain or lose. Consider the other person's language style. Make your language fit that style. Listen with true openness.

It has been said that communication is a developmental skill. You and your family will get better at it as you practice it.

REFLECT AND MEDITATE

Howard and Jeanne Hendricks wrote, "Nothing is as easy as talking; but nothing is as difficult as transparent communication." Think about the meaning of that statement.

Proverbs 25:11 says, "A word fitly spoken is like apples of gold in settings of silver." Can you estimate the value on today's market of life-size apples of solid gold arranged in a bowl of pure silver? That's how valuable and beautiful an appropriate word can be.

REACT AND RESPOND

Charlie Shedd believes that complimenting or affirming requires deliberate practice. He suggests that a husband write down 30 qualities he admires in his wife. Then each day for a month he should repeatedly mention a different quality to her. Try that for each member of your household for a week. You might want to continue for a month. By then you may be a habitually positive communicator.

REJOICE AND WORSHIP

As a Pentecostal believer, you are aware of God's ability to use human speech. Perhaps He chose speaking in tongues as an evidence of the Spirit's indwelling because, as James says, "The tongue is a little member and boasts great things....is a fire...defiles the whole body....No man can tame the tongue" (3:5, 6, 8). Communication is difficult to control, but we know that the Spirit of God can do it. Praise the Lord for the gift of the Spirit. Ask the Spirit to be in charge of your communication with your family in the same way that He can be in control of your communion with God the Father through Jesus our intercessor.

Study 3

PROBLEMS OF THE FAMILY--OUTSIDE PRESSURES

READ AND RESEARCH (Matthew 24:36-44; 2 Timothy 2:1--3:5; Ecclesiastes 4:9-12)

The earth is in a pressure cooker. Change takes place more rapidly than humankind can make adjustments. These are perilous times, and Jesus said the family would be affected (Matthew 24:38) along with the whole earth as the coming of the Son of Man approaches. One characteristic of strong families is the ability to solve problems in a crisis. Problem-solving skills must be learned as small problems arise. Then the ability to cope will be in place for the crises times. Pressure from outside the home provide major and minor problems to be solved on a daily basis. Ecclesiastes 4:9-12 suggests that one person alone is not adequate. However, two people joined together as two strands of a cord may invite God to be the third strand of a cord that can withstand outside pressures quite well.

The mass media such as newspapers, magazines, radio, theater and television constantly funnel information, concepts and values into the family. Very often these messages are counter to Scripture and to family values. One such category of messages is the acceptance of sin and the desensitization toward evil. Foul language, deceit, sex outside marriage and generally sleazy behavior are all presented as acceptable lifestyles. The ease of obtaining divorce and abortion is making commitment to marriage and to children become shallow and temporary. Overexposure can create an everybody's-doing-it attitude that may lead to sin. Careful monitoring of the media is becoming necessary for Christian adults. Frank and open discussions concerning values as projected by the media should be a regular part of family life. We cannot take ourselves out of this world, but we can learn to live in it in a manner pleasing to God.

Another outside pressure on the family is materialism. The media with its advertising and its focus on the wealthy sends a message that things are more valuable than people, that the material is more desirable than the spiritual. In our greed for things, all our priorities are disordered. The demand for more money lends to longer working hours and, in some cases, to unethical or even illegal behavior. Parents who cannot provide certain labels and brand names may begin to feel like failures. The pressure for possessions may lead to hostility among family members. This is counter to the will and Word of God.

Another source of family discord is the mixed messages from society and the church concerning roles in the family. On the one hand, Madison Avenue says the wife should pull into the driveway of a midsized mansion at 5 p.m. in her Mercedes-Benz station wagon to allow her two children to disembark, wearing color-coordinated designer outfits. She should then pick up her alligator-skin brief case and go into the spotless home. In 20 minutes or so she should serve a gourmet meal with no spots or food odors on her professionally tailored suit. She then cleans the already clean kitchen and goes off to her elegant suite to polish her nails with one hand and balance her checkbook with the other. After all, she and her husband have to go out for an evening on the town. Impossible? Yes, but TV and women's magazines tell wives they ought to be able to do it.

By contrast, ultraconservatives want the wife outside the house only for church, PTA and driving the car for the children. Some conservative spokeswomen make a fortune writing books and making speeches all over the world telling other Christian women to stay at home. These mixed messages introduce confusion and discord into the home.

The Spirit-filled Christian is not dependent on either Madison Avenue or Christian media for direction. Careful study of the Word of God, soul-searching and prioritizing by Christian spouses, and sincere praying in the Spirit can sort through the media blitz and give definite guidance for daily decision making.

REFLECT AND MEDITATE

Read Matthew 6:25-34. How do those scriptures relate to contemporary materialism?

REACT AND RESPOND

Make two lists--one of how you spend your time and one of how you spend your money. Now number the items on your list in the order of their importance to you. Ask your spouse and/or other family members to do the same thing. Compare your lists and discuss the differences.

REJOICE AND WORSHIP

We do live in perilous times, but Luke 21:28 says, "'Now when these things begin to happen, look up and lift up your heads, because your redemption draws near.'" Praise God for the promise of imminent redemption. Then pray a prayer for God's hedge to be about your family, shielding them from outside pressures.

Read Ecclesiastes 4:9-12 aloud to another family member. Ask that person to join you and the Lord in order to form that cord of three strands that is not easily broken.

Study 4

PROBLEMS IN THE FAMILY-- LOVELESSNESS

READ AND RESEARCH (1 Corinthians 13; 1 John 4)

Writers, lyricists, romantics and philosophers have tried for ages to define love. But love defies definition. It refuses to be limited to words. To contemplate the words "God is love" is to begin to realize the futility of defining love. We can, however, talk about the attributes and components of true love. If we can begin to imagine the enormity of the positive effects of love on a family, then we can begin to imagine the enormity of the negative effects of lovelessness on the family.

In this day of easy-to-obtain divorce and casual relationships, the reason for dissolution is often given as "I just don't love her/him anymore." Try to imagine the negative effects of lovelessness by thinking positively about what love is.

Love is much more than romantic emotion. Dwight H. Small wrote the following:

"Love is not something we fall into, but something we learn. It matures over time and through many shared experiences. Love isn't something that happens to us, but something at which we work hard to keep happening. Essentially, it is a commitment to care, to give oneself to the other's needs, to work through problems with patience and understanding. For Christian couples, it is letting Jesus' love shape their love until it is like Him--centered on others, relinquishing independent self-will for the sake of the beloved, and determined to assist the other to become all that he or she is meant to be."

Love is the "cleaving" of Genesis 2:24 in the King James Version. Love is the friendship of Song of Solomon 5:16. Love is the togetherness that makes the "one flesh" of Genesis 2:24 possible. Love is the partnership whereby one complements the other. Love is respect. Love is honoring each other as instructed in Ephesians 5:33 and 1 Peter 3:7. Love is caring. Love is faithfulness in intellectual and emotional as well as in physical relationships. Love is the living out of the Golden Rule in Luke 6:31. Love is mercy. Love speaks grace, as in Ephesians 4:29, rather than condemnation. Love is nourishment. Love is freedom from fear as spoken of in 1 John 4:18.

Sometimes love hurts. The purest illustration of this is when "'God so loved the world that He gave His only begotten Son, that whoever believes in Him should not perish but have everlasting life'" (John 3:16). The person who loves the most hurts the most when through death or separation love is lost.

Tony Campolo speaks of a successful approach to counseling couples who say they no longer love one another. He is convinced that actions shape feelings, so he instructs his clients to act as if they loved their spouse for a certain amount of time each day for a given number of days. The husband may be instructed to do or say three things to his wife every day that he would do or say if he did still love her. The deeds vary each day. When these loving words are said and loving deeds performed every day for several weeks, amazingly positive results are reported. Just as loving feelings produce loving deeds, loving deeds produce loving feelings.

Many families may be living in the same house but be loveless. They may not be divorced but may be disunited. Since God is love, He is the source of love and the ultimate cure for lovelessness.

REFLECT AND MEDITATE

In defining love, psychiatrist Dr. Harry Stack Sullivan says this: ''When the satisfaction or the security of another person becomes as significant to one as one's own satisfaction or security, then the state of love exists.'' How many people do you love by this definition?

REACT AND RESPOND

Open your Bible to 1 Corinthians 13. Look at verses 4-7. Substitute your name for the word *love*, and add your spouse's or another family member's name to formulate questions. For example, ''Is John patient with Mary? Is John kind to Mary? Is John envious? Boastful? Proud? Is John rude to Mary?'' and so forth.

This exercise will test to see if your actions live up to your words.

REJOICE AND WORSHIP

Sing one or more worship choruses about love:
''I Am Loved''
''God Is Love''
''I Love Him.''
Thank God for those who love you. Pray for those who love you and those whom you love.

Study 5

PROBLEMS OF THE FAMILY--SIN

READ AND RESEARCH (Proverbs 5; Romans 5:1-11)

The ultimate source of family problems is, of course, sin. Sin intruded on the very first family (Genesis 3). Sin intruded on all future families at the same time. Adam and Eve both sinned. Adam blamed Eve, and Eve blamed the serpent. They were a typical family. All families have experienced sin.

Not only did Adam and Eve sin, but their son Cain killed his brother Abel and was cursed by God. In Genesis 9 Noah's family sinned. While Noah lay naked in a drunken stupor, his son Ham made fun of him and sought to make his shame a mockery to the only surviving family on earth. Ham was cursed. In chapter 12 Abraham lied and risked Sarah's purity to protect himself. In chapter 16 Abraham and Sarah entered into a bigamous

relationship with Hagar. Jealousy ensued. Hagar fled. Later she returned and gave birth. By chapter 21 Sarah gave birth, and a jealousy and rivalry grew out of that bigamous family that still drives peace from the earth.

In Genesis 19, Lot offered his daughters as the victims of mob rape, failed to successfully witness to his sons-in-law, had to be dragged from sinful Sodom, experienced the death of his wife, watched Sodom burn, and in a drunken stupor impregnated his two daughters in two separate incestuous encounters. The trial of sin goes on and on throughout the history of humankind. Your family isn't the first to experience sin and disappointment.

The genealogy of Jesus Christ includes sin and sinners. In Genesis 38 we have the ugly story of Judah and Tamar, involving widowhood, broken promises, prostitution, seduction and incest. Tamar is in the ancestry of Jesus. Rahab the harlot was, no doubt, a disappointment to her parents, but one day she heard a message. And faith in the symbolic scarlet cord brought protection and salvation to her entire family, and Rahab became a progenitor of Jesus. Ruth was a foreigner and a descendant of Moab, the son of incest, but she became the great-grandmother of David, who figures prominently in the genealogy of Jesus. The story of David and Bathsheba included lust, adultery, betrayal, murder, polygamy and infant death. But out of this sordid family scandal came true repentance and the birth of Solomon, who was an ancestor of Jesus.

There is no recipe whereby you can predestinate your spouse and your children. Each individual is a free moral agent with a will and a choice of his or her own. Satan seeks to destroy the best and the brightest in your home. But there is hope through the redeeming blood of Jesus. Resist the intrusion of sin by the best Christian education possible, by family worship, by open communication, by nonjudgmental, unconditional love and by constant intercessory prayer. Job offered sacrifices for his children, "For Job said, 'It may be that my sons have sinned and cursed God in their hearts.' Thus Job did regularly" (Job 1:5).

If sin creeps into your family, don't deny it. Deal with it. Pray with Jacob, "'If I am bereaved [of my children], I am bereaved!'" (Genesis 43:14). Because of spiritual rebellion and death, cover your face like David and cry with a loud voice: "'O my son Absalom,...O Absalom, my son, my son!'" (2 Samuel 18:33). Let us walk and gaze with the expectant father of the Prodigal Son so that some day we can see our loved ones a great way off and in compassion run to them, fall on their necks, kiss them and hear their repentant prayer. Prepare for the day when the Prodigal, the father and the son that was always at home will link arms to form a unified family.

REFLECT AND MEDITATE

Sin often enters the life of an individual as a misguided attempt to satisfy personal need such as loneliness, lack of love or affirmation, misunderstanding or unresolved conflict. Do any of those conditions exist in your life or the lives of your family members? Observe. Ask. If the answer is yes, then prayer, love, and perhaps professional Christian counseling are needed.

REACT AND RESPOND

After prayer for wisdom, initiate a personal and private conversation with each member of your household. Talk on his or her level about personal needs as listed above. Listen openly. Plan an appropriate response to the conversation.

REJOICE AND WORSHIP

Rejoice in sins forgiven. "'Come now, and let us reason together,' says the Lord, 'Though your sins are like scarlet, they shall be as white as snow; though they are red like crimson, they shall be as wool'" (Isaiah 1:18).

DISCIPLESHIP COMMITMENT

Jesus, I pledge to You that I will do everything I can through human effort and by Your Spirit to strengthen my family by renewing my commitment to my family as You were committed to me--unto death; by spending quality time with them even as You took time to bless the little children and to hold them on Your lap; by talking to them and listening to them as You speak to me by Your word and listen to me as I pray; by expressing my appreciation to them in hope that some day You will say to me, "Well done, good and faithful servant....Enter into the joy of your lord"; by teaching them spiritual commitment by word and by deed even as You taught Your disciples; by bringing our problems to You in intercessory prayer even as You intercede for us with the Father. Amen.

CHAPTER 10

What Is the Biblical Order in the Family?

INTRODUCTION

The first human couple were created in the image of God and were told to have children. The image of God is a unity in which the Father eternally loves the Son, the Son eternally receives and reciprocates that love, and the Holy Spirit eternally serves as the medium of that love.

Since the Godhead exists in this unified and orderly mode, it follows that the human family should strive to do likewise. The Bible has provided both role models and definite instructions to help families know how to do that.

During the next five sessions the question of biblical order in the family will be explored. The following topics will be considered:

1. It Is Patterned After the Unity of God
2. It Is Based on Mutual Submission
3. It Is Modeled and Described in the New Testament
4. It Requires Responsible Parenting
5. It Requires Obedient Children

Throughout these sessions the disciple should remember that this material is to be used by adults. Therefore, even the session on the biblical requirement that children obey parents is written to adults. The emphasis is on methods whereby parents can inspire obedience in their children.

It is recognized that many adults may be neither spouses nor parents. However, a conscientious participation in all five of these sessions will bring a clearer understanding of Scripture and of those in various family roles who are struggling to fulfill them.

DISCIPLESHIP GOAL

After considering the biblical order of the family during the next five sessions, the disciple will understand that God created the family in an orderly fashion and has given instructions and role models so that it can continue to function in an orderly manner. As a result, the disciple will implement in his or her own life those steps and conditions which will contribute to biblical orderliness.

READING ASSIGNMENT

The Living Book, pp. 109 - 124

Discipleship

ORDER IN THE FAMILY--IT IS PAT-TERNED AFTER THE UNITY OF GOD

READ AND RESEARCH (Genesis 1:26, 27; 2:23, 24; John 10:25-30; 14:6-18; 17:1-26)

In the counsel of God concerning the creation of humankind, these words were spoken: "'Let Us make man in Our image, according to Our likeness'....So God created man in His own image; in the image of God He created him; male and female He created them." God's mandate was "Therefore a man shall leave his father and mother and be joined to his wife, and they shall become one flesh."

Since humankind was created in the image of God and was created male and female, then the unity of male and female can be inferred. The unity of husband and wife was established at Creation. And since the first couple were told to be fruitful and to multiply, we can infer the intended unity of the family.

The unity of God is clearly established in Scripture. Jesus spoke of His unity with the Father in the book of John in words such as these: "'I and My Father are one....the Father is in Me, and I in Him....And he who sees Me sees Him who sent Me....He who has seen Me has seen the Father'''(10:30, 38; 12:45; 14:9). And on many other occasions Jesus affirmed His oneness with the Father. This unity was intact at the creation of man, because John 1:1-4 reads:

"In the beginning was the Word, and the Word was with God, and the Word was God. He was in the beginning with God. All things were made through Him, and without Him nothing was made that was made. In Him was life, and the life was the light of men."

The New Testament uses the unity of the Godhead as an analogy to the husband and wife relationship. In his letter to the Corinthians, Paul compared the marriage relationship to the relationship of Christ and the Father with these words: "The head of every man is Christ, the head of woman is man, and the head of Christ is God" (1 Corinthians 11:3).

Since Christian families are very much a part of the church, any mention of the unity of the church includes the unity of the family. Jesus prayed for the unity of all believers in John 17:20-23: "'I do not pray for these alone, but also for those who will believe in Me through their word; that they all may be one, as You, Father, are in Me, and I in You; that they also may be one in Us, that the world may believe that You sent Me. And the glory which You gave Me I have given them, that they may be one just as We are one: I in them, and You in Me; that they may be made perfect in one, and that the world may know that You have sent Me, and have loved them as You have loved Me.'''

Paul spoke of the unity of believers in 1 Corinthians 12:12, 13. Again, Christian families are included. "For as the body is one and has many members, but all the members of that one body, being many, are one body, so also is Christ. For by one Spirit we were all baptized into one body--whether Jews or Greeks, whether slaves or free--and have all been made to drink into one Spirit."

It is clear that the Godhead exists in unity. It is clear that the first family was created in God's image. It is clear that Jesus intended the church, which He purchased, to be united. It follows, then, that Christian families should live in the same spirit of unity that Jesus prayed for in the church and that Paul admonished for the church.

Families living in discord can bring disruption to a church. Families living in harmony can be stable building blocks in a church.

REFLECT AND MEDITATE

Refer back to the prayer of Jesus in John 17. Picture your family throughout the prayer. Pray with Jesus that your family members may
· glorify God
· keep His Word
· give all they have to God
· be kept safe from the world
· have joy

· be sanctified
· be sent of God
· spread God's Word
· be united
· love.

REACT AND RESPOND

Prepare a family devotional based on Jesus' prayer in John 17. Emphasize the unity of the family. Present it in family worship time.

REJOICE AND WORSHIP

It has been said, "A family altar would alter many a family." Pray for guidance in making family worship a regular part of your home life. Act on the guidance you receive.

Study 2

ORDER IN THE FAMILY--IT IS BASED ON MUTUAL SUBMISSION

READ AND RESEARCH (Ephesians 5:1-21; Philippians 2:1-11)

Any portion of God's Word that is written to Christians in general is also written to Christian husbands, wives, and children. One of the concepts that is taught in Scripture for all Christians is that of submission--submission to God's will and submission to one another.

There are many scriptures exhorting all Christians to be submissive to the will of God. Jesus taught His disciples to pray, "'Your kingdom come. Your will be done on earth as it is in heaven'" (Matthew 6:10). Jesus himself prayed: "'O My Father, if it is possible, let this cup pass from Me; nevertheless, not as I will, but as You will'" (Matthew 26:39). James 4:7 reads: "Therefore submit to God. Resist the devil and he will flee from you."

In addition to being submitted to God, Christians are told to submit to each other. The first 21 verses of Ephesians 5 tell us how to live the Spirit-filled life every day in a manner that is becoming. We are told to love one another as Christ loved us. We are given a long list of sins from which we are to abstain. We are to be wise and to know God's will. We are to avoid drunkenness. We are to sing and praise God. And as a body of believers, we are to submit to each other as Christians. This mutual submission is not limited by gender; it applies to male and female. It is not limited by genetic or legal relationships. As Christians we must submit to both relatives and nonrelatives, to males and to females. We must be involved in "submitting to one another in the fear of God" (Ephesians 5:21).

In another letter, Paul wrote the exhortation to submission in other words: "Let nothing be done through selfish ambition or conceit, but in lowliness of mind let each esteem others better than himself" (Philippians 2:3). The Christians at Philippi were told to look out for one another. Then they were reminded that Jesus, who was God from the beginning and was a participant with the Father at Creation, was well aware of His equality with God. Yet He was willing to submit Himself not only to incarnation but even to "the death of the cross" (Philippians 2:8). Paul was telling all Christians, not just those at Philippi, to have this same submissive mind-set.

It is very easy for one member of a church or of a family to feel that he or she should be exalted above the others because of position or age or resources. But the lessons of Ephesians 5 and Philippians 2 do not support this attitude. Seek the mind of Christ in submission one to another.

REFLECT AND MEDITATE

Read Colossians 3:15: "And let the peace of God rule in your hearts, to which also you were called in one body; and be thankful."

Norm Wakefield believes that this scripture designates Jesus Christ as the umpire or arbitrator when families encounter problems. It is easy to be submissive if the Lord has the last word. With Him in control, there are no winners or losers.

Rejoice in the release from stress and antagonism that such knowledge can give. No more winners or losers! just a household of submissive loved ones!

REACT AND RESPOND

Adopt Wakefield's problem-solving strategy based on Colossians 3:15.

1. Identify the problem.
2. Bring it to the Lord in prayer.
3. Discuss the problem openly, listening with compassion.
4. Look at Scripture as it is applicable.

5. Continue praying, expecting insight from the Lord. This approach unites rather than divides.

REJOICE AND WORSHIP

Sing "Have Thine Own Way, Lord" for your private worship.

"Trust in the Lord with all your heart, and lean not on your own understanding; In all your ways acknowledge Him, and He shall direct your paths" (Proverbs 3:5, 6).

Praise the Lord for the assurance that He will help you solve family problems and make family decisions together.

If you are familiar with the tune, sing the words of Proverbs 3:5, 6.

Study 3

ORDER IN THE FAMILY--IT IS MODELED AND DESCRIBED IN THE NEW TESTAMENT

READ AND RESEARCH (Matthew 19:4-12; Ephesians 5:22, 23; 6:1-4)

The New Testament does not provide the detailed stories of the family lives of its characters as the Old Testament does. However, there are some New Testament models of family that can be given as positive examples.

Mary and Joseph of Nazareth were submissive to God as an engaged couple. An angel visited Mary with the news that she had been chosen to be the mother of the Messiah. Joseph, at first skeptical, was convinced of Mary's purity in a dream. Joseph and Mary reared Jesus along with some other children born to them later.

Zacharias was a Levite who was married to Elizabeth, a relative of Mary's. They were childless until their old age when they became the parents of John the Baptist. Their marriage seems to have been one of dedication to God.

Priscilla and Aquila were contemporaries of the apostle Paul. They were tentmakers, and Paul, also a tentmaker, worked with them for a time in

order to support himself. Apparently, this couple and the apostle studied together, because Priscilla and Aquila became teachers. On occasion, Scripture lists Priscilla's name before her husband's, leading some commentators to speculate that she might have been the stronger character.

These couples represent the nuclear family pattern that is often given as the model for the "ideal" family. The New Testament also provides excellent models of the single-person household. Jesus himself and the apostle Paul are two such examples and provide for us the two most commonly referred to ministry models for the church.

The New Testament not only provides models of the orderly family, it describes the orderly family. The basis for family order is the mutual submission required of all Christians (and examined in Study 2). In Ephesians 5 Paul described the Spirit-filled life, including mutual submission, and then went on to compare the marriage relationship to the relationship of Christ and the church.

There has been a lot of discussion about the meaning of *submit* in Ephesians 5:22. In reality the command in verse 22 is from the exact same word as in verse 21, where submission is required of all believers, both male and female.

Dissension sometimes arises when people try to interpret Ephesians 5:22 in light of Genesis 3:16. To put those scriptures together out of context can introduce confusion. Genesis 3:16-19 is a curse. It is a prophecy about the consequences of original sin. It is not a commandment or a commission. Husbands should not endeavor to enforce the curse by trying to control and rule over their wives. Neither should wives try to enforce the curse by trying to make men sweat or by planting thorns and thistles in their husband's gardens.

Another source of disagreement is the meaning of the word *head* in Ephesians 5:23. It is not something harsh and authoritarian, because Christ is not harsh and authoritarian.

Accepting the headship of a husband becomes easy for a wife when he loves her as Christ loved the church; is willing to give his life for her, not just to save her life but to develop her to her fullest potential as she is compared to a church without blemish; loves her as he does his own body; loves her as he loves himself; nourishes her and cherishes her as Christ does the church; leaves mother and father for her; and joins himself to her alone as one flesh. That is the price of headship no matter how its meaning is interpreted.

REFLECT AND MEDITATE

Linda Raney Wright in her book *A Cord of Three Strands* wrote: "The real foundation of a Christian marriage is the relationship with God of both individuals. Both partners must be sold out to Jesus Christ and individually led by Him. This will enable both parties to submit to each other as well as to encourage, serve, please, build and love each other."

Develop that kind of relationship with God, and watch your home life improve.

REACT AND RESPOND

If you are a husband, write a letter to your wife that you think Christ would write to the church He loves. If you are a wife, write a letter to your husband as the church would write to Christ. If you are single, write a letter of true submission to a family member or church family member.

REJOICE AND WORSHIP

Praise the Lord that He is perfecting you as part of the church so that He can present you glorious, spotless, wrinkle free and blemishless as His bride.

Study 4

ORDER IN THE FAMILY--IT REQUIRES RESPONSIBLE PARENTING

READ AND RESEARCH (Psalm 127; Exodus 13:8-22; 1 Timothy 3:1-7)

The parenting task for humankind began in Genesis 4:1, 2: "Now Adam knew Eve his wife, and she conceived and bore Cain, and said, 'I have gotten a man from the Lord.' Then she bore again, this time his brother Abel." In time Cain murdered Abel and was cursed by God. "And Adam knew his wife again, and she bore a son and named him Seth, 'For God has appointed another seed for me instead of Abel, whom Cain killed.' And as for Seth, to him also a son was born; and he named him Enosh. Then men began to call on the name of the Lord" (4:25, 26).

Rearing children has never been easy. It was difficult for Adam and Eve. Scripture does not tell much about their parenting practices, but the results are reported, and they are mixed. Sibling jealousy left Abel murdered and Cain cursed. But Seth had a son and, seemingly, through that line, "men began to call on the . . . Lord."

Children are born with neither a book of instructions nor a warranty. To complicate matters even further, each child in a family is different. There are, however, some general scriptural principles of parenting that should be observed.

First, family members should love one another. The best gift parents can give to children is to love them and to love each other. Love is the test for knowing God (1 John 4:7, 8). This love should be expressed in words, in affection, in touching, in deeds and in provision of life's necessities.

Second, parents should communicate to children their joy at having each individual child. Present society has devalued children. Abortions are performed by the millions annually. Overpopulation is touted as a primary environmental problem. Children are abused and abandoned. Many children in "respectable" homes are ignored or tolerated but not enjoyed or appreciated. This attitude and behavior is unscriptural and sinful.

Parents give the primary input that formulates self-esteem. Make sure the children in your household receive plenty of positive input.

Third, parents are responsible to train their children. After the Law was given, parents were admonished over and over to teach their children its precepts. They were given detailed instructions on involving children in their feasts and other religious observances, especially Passover. Proverbs 22:6 admonishes, "Train up a child in the way he should go, and when he is old he will not depart from it." Ephesians 6:4 and Colossians 3:21 are among the many New Testament scriptures instructing parents to train their children.

Fourth, parents should attempt to understand their children. This requires some understanding of the developmental characteristics of children. For example, 2-year-olds cannot comprehend abstract reasoning, so lectures do them no good. Many books are available by Christian psychologists to assist in this area.

Careful listening from the child's perspective is necessary. Consideration of the individual's personality, learning style, and birth order (oldest, only, middle or youngest child) are among the many factors involved in understanding.

Fifth, parents are responsible for providing discipline. By many different approaches and methods, children must be taught to bear the responsibility for their own behavior. Whatever methods are selected to teach this responsibility, they must all be implemented in love and not in anger. To strike a child in anger is as sinful as striking a neighbor in anger.

All five of these principles and more must be administered with large doses of prayer. Pray for the children in your home in private times as well as in their presence.

REFLECT AND MEDITATE

Howard and Jeanne Hendricks wrote: "Perhaps the reason many fail in child rearing is that they insist on ownership rather than stewardship. We can call children 'ours,' whereas the real know-how comes exclusively from the rightful Master, God." Think about it. Whose children are yours? Whose children are those in your church?

REACT AND RESPOND

Set aside a specific number of minutes to spend with each of the children in your household each day this week. Set specific communication goals for each time period, and write them down. After each visit, write down your feelings in a brief form.

REJOICE AND WORSHIP

Pray a prayer of thanksgiving for the children you have and/or the ones you know. Read Romans 8:14-18. Rejoice that you are a child of God. He is your heavenly parent. Praise God for the privilege of knowing Him as "Abba, Father."

Study 5

ORDER IN THE FAMILY--IT REQUIRES OBEDIENT CHILDREN

READ AND RESEARCH (Exodus 20:12; Proverbs 1:1-19; Ephesians 6:1-3)

The fifth of the Ten Commandments sets forth the necessity of children's obeying their parents. And as Ephesians 6:2 says, Parental obedience "is the first commandment with promise." God is the author of the principle of obedient children. But it is up to parents to expedite that obedience. Children do not come equipped with an obedience factor programmed into them.

God expects obedience by His spiritual children. Since He is a loving Father, He deals with His children in a way that inspires rather than demands obedience. He extends to us unconditional love--the kind that caused Jesus to say to the adulterous woman, "'Neither do I condemn you; go and sin no more'" (John 8:11).

Parents must inspire obedience in their children in the same manner. Love should not be dependent upon good behavior. Parental love must be unconditional. Parents must constantly measure their love and their attitudes against 1 Corinthians 13. The attributes that inspire obedience are long-suffering, kindness, not envious, not proud, not rude, unselfish, open to truth and not rumor, forbearing, enduring and unfailing.

If parents are to be obeyed, then rules and expectations must be reasonable. In speaking of God's expectations, 1 John 5:3 says, "And His commandments are not burdensome."

Parental expectations should have certain characteristics in order to be reasonable:

1. They must be appropriate for the age and developmental level of the child.

2. They must be for the good of the child and not for the gratification of the pride of the parents.

3. They must be based on Scripture while taking into account one's own culture.

4. They must be explained so that the child understands. "Because I said so" is not an appropriate explanation.

5. They must be based on an accurate perception of each individual child's temperament, interests and abilities.

6. They must be flexible.

To inspire obedience, parents must be united. Most parents have some disagreements over proper parenting procedures, particularly discipline. This is understandable since humans tend to do what has been done to them, and husbands and wives did not grow up in the same home with the same parents. But it is very important that parents stand together in the presence of the children. Disunity only sends mixed signals that confuse the children. Parents must set clear goals together, read Scripture and Christian books on parenting together, talk together privately until consensus is reached, and refuse to allow a child to pit one parent against the other.

Obedience is conditioned when children are made to bear the responsibility for their behavior. The decision to implement this form of discipline is difficult to adhere to for two reasons: (1) Parents feel sorry for the children when it is time to pay the consequences, and (2) parents make ridiculous "if...then" threats that cannot or should not be carried out. (There are excellent books on discipline by natural consequences by James Dobson, Kevin Leman and other Christian psychologists.)

Children are commanded to obey parents, but parents are responsible to make them want to do so.

REFLECT AND MEDITATE

As an adult, you have outgrown the responsibility for obeying your parents as a dependent child must. But you are still commanded to honor them and to care for them. How do you fulfill this if your parents are still living?

Proverbs 10:1 says, "A wise son makes a glad father, but a foolish son is the grief of his mother." At any age, a person should consider what joy or grief his or her behavior brings to a parent or memory of a parent.

Discipleship

REACT AND RESPOND

Do something active to honor a biological, adoptive or spiritual parent this week. Choose from these, or think of your own act of love: send or take flowers, buy a gift, do some work that is needed or desired, spend some time with them, take them on an outing, and so forth.

REJOICE AND WORSHIP

Praise God that He has chosen to make obedience easy for His children. Read Matthew 11:28-30 and rejoice in its truths. "'Come to Me, all you who labor and are heavy laden, and I will give you rest. Take My yoke upon you and learn from Me, for I am gentle and lowly in heart, and you will find rest for your souls. For My yoke is easy and My burden is light.'"

Perhaps with the guidance of Christ, you can fashion an "easy" yoke for your children.

DISCIPLESHIP COMMITMENT

I pledge to You and my family members that I will walk in Your Spirit and, thereby, will strive to contribute to scriptural order in my home.

I will love as You have loved.

I will submit myself to my family and my fellow Christians.

I will fulfill my responsibilities to my family and to You.

I will obey You in the same spirit with which children should obey their parents.

When I am to be the leader, I will do it in the same Spirit with which You washed Your disciples' feet.

If I have abused my family role through harshness or improper discipline, I will ask forgiveness of You and from the offended family member(s).

Lord, give me grace to fulfill this pledge. Amen.

CHAPTER 11

What About Family as Ministry?

INTRODUCTION

Throughout Scripture, families have been active in ministry. These ministries have taken many different forms. Early in the book of Genesis, worship to God began with families and individuals, and it continues until today. Families worship in private devotions, in pairs at bedsides, at family altars and in churches.

Besides the upward ministry of worship to God, there is the ministry within the family. Family members love, forgive, help, teach and pray for one another.

Families extend their hearts and hands outside the walls of their homes to fellow Christians in the community of faith. This ministry is to the spiritual and physical needs of other believers. They are hospitable and charitable.

Families and churches reach out to the world beyond their sanctuaries. In the spirit of Matthew 25:31-46, they attempt to feed, water, house, clothe and visit those who are in need.

The delicate part of all this ministry is to keep it all in balance.

During the next five sessions, we will examine the following answers to the question "What about family as ministry?"

1. Its Ministry Is Upward to God
2. Its Ministry Is Inward to One Another
3. Its Ministry Is Outward to the Community of Faith
4. Its Ministry Is Outward to the World
5. Its Ministry Is Balanced

The disciple should study this week in a spirit of prayer that he or she will be able to develop that balanced and anointed upreach, inreach and outreach that God has planned for his or her particular family. That goal is possible to achieve through the power of His Spirit.

DISCIPLESHIP GOAL

After considering the question "What about family as ministry?" during the next five sessions, the disciple will realize that the ministry of the family should be balanced between an upward, inward and outward ministry. This realization will result in a definite plan for his or her own family ministry.

READING ASSIGNMENT
The Living Book, pp. 124 -133

Discipleship

THE FAMILY--ITS MINISTRY IS UPWARD TO GOD

READ AND RESEARCH (Deuteronomy 6:1-9; 26; Joshua 24:14, 15; Psalms 78:1-8)

Scripture contains incidents of families worshiping as early as Cain and Abel, who each brought offerings to the Lord. One was accepted, and one was not (Genesis 4:3-5). We know that the family of Seth was involved in worship that involved "call[ing] on the name of the Lord" (Genesis 4:26). And throughout Scripture, families turned their attention upward to God in some sort of family worship. Sometimes it seemed to involve only one family. At other times families were part of corporate worship in many settings that we might refer to as "church."

Family worship includes church attendance, but the terms *family worship* and *family altar* often connote some type of devotional time that takes place inside the home. These terms elicit various images and/or memories to different people. Parents and/or children who have developed a positive model for family worship times are sure that their pattern is the best. Some people will even attempt to heap guilt on those families who prefer a different model or who have been unable to establish any successful pattern of in-home worship. The truth of the matter is that families are so very different that each family must prayerfully develop the devotional plan that works best for them.

Two patterns of family worship that are used by Christian families are daily family devotions and a weekly family night. Whichever schedule is selected, it is important to remember that Scripture actually teaches a family worship that pervades the entire day (Deuteronomy 6:1-9), not a small segment of time. It is a good practice to set aside a time for focused group worship, but awareness of God and adoration of Him should not be limited to that time. Also, individual family members still need their private times of prayer and Bible reading in addition to group worship times.

In planning daily family devotions or family altar, the following considerations should be made:

1. Allow enough variety and liveliness to keep down boredom. Some children become turned off to all worship because of boring home rituals.

2. Personalize the experience to your own family's personalities, interests and styles. What works in one home may fail miserably in another.

3. Make these worship times as regular as possible without becoming oppressive and self-defeating.

4. Have a plan, but keep it simple. You may tell a story, read a story, play a tape, share experiences, and/or sing and pray.

5. Keep the time short. This avoids boredom and burdensomeness.

6. Allow various members to participate with reading, singing, praying, sharing, and so forth. Keep everyone's abilities and interests in mind when making plans and assignments.

7. Allow some spontaneity even though you have a basic plan. This makes it possible to be Spirit-led and to capitalize on a "teachable moment."

Some families prefer one family night a week for a somewhat longer worship or Bible study time. Again, planning is required, and many of the suggestions given above should still be considered. Some religious publishers furnish curricula for the family-night-at-home format of family devotions and worship.

The exact time and format that a family chooses to worship is not so important. But it is very important that the ministry of the family reaches upward to God in devotion and in worship.

REFLECT AND MEDITATE

"But you are a chosen generation, a royal priesthood, a holy nation, His own special people, that you may proclaim the praises of Him who called you out of darkness into His marvelous light; who once were not a people but are now the people of God, who had not obtained mercy but now have obtained mercy" (1 Peter 2:9, 10).

As a priest in your home, what is your responsibility? What is your privilege?

REACT AND RESPOND

Plan and conduct at least one family worship time in your home this week. Include tithing and giving as family worship.

REJOICE AND WORSHIP

''Then little children were brought to Him that He might put His hands on them and pray, but the disciples rebuked them. But Jesus said, 'Let the little children come to Me, and do not forbid them; for of such is the kingdom of heaven.' And He laid His hands on them'' (Matthew 19:13-15).

Praise the Lord that He took time for little children and that He takes time for you.

Study 2

THE FAMILY--ITS MINISTRY IS INWARD TO ONE ANOTHER

READ AND RESEARCH (Genesis 44:18--45:28; Ruth 4:9-17)

The story of Jacob and his brother and his wives and his sons is a detailed family narrative of great importance. Jacob's story begins in Genesis 25 and ends with his death in chapter 50. Still the story of his sons continues. This narrative provides a vital part of Hebrew history, a link in the genealogy of Christ, and it furnishes many illustrations of families at their worst and at their best.

Joseph was one of the sons of Jacob. His story is one of love, hate, betrayal; yet ultimately it is one of forgiveness and provision. In spite of past sins, Joseph forgave his brothers and provided the means for his father, his brothers, their wives, their children, his sisters and all the offspring of Jacob to survive a horrible famine. Thanks to the plan of God working through Joseph, they had plenty. Joseph forgave his brothers and ministered to them.

Another beautiful story of family members providing for and ministering to one another is the story of Ruth, her mother-in-law, Naomi, and Naomi's kinsman Boaz. Ruth was committed to Naomi. Boaz was generous to Ruth, and once again the genealogy of Christ was preserved.

Families should minister to one another. Brothers, sisters, parents and extended family members should feel responsible to try to see that one another's needs are met. This responsibility should include physical as well as spiritual considerations. Four areas of family ministry that ''inward to one another'' should include are prayer, training, forgiveness and generosity.

Family members should pray for one another. In 2 Samuel 21:8-14, there is a sad story of Rizpah, a mother who guarded the bodies of her slain sons day and night for weeks so that the birds and animals would not eat them. That was a physical act of love for family. Family members should do that same thing spiritually through prayer. Pray unceasingly for your family members that they will not be devoured spiritually. Job offered sacrifices for his family's sins (Job 1:5), Abraham prayed for Ishmael (Genesis 17:18), David prayed for his infant child (2 Samuel 12:16) and for Solomon (1 Chronicles 29:19), and on many occasions parents brought their children to Jesus. That tradition must continue.

Family members must teach one another by word and by example all day long, every day (Deuteronomy 6:1-9; 2 Timothy 1:5; 3:15). Living the Christian witness constantly is, perhaps, the highest form of ministry. Actions do, in fact, speak louder than words.

Another ministry of vital importance in a family is forgiveness. Jacob and Esau forgave. Joseph forgave his brothers of gross injustices and went beyond that to literally save their lives and the lives of their wives and children. Jesus, of course, is the greatest example of forgiveness. He prayed from the cross, '''Father, forgive them, for they do not know what they do''' (Luke 23:34.) And He has taught us to pray: "'And forgive us our sins, for we also forgive everyone who is indebted to us'" (Luke 11:4). To hold a grudge against another person, family or not, is to remain unforgiven ourselves.

Family members also must minister to one another by sharing physical resources. The passage in 1 Timothy 5:1-8 admonishes families and churches to care for widows. A person who does not provide for his or her family, Paul says, "has denied the faith and is worse than an unbeliever."

Families must join hearts and hands to minister to one another. Nonjudgmental, unconditional love must be communicated within the home. Unrelenting prayer and unselfish generosity must be constant.

REFLECT AND MEDITATE

In explaining the prayer that He taught His disciples to pray, Jesus said, "'For if you forgive men their trespasses, your heavenly Father will also forgive you. But if you do not forgive men their trespasses, neither will your Father forgive your trespasses'" (Matthew 6:14, 15).

REACT AND RESPOND

Search your heart for bitterness, grudges or unforgiveness. Especially examine your attitudes toward your family members both immediate and extended. If there are unresolved conflicts there, give them to Jesus. Go to the person in question and communicate genuine forgiveness.

REJOICE AND WORSHIP

Sing a hymn of full surrender to the cleansing power of the blood of Jesus. Make it a prayer that any root of bitterness might be destroyed. Suggestions:

"Cleanse Me"
"I Surrender All"
"Just As I Am"

Accept God's forgiveness and extend God's forgiveness. Rejoice in the knowledge that as you forgive one another, you are forgiven. Sing the old gospel song "An Old Account Settled."

Study 3

THE FAMILY--ITS MINISTRY IS OUTWARD TO THE COMMUNITY OF FAITH

READ AND RESEARCH (Galatians 6:1-10; Acts 9:36-43)

Church members often discuss the responsibility of the church to the family and the responsibility of the family to the church as if the church and the home were completely separate entities. The church does not exist without people. And people generally live in families of various configurations. Therefore, the ministry of church and family is reciprocal.

Christian families have an obligation to reach outward to others. In this session, the obligation to reach outward to the community of faith will be considered.

Galatians 6:10 seems to indicate that some kind of special care should be given by Christians to each other: "Let us do good to all, especially to those who are of the household of faith." Paul gave a list of the manner in which we should be involved in helping our brothers and sisters. We are to

1. Restore someone who has sinned; this is to be done gently, because we may be tempted to sin ourselves.

2. Fulfill the law of Christ by bearing one another's burdens; this should involve sympathy, empathy, prayer and assistance.

3. Be humble.

4. Share our means with those who teach us the Word.

5. Work cheerfully knowing that God rewards faithfulness.

6. Do good to all--especially fellow believers.

Jesus in Matthew 5:42 tells us: "'Give to him who asks you, and from him who wants to borrow from you do not turn away.'" Further on in the same discourse, however, He tells us not to do these charitable deeds in order to be noticed by other people. If we do, we will not be rewarded by God (Matthew 6:1-4).

There are some scriptural examples of Christian families ministering to one another. The story of Dorcas is told in Acts 9:36-41. Dorcas had died but was restored to life by God through Peter. Dorcas was ''full of good works and charitable deeds.'' It seems that she made clothing and gave it to people in need. Those that were there mourning were identified as ''the saints and widows,'' so it may be inferred that much, if not all, of her charity was toward other believers.

Another type of family ministry that is mentioned in the New Testament is that of hospitality. The family at Bethany--Mary, Martha and Lazarus--opened their home to Jesus and His disciples. (He also was entertained in the homes of ''sinners'' who apparently were won to Him.) The disciples at Emmaus even hosted Jesus, unaware of exactly who He was until He disappeared.

The apostle Paul was housed and cared for by various church families. He and Silas were ministered to by Lydia at Philippi (Acts 16:11-15). Later, in the same city, the converted jailer and his family ministered to and fed Paul and Silas. In Caesarea, Philip the evangelist and his family kept Paul and his companions in their home. Publius and others at Malta kept Paul and provided for him. Paul, in turn, prayed for their sick, who were healed by God. Paul was ministered to by various churches, families and individual Christians. In his letters he often mentioned their prayers, their hospitality, their visits to him in prison, their letters, their offerings of money, as well as their gifts of needed supplies.

Job spoke of the poor and the evils of a lack of compassion in Job 24. In Job 29:13, however, he spoke of the blessing of causing '''the widow's heart to sing.'''

Not only should Christian families reach out to the community of faith by their hospitality, gifts and genuine Christian example, but they should do these things in the name of the Lord.

REFLECT AND MEDITATE

Think about the words of Jesus: '''He who receives you receives Me, and he who receives Me receives Him who sent Me. He who receives a prophet in the name of a prophet shall receive a prophet's reward. And he who receives a righteous man in the name of a righteous man shall receive a righteous man's reward. And whoever gives one of these little ones only a cup of cold water in the name of a disciple, assuredly, I say to you, he shall by no means lose his reward''' (Matthew 10:40-42).

REACT AND RESPOND

Have a family meeting. Share the need for family ministry to fellow Christians. Make a list of ways your family can minister to them in word, deed and example. Include both individual and group activities. Set definite dates, times and procedures for acting on your list. Read Acts 4:34, 35.

REJOICE AND WORSHIP

Read the story in Luke 21:1-4. Resolve to give cheerfully. Teach your family members to do likewise.

Discipleship

THE FAMILY--ITS MINISTRY IS OUTWARD TO THE WORLD

READ AND RESEARCH (Matthew 25:31-46; Luke 10:25-37; 6:38)

While it is urgent that Christian families minister to the community of faith, it is very important to reach out to the world as well. Jesus came first to the house of Israel, but His work was not limited to them. Likewise, Christian families must reach out beyond the walls of their homes and churches to the rest of the world.

In the giving of the Law, several instructions were included for families to provide for "strangers" and the poor. Strangers were to be treated kindly because the Israelites were once strangers in Egypt themselves. The crops in the corners of the fields were to be left for those who would need them. Gleaning was to be allowed. In fact, Ruth fed herself and her mother-in-law in that manner for a while. Strangers could eat any food from a field as long as they were not wasteful and carried none away. Jewish homes were to provide food and shelter for the traveler. In these and in many other ways, Israel was instructed to care for the poor person and the stranger.

Jesus gave a discourse on feeding, housing, clothing and visiting those who are in need. He said that in doing these things or in refusing to do them, we were either doing them or refusing to do them to Him. Furthermore, the decision concerning our inheritance of the Kingdom or our banishment into everlasting punishment will be based on our response in these matters. These scriptures in Matthew 25:31-46 emphasize the importance of an individual's and a family's reaching outward to the world.

Jesus told a parable in Luke 10:25-37 which responds to the question "Who is my neighbor?" or "To whom shall my family minister?" The Good Samaritan gave his time, gave his care and gave his money to a total stranger. That parable, along with the Matthew 25 discourse, makes our mandate for service to the world quite clear. What greater way to respond to these words of Jesus than as a family unit!

In addition to reaching out to the world by material means, the Pentecostal family must reach out to the world spiritually. When Joel prophesied about the outpouring of the Spirit, the whole family was included.

"'And it shall come to pass afterward that I will pour out My Spirit on all flesh; your sons and your daughters shall prophesy, your old men shall dream dreams, your young men shall see visions; and also on My menservants and on My maidservants I will pour out My Spirit in those days'" (Joel 2:28, 29).

When Jesus promised the Holy Spirit, He gave an overview of what that empowerment would mean: "'You shall be witnesses to Me'" (Acts 1:8).

In Acts 10 Peter was preaching to Cornelius, a Gentile, and to "his relatives and close friends" when the Holy Spirit fell on them. The receiving of the Holy Spirit was a family affair for Cornelius and his household. So it is obvious that families should seek God together. It follows, then, that families should also serve as witnesses together.

The household of Philip the evangelist was an example of a Spirit-filled family. "On the next day we who were Paul's companions departed and came to Caesarea, and entered the house of Philip the evangelist, who was one of the seven, and stayed with him. Now this man had four virgin daughters who prophesied" (Acts 21:8, 9).

The Pentecostal family today should be individually and corporately involved in an outward ministry to the world. This activity should include ministry to both material and spiritual needs.

REFLECT AND MEDITATE

Are you as an individual and your family as a group involved in ministry? Is your ministry in balance in terms of meeting both physical and spiritual needs of those inside the home and outside the home, inside the church and outside the church?

REACT AND RESPOND

Check up on your family participation in ministry to the world outside the home and the church. The chart is based on Matthew 25:31-46.

	Self	Family as a Unit	Other Family Mem.
Giving food			
Giving drink			
Giving shelter			
Giving clothes			
Visiting sick			
Visiting prison			
Benevolence			

Rating scale:
+ = very active;
o = somewhat active;
$ = give money to finance but not active;
X = no involvement
Develop plans to bring balance to your family ministry.

REJOICE AND WORSHIP

"'Give, and it will be given to you: good measure, pressed down, shaken together, and running over will be put into your bosom. For with the same measure that you use, it will be measured back to you'" (Luke 6:38).

Study 5

THE FAMILY--ITS MINISTRY IS BALANCED

READ AND RESEARCH (Isaiah 54:11-17; 2 Timothy 1:1-7)

Family living, especially parenting, is not always easy. Leadership in a family is, indeed, a grave responsibility. One of the heaviest responsibilities and one of the greatest powers of parenting is that of creating experiences. Young children form all their concepts by interacting with their environment or acting upon their environment with their senses. They learn by seeing, smelling, hearing, touching and even tasting.

Even when children grow older and can use language along with their senses to learn, their experiences are still vital. One's experiences shape everything he or she thinks, knows and believes about the world. The perception of every experience is based on the memory of all the experiences that went before it. One is never totally free of his or her past. This is true of spiritual or religious experiences as well as sensory or physical ones.

It is up to parents and other family and church leaders to select and provide experiences for children, youth and, sometimes, dependent adults. How can they make the right selections? How can a balance of activities be maintained between a family's upward, inward and outward ministries? How much time should be spent at home? In church? In the world?

Is education to be done primarily by the home, the church or the school? And is that school to be public, private or home-based?

These are questions difficult to answer, and the answers will be different for each family and may be different for various members of the same family.

In making decisions about the balance of experiences in the family, following are some of the many factors to be considered:

1. "And let us consider one another in order to stir up love and good works, not forsaking the assembling of ourselves together, as is the manner of some, but exhorting one another, and so much the more as you see the Day approaching" (Hebrews 10:24, 25).

2. "Children's children are the crown of old men, and the glory of children is their father" (Proverbs 17:6).

Young and old alike need intergenerational experiences. With our mobile society, extended families--grandparents, aunts, uncles, cousins--are not as likely to live nearby. Family and church leaders should provide activities which allow all groups to interact.

3. Deuteronomy 6:7 promotes all-day-long, in-the-home and out-of-doors religious education. "'You shall teach them diligently to your children, and shall talk of them when you sit in your house, when you walk by the way, when you lie down, and when you rise up.'" Yet the Israelites and the early Christians also were involved in teaching and being taught in the temple, in synagogues and in home churches.

4. A variety of experiences must be planned that involves readers and nonreaders, the active and the passive, all learning styles, those with differing interests, those with varying intellectual ability and those with other differences.

There are other factors to consider, but balance is the key. Satan is just as pleased to see your family get off the scriptural or spiritual tract on one side as he is to see you get off on the other. Set and seek your goals and your course in prayer!

REFLECT AND MEDITATE
Ecclesiastes 3:1-8:
"To everything there is a season,
A time for every purpose under heaven:
A time to be born, And a time to die;
A time to plant, And a time to pluck what is planted;
A time to kill, And a time to heal;
A time to break down, And a time to build up;
A time to weep, And a time to laugh;
A time to mourn, And a time to dance;

A time to cast away stones, And a time to gather stones;

A time to embrace, And a time to refrain from embracing;

A time to gain, And a time to lose;

A time to keep, And a time to throw away;

A time to tear, And a time to sew;

A time to keep silence, And a time to speak;

A time to love, And a time to hate;

A time of war, And a time of peace.''

(The preacher, commonly believed to be Solomon, is talking about balance.)

REACT AND RESPOND

Think and pray about balance in your life, your family and your church.

REJOICE AND WORSHIP

''Then Samuel took a stone and set it up between Mizpah and Shen, and called its name Ebenezer, saying, 'Thus far the Lord has helped us''' (1 Samuel 7:12).

Praise the Lord for helping you and your family to the point of spiritual growth that you have now attained. Look forward by faith to His bringing you into full maturity.

Sing the old hymn ''Come, Thou Fount.''

DISCIPLESHIP COMMITMENT

Recognizing that one of life's greatest challenges is that of ministry to and through my family, I hearwith commit myself once again to becoming the kind of supportive family member your Word commands. By your grace and through the strength of your Holy Spirit. Amen

CHAPTER 12

What Is the Church?

INTRODUCTION

The word *church* means different things to different people. To many, it refers to a building with stained-glass windows and a steeple. To others it is a denomination. And to still others it is something you experience or watch on television. While all of these ideas express our cultural orientation, they do not touch the true significance of the biblical meaning of the word *church*.

More than 100 times in the New Testament the word *church* is used. Each time, it is the translation of the Greek word *ekklesia*. Understanding the root and meaning of this word will help us gain an understanding of the question before us this week--What is the church?

Ekklesia is a compound word composed of the prefix *ek* and *klesia*. The prefix is a Greek preposition meaning "out of." *Klesia* is a passive form of the Greek verb *kaleo*, which means "to call." Together, they mean "the called out ones."

Prior to its Christian usage, *ekklesia* had a political meaning. In Greece, the *ekklesia* was a regularly summoned assembly of certain citizens of a city. At the call of a herald, these citizens came out of their homes, separated themselves from the rest of the inhabitants of the city and assembled to discuss the affairs of the city.

In the Old Testament, the assembly of Israel is synonymous with church. In fact, in the Greek translation of the Old Testament, called the Septuagint, this assembly is called the *ekklesia*. It was the assembly of the people of God who had been called out from the nations to be God's chosen people.

In the inspiration of the New Testament, the Holy Spirit selected this unique word to describe God's people under the new covenant. The church, then, is a company of people who have been called out of the world by God, who have experienced redemption by His grace through faith in Jesus Christ, and who live in the unity of the Spirit. The church is, in fact, the community of the redeemed (1 Peter 2:9, 10).

It is important that we understand the church is not a building, although the gathering of the church may be *in* a building. The church is not a denomination, although Christians may find a larger fellowship through denominational affiliation. The church is not something you go to or watch on television. The church is people, a special people--the people of God.

In the next five sessions, you will come to a fuller understanding of the nature of the church. You will have the opportunity to be guided by the Holy Spirit in your study of the Scriptures as you uncover the following truths about God's church:

1. The Divine Origin of the Church
2. The Church as the People of God
3. The Church as a Colony of Citizens
4. The Church as a Flock Under a Shepherd
5. The Church as the Temple of God

DISCIPLESHIP GOAL

To better understand the fact and the nature of Christ's church on earth and thus to develop personal faith in a secure future

READING ASSIGNMENT

The Living Book, pp. 133 - 148

Study 1

THE DIVINE ORIGIN OF THE CHURCH

READ AND RESEARCH (Matthew 16:13-19)

There are human institutions, but there are also divine institutions. The Scriptures indicate there are three institutions that are of divine origin: (1) the family (Genesis 1:28; 2:24, 25); (2) civil government (Romans 13:1; 1 Peter 2:13-17); and (3) the covenant community. In the Old Testament, the covenant community was Israel, but in the New Testament, the covenant community is the church.

In today's passage, we see the divine origin of the church. Answering the questions below will help you gain insight into this important truth. Write your answers on a separate sheet of paper.

1. How did Peter answer Christ's question, and how did he reach this conclusion (vv. 16, 17)?

2. What is the implication of the phrase "I will build" (v. 18)?

3. To whom does the church belong (v. 18)?

4. What authority did Jesus give the church (v. 19)?

The rock of the church is not Peter, but rather his confession, "You are the Christ, the Son of the Living God." This was revealed truth. Because Jesus is who He claimed to be, the church stands sure, and hell's gates will never prevail against it!

REFLECT AND MEDITATE

What type of security does it give to you personally when you consider Christ's response to Peter's declaration in this passage? Take a moment and meditate on this.

REACT AND RESPOND

Write out a prayer to the Father, thanking Him for the Church.

As you attend worship services at your church this week, look around you and realize you are part of something that transcends human ability. You are a part of a divine institution--the *church*.

Study 2

THE CHURCH AS THE PEOPLE OF GOD

READ AND RESEARCH (1 Peter 2:9, 10)

One of the most powerful and profound prophecies of the Old Testament is found in Jeremiah 31:31-33. Here God spoke of a new covenant and said in verse 33, "'I will put My law in their minds, and write it on their hearts; and I will be their God, and they shall be My people.'"

The book of Hebrews is filled with references to this new covenant and tells us that Jesus is the surety (guarantee) of it (Hebrews 7:22). Through Christ's death and resurrection, God established a new covenant, not just with Israel but with all who believe on the name of His Son. The benefit of this covenant is that believers become His people and He becomes their God (Romans 9:24-26; 2 Corinthians 6:16).

In the passage for today, Peter addressed this subject. Let the following questions help you grasp the full impact of what it means to be the people of God.

1. What four key phrases did Peter use to describe the people of God (v. 9)?

2. What is the primary task of God's people (v. 9)?

3. From what and into what did God call us (v. 9)?

4. How did Peter contrast the believer's former status with his current standing (v. 10)?

The church is not just a human gathering. It is the congregation of a special people. We are a chosen people, a called people, a covenant people. We are the people of God!

REFLECT AND MEDITATE

As a Christian you are in God's church. This means that you are part of the people of God. Reflect on what this means to you personally.

Discipleship

REACT AND RESPOND

Write out a commitment to God that would demonstrate your desire to openly show forth His praises in your life.

REJOICE AND WORSHIP

In today's vernacular, Peter said, "Once you were a nobody, but now you are a somebody!" (1 Peter 2:10). Take time now to praise God for making you somebody special.

Study 3

THE CHURCH AS A COLONY OF CITIZENS

READ AND RESEARCH (Ephesians 2:11-19)

We all remember studying about the 13 original colonies that eventually gave birth to the United States. But what exactly is a colony? A colony, by definition, is a group of people living in a location other than their homeland but remaining under the control of their parent country and maintaining all of its customs and lifestyles.

The New Testament depicts the church as a colony of citizens. We are citizens of the kingdom of God, bound in allegiance to our heavenly King and committed to living a Kingdom lifestyle (Philippians 3:20; Ephesians 2:1-6; 4:17-24). Because we are citizens of the kingdom of God, we are aliens and pilgrims in this world (1 Peter 2:11).

In today's passage, Paul talked about the marvelous work of God that brought us into our new citizenship. Look carefully at this passage as you answer the following questions:

1. How did Paul describe the Christian's pre-salvation status (v. 12)?

2. Who is represented by the pronoun *you* in verses 11-13?

3. What two groups did Jesus make one and reconcile to God (vv. 15, 16)?

4. To what does the term "one body" refer in verse 16?

5. Because of what Christ has done, what is the Christian's new standing with God (v. 19)?

Once we were strangers to God and citizens of this world. But through Christ we, the members of His church, are now citizens of the kingdom of God and strangers in this world. We can truly celebrate in the words of the old gospel song, "This world is not my home; I'm just a-passing through!"

REFLECT AND MEDITATE

Every citizen has duties to perform as a loyal resident of his country. Reflect on some of the duties a citizen of God's kingdom is called on to perform.

REACT AND RESPOND

Based on your reflection, what Kingdom duties have you failed to perform? Write out a specific plan to improve the execution of your heavenly citizenship in these areas.

REJOICE AND WORSHIP

Addressing God as your King, spend some time in personal praise for His bringing you into His kingdom.

Study 4

THE CHURCH AS A FLOCK UNDER A SHEPHERD

READ AND RESEARCH (John 10:1-16)

The word *congregation* comes from the Latin word *grex* which means "a flock." This word brings to mind an image that will help us to understand still another aspect of the nature of the church--that of a flock.

A flock is a group of sheep gathered around a shepherd. In the case of the church, that shepherd is Jesus. The writer of Hebrews called Him the "great Shepherd of the sheep" (Hebrews 13:20). Peter referred to Jesus as "the Shepherd and Overseer [Guardian] of your souls" (1 Peter 2:25).

In addition to this divine shepherd, God also gave human shepherds to tend His flock. These are the pastors Christ has placed in the church (Ephesians 4:11). (The Greek word for "pastor" and "shepherd" is the same, *poimen*. It is their duty to care for and feed the sheep and to protect them from the "savage wolves" that the enemy sends (1 Peter 5:1-4; Acts 20:28, 29).

In our study passage for today, Jesus' teaching on the Good Shepherd gives us a better understanding of the church as a flock under a shepherd. The following questions will help you in your study of this passage.

1. The church is the "called out ones." How does verse 3 relate to this definition?

2. What does the Good Shepherd do for His sheep (v. 11)?

3. Does the Good Shepherd know each of His sheep? Do they know Him (v. 14)?

4. Who are the "other sheep" of verse 16?

While there are many denominations and many local churches, Jesus made it clear there is only "one flock" (John 10:16). It is not man-made ecumenism that brings the worldwide body of Christ together. It is a common faith in the one shepherd, Jesus Christ, that truly makes us one.

REFLECT AND MEDITATE

Out of your relationship with God, meditate on some of the characteristics of the Good Shepherd you have come to realize.

REACT AND RESPOND

Christ has graciously given pastors to the church. Why not write your pastor a letter of appreciation, assuring him of your prayers?

REJOICE AND WORSHIP

The Twenty-third Psalm is the Shepherd Psalm. Read this psalm, and as an act of confession, insert your name for the personal pronouns *I, my* and *me*.

Study 5

THE CHURCH AS THE TEMPLE OF GOD

READ AND RESEARCH (Ephesians 2:19-22)

To devout Jews, the site of the ancient temple is a holy place. All that remains today is one wall. It is often referred to as the "wailing wall" because of the intercessory prayers that are constantly said before it.

The temple was of great importance to Israel. It unified the nation as the people of God. It represented their covenant relationship to Jehovah God; and it was there, in the Holy of Holies, God's presence on earth was manifest.

In the new covenant, God also has a temple. Yet this temple is not of mortar and stone. It is made of people who have been fashioned as living stones into a spiritual house--the church (1 Peter 2:4, 5). Paul said it plainly: "Do you not know that you are the temple of God?" (1 Corinthians 3:16).

In our study today, Paul was writing about the church as God's temple. Look closely at this passage as you answer the following questions:

1. What place in the church do the apostles and prophets have (v. 20)?

2. What place does Jesus have in the church (v. 20)?

3. In whom is the whole building joined together (v. 21)?

4. Into what does this building grow (v. 21)?

5. Who dwells in this temple (v. 22)?

As the Old Testament temple represented to the world the presence of God, so today the church, as God's temple, exists in the world to give evidence that God is alive and real. Unlike the physical temple, however, the church will never be destroyed, because it is built on the Rock--Jesus Christ the Son of the living God--and is held together by Christ, the chief cornerstone!

Discipleship

REFLECT AND MEDITATE

Paul offered a stern warning against defiling God's temple (the church) in 1 Corinthians 3:17. Reflect for a moment on how God's temple could be defiled.

REACT AND RESPOND

In what ways would God have you as a living stone in His temple represent Him to those around you Write this down as a commitment.

REJOICE AND WORSHIP

Sacrifices were offered in the temple. Our sacrifice is the fruit of our lips--praise (Hebrews 13:15). Take time now to audibly give thanks to His name!

DISCIPLESHIP COMMITMENT

In response to what you have learned from God's Word this week, pray this prayer to the Father as an act of worship and commitment:

Dear Father, I praise You for Your sovereign acts among men, that You have chosen to call out from every tribe and nation a people for Your name. I thank You that You called me and that I am a part of Your church. By Your grace, I will show forth Your praise, I will honor Your kingly rule, I will listen for Your shepherd's voice, and I will be a true living stone in Your temple. In Jesus' name. Amen.

CHAPTER 13

What Is the Believer's Place in the Church?

INTRODUCTION

For most Christians the first place the church-in-theory meets the church-in-fact is in church membership. Just who are the members of the church, and what place do these people have? There are two prevalent views about church membership?

First, there is the view that the local church is like a school in which people learn to become Christians. Usually, the churches that accept this view place heavy emphasis on the sacraments (baptism and Communion) as a means of God's grace. These are viewed as a way of educating and training church members in the Christian life. Baptism is administered to infants as an initiation rite into the church and the beginning of the learning process into Christianity. It provides a kind of preliminary membership. Later, usually around 10 or 12 years of age, a child must receive instruction in the Christian faith and be received into full membership by receiving his first Communion. This is sometimes called confirmation.

The second view of church membership sees the local church as a family. You do not enroll in a family; you are born into it. In this view, church membership is not inclusive, but exclusive. It is reserved for those who have been born again. Baptism is administered only to those who have professed Christ as Savior. Baptism itself is not the new birth, but it gives public witness to a personal conversion. It is a symbolic reenactment of what happens when a believer becomes a child of God--we are buried with Christ through baptism into His death that we may be raised to live a new life (Romans 6:3-6).

This latter view of church membership is most in harmony with New Testament principles. Luke wrote that following the Day of Pentecost, "the Lord added to the church daily those who were being saved" (Acts 2:47). Church membership was first viewed as a mystical union with Christ that found its visible expression in membership in a local body of believers. It is a spiritual work of the Holy Spirit that places a person in the body of Christ (1 Corinthians 12:13).

Furthermore, the Scriptures designate church members by certain names which could not apply to the unconverted--"all who believed" (Acts 2:44), "disciples" (Acts 6:2; 11:26), "saints" (2 Corinthians 1:1; Ephesians 4:12), "the brethren" (Acts 15:33), "the elect of God" (Colossians 3:12) and "Christians" (Acts 11:26).

Church membership, then, is more than a church roll. It is more than a certificate of membership. It is a relationship. It is a salvation relationship with Jesus Christ, and it is a responsible relationship with a specific group of people.

The most frequently used and best-developed image of the church in the New Testament is that of a body. Often, the church is simply called the body of Christ. It is through our understanding of this image of the church that we can grasp a better idea of our place as believers in the church. This will be this week's focus. These are the subjects you will be studying:

1. The Church as a Body
2. The Church as a Relational Body
3. The Church as a Complete Body
4. The Church as a Diversified Body
5. The Church as a Growing Body

DISCIPLESHIP GOAL

To find that personal spiritual calling God has placed on your life and to grasp how He wishes you to fulfill that calling within the body of Christ

READING ASSIGNMENT

The Living Book, pp. 148 - 160

Discipleship

Study 1

THE CHURCH AS A BODY

READ AND RESEARCH (1 Corinthians 12:12-27)

As one reads the writings of the apostle Paul, he quickly discovers that Paul's favorite term for the church is "the body of Christ." He specifically referred to it as "the church, which is His body" (Ephesians 1:22, 23) and "His body, which is the church" (Colossians 1:24). He also said that Christians are "called in one body" (Colossians 3:15), "baptized into one body" (1 Corinthians 12:13) and are "members of His body" (Ephesians 5:30).

By using this image the emphasis is placed on three things: (1) the unity of the church, (2) the interdependence of its members and (3) their vital relationship with its head, Jesus Christ.

Our passage for today is the most extensive discourse by Paul on this subject. The following questions should help you gain insight into its truth:

1. How is the unity of the body of Christ emphasized (v. 12)?

2. How does a person become a part of the body of Christ (v. 13)?

3. How is the diversity of the body pictured (vv. 14-16)?

4. How does Paul emphasize the necessity of each member's function in the body (vv. 17-22)?

5. What should each member's attitude be toward each other (vv. 23-26)?

Every believer has been baptized by the Holy Spirit into the body of Christ. Each one has his function, and none are dispensable.

REFLECT AND MEDITATE

Reflect on which part of your physical body you would like to be without. Your eyes? Your toes? Your tongue? Your liver? Obviously, you don't want to be without any of them. The same should be your attitude toward the body of Christ. No member is unnecessary. Meditate on the value of the various members of your local church.

REACT AND RESPOND

Paul said we in the body of Christ are to suffer with each other and to rejoice with each other. Is there someone in your church with whom you could obey this admonition? Make plans to do it today.

REJOICE AND WORSHIP

Thank God for your local church and the powerful network of relationships God has placed in it.

Study 2

THE CHURCH AS A RELATIONAL BODY

READ AND RESEARCH (Ephesians 4:15, 16)

If the human body is to live and develop, all of its systems must function without interruption or hindrance. A limb through which blood does not flow becomes gangrenous. An organ cut off from the nerve center becomes paralyzed.

So it is with the body of Christ. Only constant interaction among the members will maintain its life. Only through the Head (Christ) can the whole body have cohesion. By dependence on the Head, the whole body, its various parts joined together, forms a harmonious structure. By each member's fulfilling his function, the body of Christ grows to maturity.

In today's passage Paul spoke of the interdependence of the body of Christ. Let's see what he has to say.

1. What should be our manner of communication with each other (v. 15)?

2. Who is the head of the church (v. 15)?

3. Who has knit and joined the body of Christ together (v. 16)?

4. What causes the body of Christ to grow (v. 16)?

5. What does the word *edify* mean?

Your role in Christ's body is important, not only for yourself but for the well-being of the rest of the body as well.

REFLECT AND MEDITATE

Reflect on how each part of your human body works together for the common good. Now meditate on how this is to be the same in the body of Christ.

REACT AND RESPOND

What contribution are you making to the edification of your local church? If you are not satisfied with your current level of involvement, write out what plans you are making to improve in this area.

REJOICE AND WORSHIP

Write out a brief prayer of thanksgiving to God for the spiritual growth that is occurring in your life through your local church.

Study 3

THE CHURCH AS A COMPLETE BODY

READ AND RESEARCH (1 Corinthians 1:4-7)

The human body is sufficient in itself. God has provided in the body all that is necessary for life. It can nourish itself, move, work, think, feel and choose. It does not require outside aid except in infancy or in sickness. It is complete.

The same is true of the body of Christ. God has given us everything that is needed for life and godliness (see 2 Peter 1:3, *NIV*). A healthy, mature church has no need for the world's help. It is a complete body.

History has proven this to be true. Even if a local church is isolated from the rest of the Christian world or is in a hostile environment, it survives and grows by that which God provides.

Paul wrote of this truth to the Corinthian church. The following questions are to guide you in your discovery of the information found in today's passage.

1. Who bestowed God's grace on them (v. 4)?

2. How and by whom were they enriched (v. 5)?

3. In what did they not fall short (v. 7)?

Christ has given to the church grace, enrichment and every spiritual gift that is needed for its life and ministry. If the church has a need, it must look within itself to the resources God has provided, not to outside help.

REFLECT AND MEDITATE

Read 2 Peter 1:3 in the *New International Version* and meditate on the words "everything needed." This is what Christ has given to the church.

REACT AND RESPOND

Is there something you need in your spiritual life right now? God has placed the resources within your local church. He wants you to avail yourself of His grace through His body. Share your need with a mature member of your church or with your pastor. Allow ministry from the body to flow to you.

REJOICE AND WORSHIP

In worship, take time now to sing this familiar chorus to the Lord:

> *You're all I need,*
> *You're all I need,*
> *Jesus, You're all I need.*

(Repeat from the beginning.)

Study 4

THE CHURCH AS A DIVERSIFIED BODY

READ AND RESEARCH (1 Corinthians 12:4-6, 12-14)

Paul emphasized there is but one body of Christ, but within this body are many members (Romans 12:4, 5; 1 Corinthians 12:14). This speaks of the diversity of the unity.

Unity is a scriptural mandate to be pursued by all Christians in their relationships with fellow believers (Ephesians 4:3). Yet unity is not uniformity. Within the body of Christ are diversities of nationalities, cultures social classes (1 Corinthians 12:13) and spiritual gifts (1 Corinthians 12:4-6). In a local body of believers are diversities of temperament, opinions and ideas. But none of these are incompatible with essential spiritual unity. Despite our diversity, we have one body, one Spirit, one hope, one Lord, one faith, one baptism and one Father (Ephesians 4:4-6).

Let's look at how Paul emphasized the diversity of the body of Christ in today's passage.

1. What three types of diversities did Paul mention (vv. 4-6)?

2. How many times did Paul use the words *diversities* and *differences*, and how many times did he use the word *same* (vv. 4-6)?

3. What do you think the phrase "all in all" in verse 6 means?

4. What diversities did Paul mention in verse 13?

Unity, yes! Uniformity, no! This is God's plan. This is how He has fashioned the church.

REFLECT AND MEDITATE

Reflect on the diversity in your local church. Meditate on how each person's uniqueness contributes to the overall good.

REACT AND RESPOND

What unique contribution can you make to your local church? Write this down.

REJOICE AND WORSHIP

God has made you a unique person so that you may make a difference. Thank Him for His handiwork!

Study 5

THE CHURCH AS A GROWING BODY

READ AND RESEARCH (Ephesians 4:11-15)

In the human body, growth is normal. Each part of the body contributes to the growth of all the other organs as well as to its own. If a part or organ of the body ceases to grow, the body is crippled, malformed or invalid.

It is no different in the church, the body of Christ. If the church is to fulfill its function, all the members must grow and reach maturity. It is from the Head (Christ) that the whole body, supported by its joints and ligaments, receives both coordination and strength to grow to the stature Christ desires (Colossians 2:19).

In today's passage Paul addresses the dynamics of the church as a growing body. As you study this passage, the following questions will serve as your guide.

1. For what purpose were the ministry gifts given by Christ to the church (v. 12)?

2. What kind of unity is described in verse 13?

3. How is maturity described in verse 13?

4. How is immaturity described in verse 14?

5. How are we to grow up (v. 15)?

The New Testament speaks of growing churches and weak, immature churches (1 Corinthians 3:1, 2; Hebrews 5:11-14). God wants His church to grow to maturity, and this growth depends on each of us.

REFLECT AND MEDITATE

Meditate on what it means to grow to the "measure of the stature of the fullness of Christ."

REACT AND RESPOND

Evaluate the maturity level of your local church as a whole. Where is there a need for spiritual growth? In what ways would God want you to promote growth in this area?

REJOICE AND WORSHIP

Pray for your local church to be the mature body God wants it to be, and thank God that He is going to use you as a part of this growth.

DISCIPLESHIP COMMITMENT

As a result of this week's study, pray this prayer to the Father to express your commitment to Him and His church:

Dear Father, I thank You for the church, the body of Christ. I praise You for the wonderful way You have assembled us. Teach me to appreciate the unique contribution that each member makes to my church. Let me learn to pursue unity while celebrating our diversity. I confess Your truth that within our church You have given all the resources needed to do Your work. We are complete in You! Through my life and the lives of all the members of our church, may we grow to the fullness of Christ. In Jesus' name. Amen.

CHAPTER 14

What Is the Believer's Responsibility in the Church?

INTRODUCTION

We have turned Christian work into a spectator sport, a concept foreign to the New Testament. Unfortunately, the word *minister* has become a term that suggests an office in the church as a status in the community. It usually designates an educated religious leader and a professional figure in society. Such an idea dulls the impact of the New Testament principle of ministry. Ministry is not the exclusive work of the ordained clergy, but it is the privilege and the responsibility of all the saints (Ephesians 4:12).

In our modern society we have come to value the specialist. Physicians specialize. Lawyers specialize. Artists specialize. Teachers specialize. The list goes on and on. It is only natural, then, that we should look to a specialist to do the work of the Lord. In Christian circles, "Call the expert" means "Let the minister do it." This is not the biblical picture of ministry, however. God never designed Christian service to be contracted out to experts. Ministry belongs to the whole church.

What exactly is ministry? To answer this question, let's look at Jesus. He saw His purpose in the world in terms of service. He said He "did not come to be served, but to serve" (Mark 10:45). He made it clear that His followers were to follow His example. He said, "Whoever desires to become great among you, let him be your servant" (Matthew 20:26). Ministry is service.

Christian ministry is called a "'ministry of the Word'" (Acts 6:4), a "ministry of reconciliation" (2 Corinthians 5:18), and a ministry of the "new covenant" (2 Corinthians 3:6). In short, ministry is any effort we make to advance the gospel, to apply to the hearts of men and women the unique ministry of Jesus Christ.

The Greek word most often used to describe Christian service is *diakonia*. It suggests common labor, a service without status. Christian ministry means labor for Christ without regard for religious rank.

In our call to Christian service, God does not send us forth unprepared. He has placed leaders within His body to equip the saints (Ephesians 4:11, 12). Also, he has graciously bestowed spiritual gifts on each member of His body so that they may be able contributors to the church's ministry (Roman 12:6).

The focus of this week will be on the believer's responsibility for ministry. Here is what you will have the opportunity to study:

1. The Priesthood of All Believers
2. The Giftedness of All Believers
3. The Various Gifts of the Spirit
4. The Priestly (Motivational) Gifts
5. Ministering According to Your Gift

DISCIPLESHIP GOAL

To understand every believer's responsibility within the church body, especially in terms of ministry one to another

READING ASSIGNMENT

The Living Book, pp. 160 - 175

Study 1

THE PRIESTHOOD OF ALL BELIEVERS

READ AND RESEARCH (1 Peter 2:5, 9)

The Protestant Reformation was a sovereign move of God in human history. By the 16th Century the church had fallen far from its biblical heritage. This condition had brought to Europe what was justly called the Dark Ages.

God raised up men to rescue His church. These were men like Martin Luther, John Huss and John Calvin. They, along with the other Reformers, protested the church's departure from the truth. As a result, three cardinal truths were recaptured by the church: (1) The absolute authority of the Scriptures for faith and practice, (2) justification by faith alone and (3) the priesthood of all believers.

Because of the sinfulness of men's hearts, man could not enter God's presence. So to allow ministry, God sanctified (set apart) a special class of men to be His priests. They alone had access to His presence.

However, Jesus our Great High Priest has made atonement for our sins and opened up a new and living way for every redeemed person to have access to God (Hebrews 10:19, 20). This was the significance of the rending of the temple veil when Jesus was crucified.

Peter wrote about this wonderful truth in today's Scripture passage. Let's look at it carefully.

1. What adjective describes the Christian's priesthood in verse 5?

2. What type of sacrifices do New Testament priests offer (v. 5)?

3. What does it mean to say that we are a "royal priesthood" (v. 9)?

Every believer is a priest (Revelation 1:6; 5:10). We have the privilege of access to the Father. We have the responsibility of ministering God's grace to mankind.

REFLECT AND MEDITATE

Reflect on the awesomeness of man's entering God's presence. Meditate on the privilege Christ has given you to do so.

REACT AND RESPOND

As a priest you are to minister His grace to others. Find someone today to whom you can offer your priestly ministry.

REJOICE AND WORSHIP

Enter into God's presence through worship and praise. God has given you this privilege. Take advantage of it by spending some unhurried time with your Lord.

Study 2

THE GIFTEDNESS OF ALL BELIEVERS

READ AND RESEARCH (1 Peter 4:10, 11)

Everyone enjoys receiving a gift. Opening a brightly wrapped package is an excitement that both children and adults enjoy.

The New Testament states that God has given every Christian two gifts. One is the gift of eternal life through Jesus Christ (Romans 6:23). The other is a spiritual gift (Romans 12:3-6). Both are gifts of grace, meaning they are given out of God's love, not because of any merit on our part.

A spiritual gift is an endowment from God, equipping a believer with what is necessary for him to fulfill his function within the body of Christ. It is not a natural ability or talent, although these too are from God. It is a divine enablement, and no believer is without a spiritual gift.

Look at what Peter had to say on this subject and discover the answers to the questions in today's passage.

1. Who has received a spiritual gift (v. 10)?

2. What is a person to do with his spiritual gift (v. 10)?

3. How can a Christian be a good steward of God's grace (v.10)?

4. Into what two broad categories did Peter divide the spiritual gifts (v. 11)?

5. What is the ultimate goal of our ministry (v. 11)?

God does not call you to minister for Him and then frustrate you by not supplying you with what is necessary to minister. He has equipped you with the necessary gifts.

REFLECT AND MEDITATE

Stop for a moment and reflect on what your giftedness means to you.

REACT AND RESPOND

If you do not know what your spiritual gift is, make a commitment today to begin your journey to discover this important aspect of your personhood and your priesthood.

REJOICE AND WORSHIP

God has not gifted you because of your merit but because of His grace. Pride has no place here, only humility and gratitude. Pray for God to let you always walk in humility before Him.

Study 3

THE VARIOUS GIFTS OF THE SPIRIT

READ AND RESEARCH (Romans 12:6-8; 1 Corinthians 12:6-11; Ephesians 4:7-11)

In 1 Corinthians 12:4-7, Paul mentioned three types of spiritual gifts: (1) gifts (*charismata*), (2) ministries (*diakonia*), and (3) activities, or manifestations, (*energemata*). To gain insight into the nature of spiritual gifts, one must understand the distinction between these categories of gifts.

The *charismata* (gifts of grace) are the priestly gifts--sometimes called motivational gifts. They are found in Romans 12:6-8. Every believer has been given a priestly gift. The *diakoniai* are the ministry gifts found in Ephesians 4:7-11. These are the leaders that Christ has given as a gift to the church. The *energemata* are the manifestation gifts of the Holy Spirit which are not permanent gifts to an individual but are bestowed on any yielded believer as the Spirit directs (1 Corinthians 12:11). They are found in 1 Corinthians 12:8-10.

Look up the three passages for today's study, and from them answer the following questions.

1. In Romans 12:6-8, what are the seven priestly gifts?

2. In 1 Corinthians 12:6-10, what are the nine manifestation gifts?

3. In Ephesians 4:11, what are the four ministry gifts? (Note: The key to answering this question is to look at the number of times the word *some* is used. The last gift is a combination gift.)

Isn't it wonderful to realize how God has graciously gifted His church? The church is truly a complete body by God's design.

REFLECT AND MEDITATE

Reflect on a time in your life when you received a special gift. Do you remember your feelings? Now turn those emotions toward God as you meditate on the gifts He has given you.

REACT AND RESPOND

God has given you a gift. As you discover what your gift is, it becomes your responsibility to develop it and use it for His glory. If you desire to do this, write out a commitment that expresses your desire.

REJOICE AND WORSHIP

Focus your attention on the Holy Spirit, and give Him praise for the gifts He has given to the Church.

Study 4

THE PRIESTLY (MOTIVATIONAL) GIFTS

READ AND RESEARCH (Romans 12:1-8)

Romans 12 is one of the best-known passages of Scripture. A clear understanding of it, however, can be gained by seeing it in light of the believer's priestly ministry. This can be seen in two ways. First, the passage speaks of sacrifice, and only priests can offer sacrifices acceptable to God. Second, the phrase ''your reasonable service'' is the translation of the Greek word *latreia*, which refers to the service of the priests in the tabernacle.

In verse 2 we are admonished to know God's will. Then Paul launched into a teaching on spiritual gifts, thus indicating that a significant step in discovering God's will is to know what priestly gift God has given you. These seven gifts and their definitions are listed below:

Prophecy--the capacity and motivation to readily perceive the will of God, proclaim it boldly and pray for it to be accomplished.

Serving--the capacity and motivation to meet the needs of others through practical service.

Teaching--the capacity and motivation to search out truth and to present truth in a logical systematic manner.

Exhortation--the capacity and motivation to stimulate the faith of others through the application of truth to their lives.

Giving--the capacity and motivation to give liberally to meet the needs of others and the needs of the ministry of the body of Christ.

Ruling--the capacity and motivation to coordinate the activities of others for the achievement of common goals.

Showing mercy--the capacity and motivation to identify and comfort those who are hurting or in distress and to offer comfort and compassion.

Look at today's passage and discover the answers to the following questions.

1. What is the improper and the proper attitude a Christian should have toward himself (v. 3)?

2. What did Paul say about the function of the body of Christ in verse 4?

3. What are we supposed to do with our gifts (v. 6)?

The priestly gifts are often called motivational gifts. The reason for this is that a person's inner motivation toward ministry is often determined by his spiritual gift.

REFLECT AND MEDITATE

When you see a need in someone's life, what are you first inclined to do for them? Pray for them? Offer them counsel? Meet a material need? Comfort them? Instruct them? Reflect on this a moment, and write down your feelings.

REACT AND RESPOND

Your inner motivation toward ministry is an important aspect of your priestly gifts. God wants you to know your gift. Make a commitment now to do further study in this important area so that you may more fully understand your function and responsibility in the body of Christ.

REJOICE AND WORSHIP

Write out a brief prayer to God that thanks Him for His continual working in your life.

Discipleship

Study 5

MINISTERING ACCORDING TO YOUR GIFT

READ AND RESEARCH (Romans 12:6-8; 1 Peter 4:10)

God wants you to discover your priestly gift. Here are some suggestions to help you do this:

1. Ask God to give you insight into your unique gift.

2. Do a detailed study of the seven priestly gifts so that you have a good understanding of them and their characteristics.

3. Take an objective look at your own life. What characteristics of which gift do you see in your life?

4. Ask someone in the church to give you feedback as to how they see God using you in ministry.

Keep in mind, however, that merely identifying your spiritual gifts is not enough. You must use your gift to minister. As a priest you are a minister of God's grace (1 Peter 4:10). You serve as a transformer, taking God's power and adapting it to make it usable in meeting needs and serving others.

Look at the two passages for today. See what Paul and Peter have to say about using your spiritual gifts in ministry.

1. What is Paul's advice to those who have been given the various gifts (Romans 12:6-8)?

2. What is a person to do who has a speaking gift (1 Peter 4:10)?

3. What is a person to do who has a serving gift (1 Peter 4:10)?

It has been said that the prophets are the eyes of the body of Christ, the teachers are the mind, the servers are the hands and feet, the exhorters are the mouth, the givers are the hands, and the mercy showers are the heart. All the gifts are needed for the total ministry of Christ to be extended to the world.

REFLECT AND MEDITATE

Meditate on how the ministry of Christ is complete when all the gifts are functioning within His body.

REACT AND RESPOND

If you do not know what your priestly gift is, what steps should you be taking to find out? If you have discovered your gift, what type of ministry should you be pursuing?

REJOICE AND WORSHIP

As you think of how Christ has gifted the church for ministry, you will have greater appreciation for His great works. Take time now to praise Him for this.

DISCIPLESHIP COMMITMENT

In response to what you have learned this week, express your commitment to God by offering this prayer to Him:

Dear Father, I praise You that through Your grace You have opened the way for me to enter Your presence. As Your priest I commit myself to be a good steward of Your grace, faithfully using the gift You have given me. May my local church be enriched as I seek to serve You. In Jesus' name. Amen.

CHAPTER 15

What Is the Role of Leadership in the Church?

INTRODUCTION

We have just finished a study on the believer's responsibility in the church. The emphasis was on the work of the ministry of the church as the responsibility of every Christian. Yet the spiritual gifts given by the Holy Spirit to every member for ministry in the body of Christ does not negate the necessity of spiritual leadership in the church. The New Testament speaks of leaders in the church as "those. . .over you in the Lord" (1 Thessalonians 5:12).

There are many good books and material on the subject of leadership. They deal with such things as leadership styles, group dynamics and leadership development. Many of these books have proven to be very helpful to people involved in local church leadership.

However, the authority for the church's ministry must be the Bible. We can and should listen respectfully to ideas that come from man. But although we listen with respect, we must always evaluate in the light provided by divine revelation. Ultimately, commitment to any course of action must be rooted in the conviction that our choices are in harmony with revealed truth. Our goal must be to see the biblical perspective. Our commitment must be to let that perspective shape us and our church's ministry.

At first glance, however, the New Testament seems indecisive about the specific kind of leadership and church government God had in mind for His church. The primary emphasis of the New Testament is the life and mission of the church, not its leadership. Yet as we look closer, we see it is the life and mission of the church that gives birth to its leadership.

Our struggle to understand church leadership must begin with a recognition that the church is not a human organization or institution. It is a living organism, and at the head of this living organism is the living Christ (Ephesians 1:22, 23; 4:15). Whatever role human leadership may play in the church, it must not intrude into the realm of Christ's headship nor claim His prerogatives.

Leadership in the church is not *institutional* leadership but *body* leadership. This is Paul's point in Ephesians 4:11-16. The goal of the leadership of the church is to maintain and foster the health of the body of Christ. A healthy church is growing in unity and in love in the context of mutual ministry. Leaders must see that their primary concern is to help each believer make his own unique contribution to the maturity of the whole Body. Therefore, in the truest sense a New Testament church leader is a servant--a servant of Christ and of the body of Christ.

In your daily studies this week, you will have the opportunity to learn more about the role of leadership in the church. Here are the five topics you will be studying:

1. The Headship of Christ
2. The Nature of New Testament Leadership
3. The Ministry Gifts of Christ to the Church
4. The Office of Elder
5. The Office of Deacon

DISCIPLESHIP GOAL

To see more clearly the role of leadership in the church and especially the need for yieldedness to Christ

READING ASSIGNMENT

The Living Book, pp. 175 -186

Discipleship

Study 1

THE HEADSHIP OF CHRIST

READ AND RESEARCH (Ephesians 1:17-23)

We must begin our discussion of leadership in the church with Jesus. Scriptures make it plain that He is the head of the church (Ephesians 4:15; 5:23; Colossians 1:18). He is not head emeritus. He is not a figurehead giving nodding acknowledgment while others run His organization. He is not the retired founder of the firm. No, God has appointed Jesus "to be head over everything for the church" (Ephesians 1:22, *NIV*).

In the church, we are dealing with the living Lord. We must recognize that Jesus acts in this present age as He did during biblical times and as He will in the age to come.

As our head, Jesus is the source of our life (Ephesians 1:17-23). He sustains the whole Body and supplies what is needed for growth (Ephesians 4:15, 16). He is committed to bring saving transformation to our lives and to present us without stain or wrinkle or blemish (Ephesians 5:25-29).

In today's passage, you will see the exalted position of Christ. The following questions will guide you in your study.

1. What is Christ's inheritance (v. 18)?
2. Where is Christ seated (v. 20)?
3. Who exalted Christ (v. 20)?
4. What is under Christ's feet (v. 22)?
5. Of what is Jesus the head (vv. 22-23)?

The church has only one leader--Jesus Christ. All earthly leadership, to be valid, must be in submission to Him.

REFLECT AND MEDITATE

Reflect on the exalted position of Jesus. Meditate on the significance of this exaltation for the church.

REACT AND RESPOND

Pray that your church may truly be submitted to the headship of Jesus Christ.

REJOICE AND WORSHIP

As an act of praise and worship, sing the familiar chorus "He is Lord."

Study 2

THE NATURE OF NEW TESTAMENT LEADERSHIP

READ AND RESEARCH (Matthew 20:25-28)

Since Jesus is the only head of the church, the obvious question is "What role do human leaders (that is, pastors, elders, deacons, overseers, and so forth) play?" This is what we will address in today's study.

Christ, as the head of the church, limits us to a leadership that finds its expression in servanthood and relies on a servant's seeming weakness. Servant leadership is the New Testament style of leadership. It was modeled by Jesus himself, who came as the servant of the Lord (Isaiah 42:1; Mark 10:45). He gave us a picture of servant leadership when He washed the disciples' feet (John 13:1-17).

Jesus' most extensive teaching on servant leadership is found in the passage for today. The following questions will help you in your study:

1. How do leaders of this world exercise their leadership (v. 25)?
2. How is leadership in God's kingdom different from leadership in the world (v. 26)?
3. What attitude should a person have who aspires to greatness (v. 26)?
4. What did Jesus come to do (v. 28)?

The servant leader brings the body of Christ into a harmonious relationship and leads its members to maturity. The living Lord, as the head of the church, will act through His servants to work out His good will. The attitude of the servant leader is humility. His resource is the quality of his life, and his expectation is that God will act in the midst of His people.

REFLECT AND MEDITATE

Read Philippians 2:5-8 and meditate on what it means to have the mind of Christ.

REACT AND RESPOND

Evaluate the level of your servanthood. In what ways do you need to improve in this area. Write out your plan.

REJOICE AND WORSHIP

How has Jesus personally served (ministered to) you? Offer a prayer of thanksgiving to Him in response to His ministry.

Study 3

THE MINISTRY GIFTS OF CHRIST TO THE CHURCH

READ AND RESEARCH (Ephesians 4:11-15)

You will remember that there are three categories of spiritual gifts: (1) priestly (motivational) gifts (Romans 12:3-8), (2) manifestation gifts (1 Corinthians 12:8-11), and (3) ministry gifts (Ephesians 4:11-13). This final category has to do with leadership in the church, and we will look at these gifts in this session.

The Greek word for *gifts* in Ephesians 4:8 carries the idea of "a present." The fourfold ministry of apostles, prophets, evangelists and pastor-teachers are Christ's *presents* to His church. Some have called these gifts leadership gifts, and others have called them Ascension gifts because Christ bestowed them on the church when He ascended back to the Father (Ephesians 4:8).

Each of these ministry gifts has a unique function within the body of Christ. The apostles are to govern. They have the broad ministry role of supervising the local churches and appointing the pastoral leadership. The prophets are to guide. They are revivalists, ministering spiritual renewal to the church. The evangelists are to gather. They minister to those who are outside the church by proclaiming the gospel to the unsaved. The pastor-teachers are to guard. They are the shepherds,

tending to the spiritual well-being of a local congregation. It is the only one of the four offices that is centered in the local church.

Take a close look at today's passage, which deals with the ministry gifts, by answering the following questions:

1. What two things are emphasized in verse 12 as the purpose of the ministry gifts?

2. How long will the ministry be needed in the church (v. 13)?

3. How did Paul describe spiritual immaturity (v. 14)?

Christ has made an extraordinary deposit to the church by providing the church leaders in these four offices. Together the full ministry of Christ, who embodied all of the gifts, will be experienced by the church.

REFLECT AND MEDITATE

Reflect on the four ministry gifts. Can you name someone who fills these offices today?

REACT AND RESPOND

Can you think of a time when you benefited from the ministry of someone in one of these offices? Why not write this person a letter informing him of the fruit of his ministry?

REJOICE AND WORSHIP

Take a moment to thank God for the leaders He has given to the body of Christ.

Discipleship

Study 4

THE OFFICE OF ELDER

READ AND RESEARCH (1 Peter 5:1-4)

When the apostle Paul wrote to the church at Philippi, he addressed three groups in the church: "To all the saints in Christ Jesus. . .with the bishops [elders] and deacons" (Philippians 1:1). The terms *pastor, shepherd, elder, bishop,* and *overseer* are used interchangeably in the New Testament to refer to the same office.

The pastor-teacher, or elder, is the only one of the ministry gifts that is centered completely in a local church. Paul and Barnabas appointed elders in Iconium, Lystra and Derbe (Acts 14:21-23). The elders of the various churches were part of the Jerusalem Council in A.D. 50 (Acts 15:23). Paul exhorted the Ephesian elders concerning their duties (Acts 20:17-38).

The elder ministry of a local church usually consists of a pastor and/or a pastoral staff who are supported financially by the local church (1 Timothy 5:17, 18). Many churches are also raising up an elder ministry consisting of spiritual leaders from the congregation to assist the pastoral staff.

Qualifications for elders are found in 1 Timothy 3:1-7 and Titus 1:5-9. The elders are to guard the church from false doctrine (Acts 20:28-30). They are to be ministers of divine healing (James 5:14, 15) and are to labor in teaching the Word and doctrine (1 Timothy 5:17).

Peter wrote about the ministry of the elder in our passage for today. Take a close look at this passage as you answer the following questions:

1. What are the elders instructed to do (v. 2)?
2. What are unacceptable motivations for serving as an elder (v. 2)?
3. How are the elders to minister to those entrusted to them (v. 3)?
4. What reward is promised to the elders who are faithful (v. 4)?

The leadership of the elder should not be viewed primarily as administrative but spiritual in nature. The first indicates management and control; the second, ministry and service.

REFLECT AND MEDITATE

Reflect on the various duties of your pastor. Pray for him to have God's strength as he leads your church.

REACT AND RESPOND

Is your pastor encumbered with activities that do not relate directly to his spiritual work? Would you consider volunteering to help with one of these tasks? If so, make a commitment to do so now.

REJOICE AND WORSHIP

Thank God for your pastor and the other spiritual leaders of your church. They are Christ's gifts to your local body of believers.

Study 5

THE OFFICE OF DEACON

READ AND RESEARCH (Acts 6:1-7)

In addition to its spiritual ministry, the church has other concerns as well. These include the management of church funds, business matters and the maintenance of church properties. To free the elders from these tasks, the New Testament authorizes another type of leader in the church--

the deacon.

The office of deacon is a vital one. Paul laid down specific qualification guidelines for a person desiring to serve in this position (1 Timothy 3:8-13). This underscores the importance of this office.

The selection of the first deacons is found in today's scripture. The following questions will help you understand this historical passage:

1. What problem gave occasion to the selection of the first deacons (v. 1)?

2. Why didn't the apostles do this job themselves (v. 2)?

3. How were the deacons selected (v. 3)?

4. What type of men were needed for this task (v. 3)?

5. Who were the first deacons (v. 5)?

6. What was the result of how the church handled this problem (v. 7)?

The position of deacon may be called different things in different churches. Some call the deacons the Church Council: others may use the term Administrative Council or Board of Stewards. The name doesn't matter as much as that the biblical office is being filled.

REFLECT AND MEDITATE

Reflect on how a problem was turned into a blessing in Acts 6. Meditate on the truth that by following God's Spirit, every church problem can result in victory.

REACT AND RESPOND

Pray specifically for those in your church who serve in the office of deacon. When you see them at church, let them know they have your prayers and appreciation.

REJOICE AND WORSHIP

God in His infinite wisdom has provided everything that your church needs. Praise Him for His great provision.

DISCIPLESHIP COMMITMENT

In response to your study this week, pray this prayer to the Father:

Dear Father, I thank You for my church and the leaders You have given to us. I commit to be responsive to their leadership as they seek to lead our church according to Your will. Give our pastor the grace and wisdom needed for his spiritual tasks. May our deacons be guided in all their decisions by Your Spirit. In Jesus' name. Amen.

CHAPTER 16

What Is the Mission of the Church?

INTRODUCTION

The Bible divides the human family into two groups. Not just male and female or rich and poor. The most basic distinction in human society, from the Christian perspective, is the church and the world.

As Jesus approached His arrest, trial and death, He warned His disciples they could expect opposition from the world. He said, "If you were of the world, the world would love its own. . . .You are not of the world, but I chose you out of the world" (John 15:19).

The fundamental teaching of the New Testament concerning the mission of the church can be expressed in this simple statement: Christ has called His church out of the world in order to send the church back into the world with the gospel. This means that the mission of the church is a rhythm between separation from the world and penetration of the world.

The tension between these two directions--separation and penetration--can often cause a struggle for Christians. As members of the church we must be enough in touch with the world to speak to its needs without being so much like the world that we have nothing to say.

However, while we emphasize that the church has a mission to this world, we must not neglect the other responsibilities of the church. The church has a responsibility to God. We are to worship Him and enjoy His fellowship.

The church also has an internal responsibility. The body of Christ is to minister to itself. This ministry will take the form of edification, fellowship, teaching and training.

The church's reaching in all three directions--toward God, toward itself and toward the world--form its mission. The body of Christ is to be a worshiping community, a teaching community and a reaching community.

During this week's study you will be focusing on these areas:

1. The Church and the Kingdom of God
2. The Church and Christ's Commission
3. The Church and Its Ministry to God
4. The Church and Its Ministry to Itself
5. The Church and Its Ministry to the World

DISCIPLESHIP GOAL

To understand how the great commission has a direct bearing on your personal thoughts, priorities and life objectives

READING ASSIGNMENT
The Living Book, pp. 186 -198

Study 1

THE CHURCH AND THE KINGDOM OF GOD

READ AND RESEARCH (2 Corinthians 5:20)

The central message of the Gospels was that the kingdom of God had arrived. John the Baptist came preaching that God was ready to bring in the new age and that it would be here soon (Matthew 3:2). This new age was foretold in the Old Testament as a time when Satan's power would be broken and his kingdom destroyed. John called this new age the kingdom of God and said that the appearance of the Messiah, God's anointed King, signaled its arrival.

When Jesus went forth preaching, the Scriptures say, He preached the ''gospel of the kingdom'' (Matthew 4:17; 4:23). The miracles He performed and that He commissioned His disciples to perform were signs of His kingdom (Matthew 9:35; 12:28; Luke 9:1, 2; 10:8, 9).

The kingdom of God can best be understood as the rule of God. By Christ's coming, He was announcing that the kingly reign--the authority of God--had broken in on the present evil age and that all who would come to Him by repentance and faith would be citizens of this Kingdom.

The church stands in a central place with respect to God's kingdom rule. We are told that we are to be proclaimers of the gospel of the Kingdom even until the final hour (Matthew 24:14). We are to constantly pray for the kingdom of God to come to the hearts of men and in our world (Luke 11:2). We are to have signs following us as confirmation of the presence of the kingly rule of Christ (Mark 16:17, 18; Acts 2:43). In short, the church stands as a embassy of the kingdom of God.

An embassy is the official residence of an ambassador of a government located in a foreign country. It represents the concerns of that government in a foreign land. Likewise, the church represents God and His kingdom in this world. We are to impact our communities with the gospel of the kingdom of God.

In our scripture for today, Paul spoke of our ambassadorship. Look at it closely as you answer the following questions:

1. Whose ambassador are we?
2. What is our message to the world?

REFLECT AND MEDITATE

Reflect on what an ambassador does, and meditate on how this applies to the Christian life.

REACT AND RESPOND

To more fully understand the kingdom of God, why not make a commitment to do an in-depth study of the biblical subject.

REJOICE AND WORSHIP

Praise God for the fact that you are part of His kingdom!

Study 2

THE CHURCH AND CHRIST'S COMMISSION

READ AND RESEARCH (Matthew 28:18-20)

Before Christ left this earth to return to the Father, He gave the church what has become known as the Great Commission. This commission represents the predominant theme of the church's mission.

In Matthew 28:19, 20 are four Greek verbs. These have been translated, ''go,'' ''make,'' ''baptizing'' and ''teaching.'' Two of these are commands. They are ''go'' and ''make.'' The other two verbs are participles, indicating how the commands are to be fulfilled.

Christ has called us to make disciples. To understand this, we must understand the meaning of *discipleship*.

A disciple is one who has accepted Jesus Christ as Savior and Lord, has publicly acknowledged his allegiance to Christ, and is seeking to submit all areas of his life to the Lordship of Christ. It is the church's responsibility to make disciples and to assist the new convert in attaining these discipleship goals. Today's passage is the Great Commission. The following questions will help you gain a fuller understanding of it.

1. What did Jesus say concerning his authority (v. 18)?

2. What formula for baptism did Jesus give (v. 19)?

3. What is to be the direction of the teaching of the church (v. 20)?

4. What promise did Christ give to the church (v. 20)?

Someone has said that every Christian should either be becoming a disciple or helping to make disciples. The goal of true discipleship is that each disciple becomes a disciple maker.

REFLECT AND MEDITATE

Reflect on the qualities of a true disciple of Christ. Meditate on how Christ is magnified through them.

REACT AND RESPOND

All of us have known Christians who were especially influential in helping us develop our own discipleship. Why not write a letter to one of these individuals (a relative, a friend, a pastor, a teacher, and so forth) and express your gratitude for the important role he or she has played in your life?

REJOICE AND WORSHIP

Take a moment to thank God for the spiritual growth that is taking place in your life.

Study 3

THE CHURCH AND ITS MINISTRY TO GOD

READ AND RESEARCH (John 4:21-24)

When the average Christian hears the word *ministry*, he rarely thinks of ministering to God. We usually picture God ministering to man rather than ministering to God. However, the Scriptures present worship as our ministry to God.

The psalmist implied that our sincere praise blesses God (Psalm 103:1, 2). He said God inhabits the praises of His people (Psalm 22:3) and takes pleasure in His people (Psalm 147:11).

Peter said that God has called us to be His people so that we might proclaim His praises (1 Peter 2:9). The early church exemplified this and praised God continually (Acts 2:47). Also, the church that is in heaven is always viewed as worshiping the Lord (Revelation 4:10, 11; 5:9, 10).

To be a true New Testament church, a local congregation must have worship as the central focus of its life. All the other areas of ministry will flow from this ministry to God.

In the passage for today, Jesus spoke to the Samaritan woman about the nature of true worship. Refer to these scriptures as you answer the following questions.

1. Has the hour of true worship arrived (v. 23)?

2. How are true worshipers to worship the Father (v. 23)?

3. What is the Father seeking (v. 23)?

4. What does verse 24 tell us about the nature of God?

The life of the church flows through praise and worship. It is the hub of all that we do. A church will never move for God if worship is missing from the wheel.

REFLECT AND MEDITATE

Meditate on the meaning of worshiping in spirit and in truth.

REACT AND RESPOND

Worship is both a private and a corporate matter. The effectiveness of your experience in corporate worship is directly related to the consistency of your private devotional life. What changes should you make in your devotional life to make it more meaningful? Write out your plan.

Take time now to experience the presence of God through a period of unhurried praise and worship.

Study 4

THE CHURCH AND ITS MINISTRY TO ITSELF

READ AND RESEARCH (Acts 2:42-47)

We have already seen that the church is like a body, and like the human body it can become sick and weak. To prevent this from occurring, the church must have a ministry to itself. This ministry can best be seen in two key words: *fellowship* and *edification*.

The word *fellowship* (Greek, *koinonia*) carries the idea of a shared life. As believers we share a common faith in one Lord. This common faith is to lead us to share our lives with fellow believers. This means that we are devoted to one another through a meaningful commitment of love, caring and partnership.

Edification comes from a Greek word meaning "house building." It shows us the reason for our fellowship. We are to share together so that we may build each other up. Not only are we responsible for our own spiritual growth, but each one of us is to help the others to mature as well. Edification occurs through the church's teaching and training ministries, and it is the responsibility of the church to provide such ministries.

We can see the early church ministering to itself in today's passage. Allow the Holy Spirit to guide you in your study:

1. In what did the early church continue steadfastly (v. 42)?

2. What impact did the early church have on the world (v. 43)?

3. How did the early church practice fellowship (vv. 44-46)?

4. How did the church grow as a result of these activities (v. 47)?

Paul said that we must pursue those things which make for peace and which edify others (Romans 14:19). He also said the body of Christ is built up as each separate part fulfills its role (Ephesians 4:16). When the church ministers to itself, it remains strong and healthy.

REFLECT AND MEDITATE

Meditate on the attributes of a healthy church. Reflect on how many of these attributes can be found in your local church.

REACT AND RESPOND

In prayer, ask God what you can do to help build up the church. Ask Him if you have kept your church from growing to maturity. If you feel He is speaking to you, write down your plan of action.

REJOICE AND WORSHIP

Lift your voice and your hands to God in worship and praise for your church and the rich opportunities for fellowship God has given you through it.

Study 5

THE CHURCH AND ITS MINISTRY TO THE WORLD

READ AND RESEARCH (John 17:16-18)

The church's ministry to the world may be summed up in one word--evangelism. It is the responsibility of the church to share the good news of the gospel with the unsaved, and no church that neglects this important ministry is fulfilling its mission.

Christ specifically promised the power of the Holy Spirit to enable the church to evangelize (Acts 1:8). It is through His power that the church proclaims the gospel and sinners are convinced of its truth.

As a part of our evangelistic mission, the church also is to impact its society and culture. Jesus described the positive influence of the church on its community and world in terms of salt and light (Matthew 5:13-16). As salt, the righteousness of the church preserves and holds back decay. As light, the church dispels the darkness of sin, corruption and injustice. Every community where a local body of believers is located should be a better community because of the influence of the church.

In today's scripture, Jesus was praying not only for His disciples but for His church as well (v. 20). A part of this prayer deals with the church's ministry to the world. Look carefully at what Jesus was praying.

1. How did Jesus describe believers' relationship with the world (v. 16)?

2. *Sanctify* means to be set apart for a purpose. How does Christ sanctify the church (v. 17)?

3. In what manner has Christ sent the church into the world (v. 18)?

The church is to have an impact on the world. The worst thing that can happen to the church is not persecution but that the church would simply be ignored by the world.

REFLECT AND MEDITATE

Jesus said that we are sent as He was sent. Meditate on how the Father sent Jesus and what this has to do with the church's mission in the world.

REACT AND RESPOND

Have you ever shared your faith with someone? It is every Christian's responsibility to witness. What plans would you like to make to share your faith and the gospel with another person?

REJOICE AND WORSHIP

Aren't you glad that someone brought the gospel to you? Give thanks to God right now for sending someone to share the good news with you.

DISCIPLESHIP COMMITMENT

In response to what you have learned this week, pray the following prayer to the Father as an act of personal commitment:

Dear Father, I thank you for my church. I praise You that You have called us and commissioned us to be ambassadors of Your kingdom in our community. I pray that we will represent You well. Give us the power of Your Spirit to make disciples. Let our worship be anointed by You that we may worship You in spirit and in truth. May unity and fellowship abound in our church as we build up one another. May souls be saved through our ministry. And may I be used as a part of the accomplishment of Your will in my church. In Jesus' name. Amen.

CHAPTER 17

Who Is the Holy Spirit?

INTRODUCTION

Every Sunday millions of Christians around the world recite the words of the Apostles' Creed: ''I believe in God the Father Almighty . . . and in Jesus Christ His only Son our Lord; . . . I believe in the Holy Ghost.'' What do Christians mean by this confession of faith in God, in Jesus Christ and in the Holy Ghost?

Most Christians find it much easier to explain who Jesus is than to explain who God is. We readily identify Jesus as the Son of God and Messiah (Christ), who lived and died on this earth as a man. We recognize and identify with the humanity of Jesus while also believing that He is Lord and God, for He died for our sins and rose from the dead.

But who is God? Well, we say in the words of the Creed that He is ''God the Father Almighty, Creator of heaven and earth.'' Still, we find it quite difficult to describe or explain who God is because He is Spirit (John 4:24) and ''No one has seen God at any time'' (1 John 4:12).

We have much the same difficulty (and even more so) when it comes to describing or explaining who the Holy Spirit is. Since the Holy Spirit is represented to us in Scripture as ''Spirit,'' it is easy for us to make the mistake of thinking of the Holy Spirit as a force, power or influence rather than as a person. The personhood of God is communicated to us in the expression ''God the Father.'' The personhood of Jesus Christ is clearly revealed to us in His human life on this earth. But do we think of the Holy Spirit as a person?

It is important for every Christian to understand that the Holy Spirit is a divine person and not merely a divine power or influence. Our understanding of who the Spirit is will determine how we seek to relate ourselves to the Holy Spirit. If we think of the Holy Spirit as being an impersonal power or influence, our approach will be, How can I get the power of the Spirit and use it? If, however, we understand the Holy Spirit to be a person, our attitude will be, How can the Holy Spirit use me to bring glory to God?

The Holy Spirit is personal. He is God with us and God in us--Christ with us and Christ in us. The object of Christian worship is God the Father, God the Son and God the Holy Spirit. If the Holy Spirit is regarded as an impersonal force, we rob Him of the worship due to Him as God.

During the five discipleship study sessions following, we will explore what the Bible says about who the Spirit is:

1. The Holy Spirit Is God
2. The Spirit of God
3. The Spirit of Christ
4. The Source of Spiritual Life
5. The Christian's Helper

DISCIPLESHIP GOAL

To better understand and appreciate who the Holy Spirit is so I will be more alert and yielded to His direction and enabling power for Christian worship, living and service

READING ASSIGNMENT
The Living Book, pp. 199 - 213

Discipleship

THE HOLY SPIRIT IS GOD

READ AND RESEARCH (Acts 5:1-6; 1 Corinthians 3:16, 17)

The church was young. Only a short time had passed since the Holy Spirit was poured out on the disciples of Jesus on the Day of Pentecost (Acts 2:1-4). The young church had not had much time to formulate the Christian understanding of God, but the passage in Acts 5:1-6 reveals that they knew the Holy Spirit is God.

When a man named Ananias was dishonest with the apostles about a contribution to the church, Peter warned him that Satan had filled his heart "to lie to the Holy Spirit" (v. 3) and in so doing he had lied "to God" (v. 4). This shows that the early church believed in God the Father, God the Son and God the Holy Spirit (or Holy Ghost).

In the passage in 1 Corinthians 3:16, 17, the apostle Paul spoke of the believers in Christ as being "the temple of God" and said the "Spirit of God" dwells in believers. Later, he reinforced this thought by saying emphatically, "Your body is the temple of the Holy Spirit" (1 Corinthians 6:19). It is clear from these statements that the Holy Spirit indwelling the believer in Christ is God indwelling the believer in Christ.

Who is the Holy Spirit? The Holy Spirit is God. Although we Christians speak of the Holy Spirit as being the third person in the Holy Trinity (Father, Son and Holy Spirit), this does not mean the Holy Spirit is third in rank or importance. Father, Son and Spirit are coequal. The Father is God, the Son is God, and the Holy Spirit is God. Therefore the Holy Spirit is not *it*, not an impersonal force, power or influence emanating from God, but a person.

REFLECT AND MEDITATE

1. Read the passages in Matthew 28:19 and 2 Corinthians 13:14. What persons are clearly identified by these passages as being God, the Holy Trinity?

2. How does the recognition that the Holy Spirit is a person rather than a mere force, power or influence affect your relation to the Holy Spirit?

REACT AND RESPOND

What can you do to make your relationship with the Holy Spirit more personal? What can you do to become more sensitive to the Holy Spirit's presence and guidance? Examine and compare your attitude toward Jesus Christ, your attitude toward God the Father and your attitude toward the Holy Spirit. Do you actually worship and listen to the Holy Spirit as you worship and listen to Jesus Christ or God the Father? If not, you can make your relationship with the Holy Spirit more personal and sensitive by a change in your attitude. Worship and welcome the Holy Spirit into your life just as you worship and welcome Jesus Christ and God the Father into your life.

REJOICE AND WORSHIP

Holy Spirit use me, I surrender now,
I want to serve Thee, please show me how;
I will wait in patience till I hear from Thee,
O Holy Spirit, grant this, my plea.
Holy Spirit use me, take my life today,
Use me in Thy service, this I daily pray;
Make my life a blessing, fill me with Thy fire,
Holy Spirit use me, that's my desire.
--Leon H. Ellis, *Hymns of the Spirit*, p. 109

Study 2

THE SPIRIT OF GOD

READ AND RESEARCH (Genesis 1:1-27; Job 33:4)

The Spirit of God is mentioned in the second verse of the Bible. The Bible begins by saying "In the beginning God created" and immediately goes on to say that the Holy Spirit was also active in the work of Creation. The Spirit of God is represented as hovering like a female bird over the formless earth, bringing life and order to the earth. The implication of the Creation account in Genesis 1 is that when God spoke the creative word ("Then God said, 'Let there be...,'" vv. 3, 6, 14; compare vv. 9, 11, 20, 24), the Holy Spirit was active in bringing God's creative word to pass.

In Genesis 1 the final creative word is "'Let Us make man'" (v. 26). The participation of God the Father, God the Son and God the Holy Spirit in the work of creation is strongly implied by the words "'Let *Us* make man in Our image, according to Our likeness'" (v. 26). This understanding of the Holy Spirit's participation in the creation of mankind is reflected in Elihu's words, "'The Spirit of God has made me'" (Job 33:4).

The One who is called *Spirit of God* or *Spirit of the Lord* throughout the Bible (especially in the Old Testament) is the very same One whom the Bible calls *Holy Ghost* or *Holy Spirit*. And frequently in the Bible the Holy Spirit is referred to simply as *the Spirit*.

God is Spirit (John 4:24), and the Holy Spirit is the Spirit of God. God is holy (Isaiah 6:3), and when we speak of the Holy Spirit, we mean that the Spirit of God is holy just as God is holy.

REFLECT AND MEDITATE

1. Read the passage in Ephesians 4:30. Notice that in this passage of Scripture the two terms *Holy Spirit* and *Spirit of God* are combined to make the term *Holy Spirit of God*. Isn't this a clear example of the fact that the Holy Spirit is the Spirit of God?

2. When you say to yourself, "'The Spirit of God has made me, And the breath [Spirit] of the Almighty gives me life'" (Job 33:4), does this suggest to you that God has an intense interest in your life? What does it do for your sense of self-worth or self-esteem to recognize that you are a creature of God's Spirit?

REACT AND RESPOND

Respond to the Holy Spirit as your Maker. Respond to the Holy Spirit as One sent by God the Father to represent and do the work of God the Father. Allow the Spirit to make you all God would have you to be.

Endeavor to see every other person as one whom God has created and given life by His Spirit. Ask yourself, "How then shall I live with my fellow humans since we share a common bond as creatures of God's Spirit? Does this leave any room in my life for arrogance, prejudice or bigotry toward others?"

REJOICE AND WORSHIP

O Lord, You have searched me and known me....
Where can I go from Your Spirit?
Or where can I flee from Your presence?...
For You have formed my inward parts;
You have covered me in my mother's womb.
I will praise You, for I am fearfully and wonderfully made;
Marvelous are Your works,
And that my soul knows very well.
--Psalm 139:1, 7, 13, 14

Study 3

THE SPIRIT OF CHRIST

READ AND RESEARCH (Romans 8:1-11; Galatians 4:4-7)

The Holy Spirit is the Spirit of Christ. Knowing this fact can be of immeasurable help to us in living the Christian life. By what power is a person enabled to live a Christlike life? The passage in Romans 8:1-11 explains that the power for Christlike living is imparted to us by the Holy Spirit. In this passage the Holy Spirit is called ''the Spirit'' (v. 1), ''the Spirit of life'' (v. 2), ''the Spirit of God'' (v. 9), ''the Spirit of Christ'' (v. 9) and ''the Spirit of Him who raised Jesus from the dead'' (v. 11).

The Holy Spirit is the Spirit of Christ because He represents Christ and does the work of Christ. In fact, when a person becomes a Christian, God sends the Holy Spirit, ''the Spirit of His [God's] Son'' (Galatians 4:6), into the heart of that individual as a witness that he or she has become a child of God.

The Spirit of Christ in us grants us the freedom and the ability to live a spiritual life--a life in harmony with God. ''For the law [power and authority] of the Spirit of life in Christ Jesus has made me free from the law [force, power] of sin and death'' (Romans 8:2). Thus freed from the force and power of sin and death by the Spirit of Christ, we are enabled to live by the law of God, not according to the desires of our sinful nature.

More and more of the Holy Spirit in my life means more and more of Christ in my life. More and more of the Spirit of Christ--this is the only way to victorious Christian living.

REFLECT AND MEDITATE

1. Think about Jesus Christ. He was the best man who ever lived--full of love, understanding, compassion, mercy and goodwill toward all. Now think about the fact that the Holy Spirit is the Spirit of Jesus Christ--His exact and perfect representative to your heart and mind.

2. Now think about this: The Holy Spirit is as good as Jesus--just as approachable and just as concerned about and interested in your life.

REACT AND RESPOND

If you could appear before Jesus Christ today and speak to Him about your needs, what would you say? Of course, Jesus Christ is no longer present in human form, and you cannot have an audience with Him as in the days of His incarnation. But the Spirit of Jesus Christ is present with you and in you. Now speak to the Holy Spirit as the Spirit of Christ; speak to Him about your needs.

REJOICE AND WORSHIP

God my Father, thank You for sending the Spirit of Christ into my heart.

Thank You for letting me know by the witness of Your Holy Spirit with my spirit that Jesus Christ is my Savior and Lordand You are my heavenly Father.

Thank You for giving to me by the Spirit of Christ the assurance that Jesus Christ is alive and that I have eternal life because His Spirit lives in me.

Thank You for giving to me the freedom and ability by the Spirit of Christ to live a Christlike life this day. Hallelujah and amen!

Study 4

THE SOURCE OF SPIRITUAL LIFE

READ AND RESEARCH (Ezekiel 37:1-14)

Of all the Old Testament books, none places as much emphasis on the doctrine of the Holy Spirit as does the book of Ezekiel. This prophet of the Lord spoke frequently about the presence and work of the Holy Spirit.

While "in the Spirit of the Lord" (v. 1), Ezekiel was shown in a vision that the Holy Spirit is the source of spiritual life. In the vision Ezekiel was shown a large valley full of the dried bones of dead men. The Lord said these dead bones represented the nation of Israel--spiritually dead because of their sins. But the Lord informed Ezekiel that Israel could be spiritually alive again by the power of the Holy Spirit.

In response to the Lord's command, Ezekiel prophesied to the wind or breath (Spirit) of God to come and breathe life into the dead who lay in the valley. The breath (Spirit) of the Lord came into them, and they lived again. The Lord then told Ezekiel the meaning of this vision for Israel: "'I will put My Spirit in you, and you shall live'" (v. 14).

Read the passage in John 7:37-39. Jesus said the Holy Spirit is a source of boundless spiritual life--the source of "rivers of living water." And in the book of Revelation, the Holy Spirit is represented as inviting all who will to come "take the water of life freely" (22:17).

What is the difference between spiritual life imparted by the Holy Spirit and biological life? To be spiritually alive by the Holy Spirit means an individual is alive to God, a partaker of eternal life by faith in Jesus Christ and tuned in to things eternal. A person who is spiritually dead may abound in physical health and energy and may be brilliant and successful in the eyes of the world. But without the life which the Holy Spirit gives, that person is dead.

REFLECT AND MEDITATE

1. Without the life imparted to me by the Holy Spirit, what real hope could I have? I would have only the kind of hope the world has. I might hope for a larger salary, a finer home, a three-month winter vacation--but what would such things be worth to one who is spiritually dead?

2. Without the life-giving presence of the Holy Spirit, could my brief life on earth count for much? Would my life really have a good influence on others? The Spirit gives me real life, a life that counts for something--now and forever.

REACT AND RESPOND

Self-examination: Am I spiritually alive? What do I cherish most in life? What are my priorities? Is living for Jesus Christ the most important thing in my life? Can other people see that the life-giving Spirit lives in me? Is my life really different from those who do not claim to have spiritual life? Answers to these questions are strong indicators of whether I am alive by the Spirit.

REJOICE AND WORSHIP

Breathe on me, Breath of God,
Fill me with life anew,
That I may love what Thou dost love,
And do what Thou wouldst do.
Breathe on me, Breath of God,
Till I am wholly Thine,
Till all this earthly part of me,
Glows with Thy fire divine.
--Edwin Hatch, *Hymns of the Spirit*, p. 100

Study 5

THE CHRISTIAN'S HELPER

READ AND RESEARCH (John 14:15-26; Romans 8:18-27)

Jesus' disciples were saddened and bewildered as He spoke to them about His approaching death. Jesus said He would be leaving them, but He promised to ask God the Father to send them "'another Helper . . . the Spirit of truth'" (John 14:16, 17). Moreover, Jesus promised not to leave them alone permanently--He would come to them again in the promised Helper (v. 18).

In the passage in John 14:16, the word another comes from the Greek word *allos*. This word *allos* means another of the same kind, not another who is different. In effect, Jesus said to His disciples that when the Holy Spirit (the Spirit of truth) came to be their helper (Comforter), He would be a helper just like Jesus had been to them.

As the Christian's Helper, the Holy Spirit seeks to help us in the same ways that Jesus would help us if He were incarnate among us today. Through the Holy Spirit, Jesus Christ is present with us as our Helper forever.

During His earthly ministry Jesus was the most excellent teacher. Like Jesus, the Holy Spirit is a teacher. Jesus said of the Holy Spirit, "'He will teach you all things, and bring to your remembrance all things that I said to you'" (John 14:26). Jesus also said that the Holy Spirit in His role as helper and teacher "'will guide you into all truth'" (John 16:13). So although we do not have the incarnate Jesus to teach and guide us, we do have His Holy Spirit to teach and guide us as we read the Bible, pray and seek to do God's will.

The passage in Romans 8:26, 27 calls attention to another very special way in which the Holy Spirit is our helper. The Holy Spirit helps us with our human weaknesses by making intercession for us according to the will of God. Jesus would surely help us by praying for us, and He does pray for us at the right hand of God (Romans 8:34). Like Jesus, the Holy Spirit makes intercession for us, thus strengthening us and directing us into God's good will.

REFLECT AND MEDITATE

Think about what a wonderful and sufficient helper you have in the Holy Spirit. In what way do you want most the help of Jesus right now? The Holy Spirit will be your helper in the same way the incarnate Jesus would.

REACT AND RESPOND

Are you really depending on the Holy Spirit to be your helper? Respond to Him by throwing off proud self-sufficiency and self-pity. Be strong in the Lord by depending on the help of the Holy Spirit.

REJOICE AND WORSHIP

Come, Holy Comforter,
Thy sacred witness bear,
In this glad hour!
Thou, who almighty art,
Now rule in ev'ry heart,
And ne'er from me depart,
Spirit of pow'r.
--Hymns of the Spirit, p. 11, v. 3

DISCIPLESHIP COMMITMENT

I resolve to be more conscious of the Holy Spirit's presence and more responsive to His help and direction. I resolve to do this not only for my personal growth as a Christian but also to be a more helpful Christian to other people.

CHAPTER 18

What Does It Mean to Be Born of the Spirit?

INTRODUCTION

In 1976 the people of the United States elected Jimmy Carter to be their president. Since President Carter unashamedly testified that he was a "born-again Christian," for a while it became almost a fad in America for people to talk about being born again. However, the new birth (being born again by the Holy Spirit) is not a fad; it is the central reality of being a believer in Jesus Christ. From a New Testament perspective all true Christians are of necessity born again of the Spirit.

When we speak of the Christian life, we should understand that by "Christian life" is meant the spiritual life, the new life in Christ, the life transformed by the Holy Spirit. The Bible says the Christian life begins with a new birth by the Holy Spirit (John 3:3-6), by which "if anyone is in Christ, he is a new creation" (2 Corinthians 5:17).

The Christian life is so radically different from the natural life of the sinner that a person can neither understand nor receive the spiritual life in Christ without the help of the Holy Spirit and the new birth by the Spirit (1 Corinthians 2:14).

The spiritual process by which a person passes from living the natural life of the sinner to living the Christian life by faith in Christ is generally referred to as conversion.

The word *conversion* gathers into one term several aspects of the experience of being saved from sin by faith in Christ. This includes the conviction of the sinner for sins committed, sorrow for sins and repentance in turning from one's sins, faith in turning to Christ as one's personal Savior and Lord, justification by faith (being freed from the guilt of sin by God), regeneration or the new birth (receiving spiritual life from God), and adoption into the family of God as a result of repentance, faith and the new birth.

The Holy Spirit works in every aspect of the conversion experience to bring about the salvation of the sinner. When this work of conversion is complete, evangelical and Pentecostal Christians generally refer to the converted individual as being "a born-again Christian."

Every person who becomes a Christian does not undergo a dramatic or sensational conversion experience, but every person who becomes a Christian is born again of the Spirit and will live a life that is transformed by the Holy Spirit. When a person is born of the Spirit, the transformation is not only apparent to that individual, it will be evident to others as well. Under the following headings we will explore the difference it makes in one's life to be born of the Spirit:

1. Spiritual Rebirth--Regeneration
2. Spiritual Transformation
3. Spiritual Enlightenment
4. Spiritual Motivation
5. Spiritual Fellowship

DISCIPLESHIP GOAL

To gain a better understanding of the practical results of my conversion to Christ so as to live a more Christlike life and to help others come to know Christ as their Savior and Lord

READING ASSIGNMENT

The Living Book, pp. 213 -225

Discipleship

SPIRITUAL REBIRTH--REGENERATION

READ AND RESEARCH (John 3:1-17; 2 Corinthians 5:14-21)

Nicodemus must have been somewhat stunned and confused by Jesus' suggestion that he needed to be born again. It was not that Nicodemus had never heard anyone speak about being born again. Gentiles who were converted to Judaism and baptized as Jewish proselytes were said to be born again. And even among pagan Gentiles the devotees of the mystery religions spoke of themselves as being born again. But Nicodemus could not see immediately any need on his part to be born again. After all, he was born a Jew, a son of Abraham, and lived his life as a devoutly religious Israelite. Why would Jesus suggest that he needed to be born again from above by God's Spirit?

The conversation between Nicodemus and Jesus reveals that a person (such as Nicodemus) might be religious and lead a life that is socially and morally commendable and yet not be born of the Spirit. The spiritual rebirth Jesus calls for in the life of every person is not something we can do but something God does for us as we respond to His love and grace. By believing that Christ died for our sins to save us from sin and by accepting Christ as our Savior and Lord, God performs in us the miracle of spiritual rebirth by the Spirit. We are regenerated--given a new life--and become new creatures in Christ Jesus.

Regeneration is the spiritual change brought about in an individual's mind and heart by an act of God in which one is freed from the will to sin and can respond to God in faith. Although the word *regeneration* is used only twice in the New Testament (Matthew 19:28; Titus 3:5), it is suggested by such terms as ''born again'' (John 3:3, 5, 7), ''born of God'' (John 1:13; 1 John 3:9), ''made alive'' (Ephesians 2:1, 5) and ''renewed'' (Romans 12:2; Titus 3:5).

''Regeneration is, therefore, an act of God through the immediate agency of the Holy Spirit operative in man (Colossians 2:13), originating in him a new dimension of moral life, a resurrection to new life in Christ'' (*The New International Dictionary of the Bible*).

REFLECT AND MEDITATE

1. Recall the time when you first surrendered your life to Christ and accepted Him as your Savior and Lord. Remember the ways in which you first experienced and recognized that you were born of the Spirit.

2. Next, think about the ways in which you are continuing to experience your new life in Christ. In what ways has your experience of your new life in Christ changed? Are you pleased or dissatisfied with your progress as a born-again Christian?

REACT AND RESPOND

What privileges are mine as a born again child of God! What honorable responsibilities are mine to live as one born again of the Spirit! I will endeavor to live more fully in keeping with my privileges and responsibilities as one who lives anew by the life of God.

REJOICE AND WORSHIP

Thank You, God my Father, for the new birth. Thank You for sending Christ to die for my sins to make my rebirth by the Spirit a possibility. Thank You for laying claim to my life with Your love and grace, enabling me by your Spirit to respond to You in faith and obedience.

I really want to live as a born-again Christian today and every day.

I want to be an effective witness for Christ as others see this new life in me.

Thank You, Lord, for saving me. Amen.

Study 2

SPIRITUAL TRANSFORMATION

READ AND RESEARCH (Romans 12:1, 2; 2 Corinthians 3:1-18; Titus 3:3-7)

Be not conformed to the world; be transformed. This is God's commandment to every person who is born of the Spirit. In effect the Bible says that if we are born of the Spirit, we must not allow ourselves to be molded by this evil age. The lifestyle of the Christian is to be formed not by the misguided values of this sinful world but by the example and character of Christ.

Being born of the Spirit is a transforming experience, and it also sets us free to continue to be transformed. The Bible explains how this can happen:

Now the Lord is the Spirit; and where the Spirit of the Lord is, there is liberty. But we all, with unveiled face, beholding as in a mirror the glory of the Lord, are being transformed into the same image from glory to glory, just as by the Spirit of the Lord (2 Corinthians 3:17, 18).

As we live by faith in Christ--believing and obeying the gospel--"the light of the knowledge of the glory of God in the face of Jesus Christ" (2 Corinthians 4:6) shines into our heart, changing us into the image of Christ. To put it in simple terms, as we live with devotion to Christ, we become more and more like Christ.

Yes, the life of an individual who is born of the Spirit is different from the individual who is conformed to this world. The life of a person who is transformed by the Spirit is elevated spiritually and morally above that of the natural life of the sinner.

Spiritual transformation by the Holy Spirit is our only hope of salvation from sin. "According to His mercy He [God] saved us, through the washing [cleansing from sin] of regeneration and renewing [transforming work] of the Holy Spirit" (Titus 3:5).

REFLECT AND MEDITATE

1. On the practical level of daily living, what does it mean for me to be transformed by the Holy Spirit? Are my attitudes Christlike or worldly? Do I speak and act like a Christian?

2. The highest privilege I have in this life is to be Christlike. Therefore I have no need to impress people with worldly status symbols. Christlikeness is the ground of my self-esteem.

REACT AND RESPOND

I am resolved no longer to linger,
Charmed by the world's delight;
Things that are higher, things that are nobler,
These have allured my sight.

I am resolved to follow the Saviour,
Faithful and true each day;
Heed what He sayeth, do what He willeth,
He is the living way.

--Palmer Hartsough, *Hymns of the Spirit*, p. 289

REJOICE AND WORSHIP

Holy Spirit, I thank and praise You for giving me the spiritual liberty to become the best person I can be by the grace of God. Help me to use my liberty to be more devoted to the imitation of Jesus Christ in my daily living. Keep before my mind the fact that as I am transformed into the image of Christ, my Christian influence will increase. Holy Spirit, I submit myself to You for the renewing of my mind. Amen.

Study 3

SPIRITUAL ENLIGHTENMENT

READ AND RESEARCH (John 16:5-15; 1 Corinthians 2:1-16)

Two men look at a beautiful poem inscribed on a piece of parchment. One man has a deep sense of appreciation for the poem because he is touched by the words penned by the poet. The other man sees the words on the parchment, but they mean nothing to him--he cannot read. Only if he can learn to read and understand the words will he be enlightened to the meaning of the poem.

An individual in bondage to his sinful nature is spiritually illiterate regarding the things of God. He does not have the appreciation for God, the Bible, Jesus Christ, and all things good and eternal that one has who is born of the Spirit. As the apostle Paul put it, "The natural man does not receive the things of the Spirit of God, for they are foolishness [meaningless] to him; nor can he know them, because they are spiritually discerned" (1 Corinthians 2:14).

It is essential for an individual to be enlightened by the Holy Spirit to become a believer in Christ. The Holy Spirit opens the spiritual eyes of the sinner to the fact that he is lost in sin and that he can be saved only by faith in Christ.

Thus the Spirit seeks to move the sinner to become a believer in Christ. This initial enlightening work of the Spirit is called conviction. Every person who is convicted by the Spirit does not become a believer, but no person becomes a believer without first being enlightened and convicted by the Spirit.

Spiritual enlightenment begins with conviction, pervades the entire conversion process and then continues throughout the whole lifetime of the Christian.

The person who is born of the Spirit is spiritually literate. He is deeply moved by spiritual truths because he understands and appreciates the things of God. And from whom does he have this enlightenment to the spiritual dimension? "God has revealed them to us through His Spirit . . . . that we might know the things that have been freely given to us by God . . . . comparing spiritual things with spiritual" (1 Corinthians 2:10, 12, 13).

REFLECT AND MEDITATE

1. What a wonderful gift is the enlightenment of the Holy Spirit! This enlightenment makes the Bible come alive to me, draws me to God, and gives me an appreciation for all that is true and good.

2. How privileged I am to be born of the Spirit! This gives me an eternal perspective of all things-- a perspective I would not have without the enlightenment of the Spirit.

REACT AND RESPOND

I will endeavor to be more open to the enlightenment of the Holy Spirit. I desire to know and appreciate more all that God has given to me in Christ. I will also endeavor to be more patient toward those who are unsaved and do not yet appreciate the things of God. I will pray for their conversion.

REJOICE AND WORSHIP

Thank You, Holy Spirit, for placing within my heart a love for God and a desire to follow Jesus Christ. I acknowledge that every inclination I have to do what is right and to cherish what is good is because You have enlightened my mind. Thank You for giving to me the mind of Christ. Amen.

Study 4

SPIRITUAL MOTIVATION

READ AND RESEARCH (Jeremiah 31:31-34; Hebrews 8:7-13; 10:15-17

In ancient times it was a common practice for kings or rulers to enter into covenants with their subjects. Both parties to the covenant stated what their responsibilities and benefits would be in the covenant relationship. Because of this ancient practice, in the Bible the terms of the relationship between God and man are often described as being a covenant.

After God led Israel out of Egypt, He spoke to the nation at Mount Sinai, offering to them a covenant. God promised to have Israel as His very own people and to protect, provide for them and bless them in countless ways if they would keep His commandments. When the Ten Commandments were given as the terms of this covenant of law, Israel said, "'All that the Lord has spoken we will do'" (Exodus 19:8; compare Deuteronomy 5:27). The Lord's response to Israel was, "'"Oh, that they had such a heart in them that they would fear Me and always keep all My commandments"'" (Deuteronomy 5:29).

The weakness of the covenant of law was that man in his natural sinful state does not have a sufficient inward motivation to cause him to reverence and obey God as he should. Under the new covenant of grace--we are brought into right relationship with God by grace through faith in Jesus Christ--the Holy Spirit gives the Christian an inward, spiritual motivation to love, reverence and obey God. Under the covenant of grace, God gives the believer in Christ a new heart and mind, putting His law in the heart and mind of the believer.

In the person born of the Spirit, the inward compulsion of the Spirit to do God's will is stronger and more effective for producing a life of righteousness than any external motivation can be. This new motivation is, in fact, the power of a new affection--love for God born of God's love for us (1 John 4:19; Romans 5:5).

REFLECT AND MEDITATE

1. Why is it that I have the inward desire and will to obey God? Isn't it because God has given me a new heart and mind by His Spirit--a heart and mind to do His will?

2. Why does it grieve my heart and trouble my mind when I disobey God's Word? Isn't it because God by His Spirit has written His law in my heart and mind?

REACT AND RESPOND

I resolve to be more appreciative of the fact that my new life as a born-again Christian works from the inside out, not from the outside in. When I am tempted to think that outward motivations can make me sufficient for the Christian life, I will recall that the inward motivation of my new heart and mind causes me to love, reverence and obey God.

REJOICE AND WORSHIP

God of all grace, I confess that in my own strength I cannot live the Christian life. I rejoice in knowing that You help me to go beyond myself in loving and obeying You. Thank You for giving me a new heart and mind, for writing Your law on my heart and mind, and for giving me the power of a new love for You to do Your will. Amen.

Discipleship

SPIRITUAL FELLOWSHIP

READ AND RESEARCH (1 John 1:1-10; 4:7-16)

In Christian circles today, *fellowship* is often spoken of as a verb--something we do. In the Bible, *fellowship* is a noun--the family relationship we have with God and with other Christians because of our new birth by the Spirit.

Describing the Christians' relationship with God, John wrote, "Our fellowship is with the Father and with His Son Jesus Christ" (1 John 1:3). How do we enter into this close relationship of communion with God and His Son? John answered by saying, "Beloved, now we are children of God" (1 John 3:2). We have spiritual fellowship with God and His Son by virtue of our new birth by the Spirit into God's family.

One of the best indicators of what it means to have spiritual fellowship with God is to notice the way born-again Christians speak about God. To an individual who is born of the Spirit, God is not merely something or someone he believes in with intellectual assent; God is real in his own experience.

For example, we might say that we know about George Washington because of what we have read and heard about him. However, we would never think of saying that we actually know George Washington. The truth is that we only know about him. But when it comes to God, we can know about Him from what we have read and heard, and we can know Him presently, spiritually, personally, by faith.

The spiritual fellowship of the Spirit-born Christian is to know God--not merely know about Him--and to know that He loves us as His own dear children. Then, out of this fellowship comes our fellowship (brotherhood, communion) with every other Christian, who is also a child of God (1 John 4:7).

REFLECT AND MEDITATE

1. What a privilege it is to know God for myself and to experience His love and presence! How very poor I would be spiritually if I only knew about God and did not know Him as my loving heavenly Father!

2. How wonderful it is to live in fellowship with God, with Jesus Christ and with the Holy Spirit! How wonderful it is that this spiritual fellowship also binds me to all my brothers and sisters in Christ--all members of the same family of God!

REACT AND RESPOND

I will remember that my spiritual fellowship with God is not something I do, but a relationship the Holy Spirit created between me and God when I was born of the Spirit. I will continually acknowledge that my spiritual fellowship with God is also the source of my fellowship with all other believers in Christ.

REJOICE AND WORSHIP

Praise God for so loving me as to make me His own dear child!

Praise God for bringing me into His family, making Jesus Christ my elder brother!

Praise God for bringing me into the fellowship of the Holy Spirit and the household of faith!

Praise God for my brothers and sisters in Christ!

DISCIPLESHIP COMMITMENT
Having been born again by the Spirit, I will endeavor to live every day as the new creature I am by faith in Jesus Christ. Through a daily discipline of devotions to God, I will seek to become more like my heavenly Father.

CHAPTER 19

What Does It Mean to Be Sanctified by the Spirit?

INTRODUCTION

The relationship between sanctification and holiness of life is borne out by the fact that the words *holy, holiness, sanctify* and *sanctification* all come from the same root words. In the original language of the Old Testament (Hebrew), the root word for *sanctification* and its synonymns occurs some 700 times. The root word in the original language of the New Testament (Greek) occurs about 400 times. This leaves no doubt that sanctification and holiness of life must be regarded as a major doctrine of the Bible.

The historic understanding of sanctification is stated thus in *The Encyclopedia of Religion and Ethics:*

> *In general, sanctification is the work of the Holy Spirit of God, in delivering men from the guilt and power of sin, in consecrating them to the service and love of God, and in imparting to them, initially and progressively, the fruits of Christ's redemption and the graces of a holy life.*

The Holy Spirit is the agent of God who performs the work of sanctification in our lives (Romans 15:16). Our salvation comes through sanctification by the Spirit and faith in the truth (2 Thessalonians 2:13). The Holy Spirit sanctifies the Christian through the instrumentality of the Word of God. As the Spirit of truth, the Holy Spirit sanctifies us by bringing our life into conformity with the truth of God's Word (John 15:3; 16:13; 17:17).

The sanctifying work of the Spirit in our lives is so we may obey Jesus Christ (1 Peter 1:2). Sanctification is the continuing activity of God in the Christian, by His Word and Spirit, which makes holiness of life possible. The Holy Spirit, as the Spirit of holiness (Romans 1:4), produces holiness in the Christian. He is the author of any longing we have in our heart for holiness of life. Even the most vile, offensive and violent sinners can be transformed and sanctified by the Spirit of our God (1 Corinthians 6:11).

All the facts considered, sanctification embraces four important spiritual facts for the Christian:

1. Separation to God from sin. This is the fundamental meaning of sanctification in both the Old and New Testaments.

2. The holiness of Christ imputed to the Christian. That is, the Christian is made holy in God's sight by the righteousness of Christ.

3. Purification from moral evil. The holiness of Christ is imparted to the Christian, making him a "saint" in Christ Jesus.

4. Conformity to the likeness of Christ. Through sanctification the Christian becomes Christlike.

Under the following headings we will examine more thoroughly what it means to be sanctified by the Spirit:

1. Cleansing and Separation From Sin
2. Consecration to God
3. Living a Life of Holiness
4. Sanctification--Our Position in Christ
5. Sanctification--A Continuing Work of Grace

DISCIPLESHIP GOAL

To come to a better understanding and appreciation of the biblical doctrine of sanctification and holiness and to consecrate my life more completely to Christ, allowing the Holy Spirit to produce holiness in me

READING ASSIGNMENT

The Living Book, pp. 229 - 242

Study 1

CLEANSING AND SEPARATION FROM SIN

READ AND RESEARCH (Romans 6:1-23)

Although the Holy Spirit is not mentioned as the divine agent in sanctification in this passage, Romans 6 is regarded by virtually all Bible scholars as one of the primary texts of the New Testament on the subject of sanctification.

The progression of thought in the book of Romans is that believers in Christ are cleansed of sin and justified (set free from the guilt of sin) by conversion (repentance, faith in Christ, the new birth). Romans 6 says in effect we are justified by faith; therefore we should not sin. To put it another way, we are born of the Spirit and justified by faith, thus we will also be sanctified and live a holy life. It is in this sense that we speak of sanctification as being subsequent to, or following, the new birth.

The idea that one who is sanctified must necessarily be cleansed and separated from sin arises from the fact that God is holy. Since sin separates man from God, the sinner who would return to God must be cleansed from sin and then pursue a way of life separate from his former sinfulness. This does not mean that a sanctified person never sins, but it does mean that the dominating force in one's life is not sin but righteousness.

From the practical standpoint of separation from sin, sanctification is described this way:

> *Do not let sin reign in your mortal body, that you should obey it in its lusts....But now having been set free from [the bondage and power of] sin, and having become slaves [servants] of God, you have [as a result] your fruit to holiness, and the end, everlasting life* (Romans 6:12, 22).

God does the work of cleansing and separating us from sin--freeing us from the bondage and power of sin. In turn we can respond to God's sanctifying work in our life by choosing to continue in the way of freedom from sin. As the servants of God we can reject sin and do God's good will.

REFLECT AND MEDITATE

1. Have I entered by the strait (narrow) gate, and am I walking in the narrow way that leads to life (Matthew 7:14)? Conversion to Christ might be viewed as the ''strait gate,'' and sanctification is the ''narrow way'' that leads to life.

2. Because of God's sanctifying work in my life, I can reckon myself to be dead to sin (Romans 6:11). This means I do not have to yield to temptation; I do not have to sin. Sin does not have dominion over me. I am God's servant.

REACT AND RESPOND

> *The thing my God doth hate,*
> *That I no more may do;*
> *Thy creature, Lord, again create,*
> *And all my soul renew.*
> *My soul shall then, like Thine,*
> *Abhor the thing unclean,*
> *And, sanctified by love divine,*
> *Forever cease from sin.*
> --Charles Wesley

REJOICE AND WORSHIP

Thank You, God, for forgiving my sins for Christ's sake. Thank You, too, for setting me free from sin's dominion over my life, giving me the opportunity to live in sanctification and holiness before You. Help me to live this way not only for my own sake but also that my life may be a Christlike influence on others, bringing glory to You. Amen.

Study 2

CONSECRATION TO GOD

READ AND RESEARCH (2 Thessalonians 2:13-17; 1 Peter 2:1-10)

If we look at sanctification as being both negative and positive in its results, separation from sin would be viewed as the negative aspect, and consecration to God would be the positive aspect. As Christians we are not called merely to abstain from sin; we are also called of God to actively engage in deeds of righteousness. Through sanctification we are set apart to God to be established "in every good word and work" (2 Thessalonians 2:17).

In the Bible, not only people but even objects which are set apart to God are regarded as being sanctified or holy. In the Old Testament, altars, the furnishings of the temple, and even the temple itself were all regarded as being sanctified or holy because these material objects were dedicated to the worship and service of God. In like manner, the priests who served in the temple were consecrated to God and therefore sanctified or holy (Leviticus 21:8).

But the idea of sanctification extended beyond sacred objects and priests in the Old Testament. Since the whole nation of Israel was set apart as God's chosen people, the whole nation was regarded as being sanctified and holy (Exodus 19:6; 31:13). The New Testament's description of the church (believers in Christ) as being chosen for salvation "through sanctification by the Spirit" (2 Thessalonians 2:13) and being "a holy nation" (1 Peter 2:9) is based on the Old Testament passages which describe Israel as being sanctified and holy.

The idea underlying sanctification as consecration to God is that anything or any person set apart to God is made holy by identification with God, who is holy. While God is the One who sanctifies those who are consecrated to Him, the responsibility falls on us to consecrate ourselves to God. This responsibility for personal consecration to God is expressed in the apostle Paul's well-known exhortation: "Present your bodies a living sacrifice, holy, acceptable to God" (Romans 12:1).

REFLECT AND MEDITATE

1. What does it mean to me to be sanctified--chosen of God, holy, set apart to God? Do I understand and appreciate both the privileges and responsibilities of being one of God's chosen people?

2. Yes, I consecrated my life to God when I accepted Jesus as my Savior and Lord. God forgave me and washed my sins away. Am I consecrating myself to God daily? Am I now, this very moment, set apart to serve God?

REACT AND RESPOND

I will not live a negative life, focusing my attention only on the sins I must avoid and the things I should not do. I will respond in a positive way to God's sanctifying grace. I will do good and serve God and my fellowman in response to God's sanctifying work in my life. Consecration to God will be my constant way of living.

REJOICE AND WORSHIP

Take my life, and let it be
Consecrated, Lord, to Thee;
Take my hands and let them move
At the impulse of Thy love.
Take my will, and make it Thine,
It shall be no longer mine;
Take my heart, it is Thine own,
It shall be Thy royal throne.
--Frances R. Havergal, *0*, p. 276

Discipleship

LIVING A LIFE OF HOLINESS

READ AND RESEARCH (Ephesians 4:17--5:7; 1 Peter 1:13-16)

The New Testament makes plain that holiness of life is God's standard of living for Christians. The New Testament does not provide a specific answer to every question we might raise about what is right or wrong for a Christian, but the New Testament does provide detailed instructions on the way Christians should live.

The passage in Ephesians 4:17 through 5:7 is but one example of how thorough the New Testament is in outlining holy living as God's standard. In attitudes, words and deeds, Christians are to be Christlike--not like unsaved people who follow their sinful desires. What the Holy Spirit produces in the life of a Christian is consistent with ''goodness, righteousness, and truth'' (Ephesians 5:9).

Sanctification by the Spirit will result in a life of holiness because God is holy and He has called His people to be holy. Sanctification by the Spirit makes it possible for the Christian to obey God's call to holiness.

Holiness of life is sanctification in practice. As Christians we are sanctified (set apart from sin to God) to be sanctified (holy, righteous, pure, morally good) in our living. In simplest terms, *Christlikeness* is a synonymn for *holiness*. When we say that holiness is God's standard of living for His people, we could as well say that Christ's example is God's standard of living for His people. Since holiness of life is a Christlike life, shouldn't every Christian aspire to live a holy life?

Some people have turned away from holiness of life because they have wrongly thought that to live a life of holiness means an individual must be absolutely perfect. Of course, no person is absolutely perfect, but people who are sanctified by the Spirit are constantly striving toward perfection in Christlikeness. Like Christ himself, God's standard of holiness will forever be a challenge to us to become better people. But instead of giving up on holy living, we should yield ourselves more completely to the sanctifying grace of the Holy Spirit and accept the challenge of living a holy life to the glory of God.

REFLECT AND MEDITATE

1. What is my concept of holy living? Is it derived from the example and teachings of Christ, or is it to some extent a man-made concept? Do I actually know enough about Jesus as He is presented in the Gospels to have a concept of holiness based on His example?

2. Without question I need to see more clearly Jesus' example and to know better His teachings. Only thus can I have a correct understanding of God's standard of holiness. Christ must be my example for holy living!

REACT AND RESPOND

Daily I will ask God to sanctify me by His Word and His Spirit, thus enabling me to live a holy life. I will keep in mind that God's standard of holiness is not a man-made standard; it is Jesus Christ. I will aspire to be like Jesus.

REJOICE AND WORSHIP

I praise You, Lord God, for your holiness!

Hallowed be Your name in heaven and on earth.

Thank You for redeeming me from sin by the blood of Your own dear Son, to Whom be glory forever!

Thank You for sanctification by the Spirit and for calling me to live a holy life.

Make me Christlike; make me a blessing to others.

Amen.

Study 4

SANCTIFICATION--OUR POSITION IN CHRIST

READ AND RESEARCH (1 Corinthians 1:1-9; 6:9-11)

The Bible speaks of sanctification in different ways. In some passages sanctification is presented as an accomplished fact in the life of the Christian. In other passages sanctification appears to be an ongoing work of grace in the life of the Christian. These two different perspectives of sanctification have given rise to various ways of trying to define sanctification. Those who focus attention on sanctification as an accomplished fact might say that sanctification is a "second definite work of grace," or they might say it is "instantaneous" rather than gradual or progressive.

From a biblical standpoint, sanctification is definite, immediate and progressive. Through sanctification by the Spirit, God imparts to us both initially and progressively the graces of a holy life. The legal position (in relation to God) of one sanctified in Christ Jesus is definite and immediate (Acts 26:18; 1 Corinthians 1:2), but sanctification as a practical reality in the daily life of the Christian is a continuing work.

When the Bible speaks of the Christian as being sanctified (an accomplished fact), it refers to the Christian's status or standing in relation to God by faith in Jesus Christ. The Bible says of the sanctified believer in Christ, "You are in Christ Jesus, who became for us . . . righteousness and sanctification and redemption" (1 Corinthians 1:30). Christ is our representative before God. When we trust in Christ as our Savior and Lord, God sees us as being "in Christ." Therefore Christ becomes our righteousness, sanctification and redemption. Thus in the New Testament the believer in Christ is described as being already (objectively) sanctified in Christ.

Even though some of the Christians at Corinth were carnal-minded and spiritually immature, the apostle Paul regarded all of them as being "called to be saints" because they were "sanctified in Christ Jesus" (1 Corinthians 1:2). Paul knew there was much room for spiritual improvement in the lives of the Corinthians. Still God viewed them as His sanctified people because of their faith in Christ.

REFLECT AND MEDITATE

1. I can regard my sanctification by the Spirit as being an accomplished fact--not because I am as good as I should be but because of the goodness of Christ on my behalf. Jesus Christ is my sanctification.

2. What does it mean to me that I am sanctified in Christ Jesus and called to be a saint? What does this say about my security as a Christian? What does this say about the kind of person I should be?

REACT AND RESPOND

I will endeavor to see myself as God sees me in Christ. Moreover, I will commit myself to become the person God sees me to be in Christ. I want my sanctification to be demonstrated in my daily living and relationships with others because it is already an accomplished fact in my life by faith in Christ.

REJOICE AND WORSHIP

Jesus Christ is made to me,
All I need, all I need;
He alone is all my plea,
He is all I need.

Wisdom, righteousness and pow'r,
Holiness [sanctification] forevermore,
My redemption full and sure,
He is all I need.

Glory, glory to the Lamb,
He is all I need!
--C. P. Jones, *Hymns of the Spirit*, p. 138

Discipleship

SANCTIFICATION--A CONTINUING WORK OF GRACE

READ AND RESEARCH (1 Thessalonians 4:1-8; 2 Peter 1:1-11)

Many scriptures urge the Christian to progress in Christlike living. Since we are not yet perfect in Christlikeness, sanctification must be a continuing work of grace. It could be said that we are to be continuously sanctified because we are sanctified. Although we are set apart in Christ for God, and for Christ's sake we are viewed as being holy by God, we must continue in the way of holiness, showing by our consecration to God that we are sanctified.

Sanctification as a continuing work of grace means that God is working in us and we are working with God to live the Christian life. The holiness of God introduced into our life by the grace of sanctification must be sustained by continuing sanctification.

Not only does God sanctify and continue to sanctify the believer in Christ, but as believers we too must strive toward sanctification. One example of how this is done is the apostle Paul's exhortation to the Thessalonian Christians to abstain from sexual immorality: ''For this is the will of God, your sanctification'' (1 Thessalonians 4:3). In the same vein of thought, Paul wrote to Timothy, ''If anyone cleanses himself from. . .[evil], he will be a vessel for honor, sanctified and useful to the Master, prepared for every good work'' (2 Timothy 2:21).

Sanctification as a continuing work of grace is preparation for every good work. Therefore the Christian is challenged to always be adding more and more of the graces of Christ to his life. We are commanded to add to faith virtue, to virtue knowledge, then self-control, perseverance, godliness, brotherly kindness and, above all, love (2 Peter 1:5-7). Of course, we cannot increase in Christian graces by our own effort without God. The graces of Christ are imparted to us *initially* and *progressively* as we pursue the sanctified life in Christ by the Spirit.

REFLECT AND MEDITATE

1. There would be no way for me to become a more Christlike person if God did not continue to dispense His grace to me through His continuing work of sanctification. I see my need to be continuously sanctified because I am sanctified.

2. God is working in my life to make me a Christlike person. His purpose for my life is very good. I must work with Him to receive, as He works in me to impart, the graces of Christ.

REACT AND RESPOND

I will express my gratitude and appreciation for my sanctification by the Spirit by abstaining from sin and embracing righteousness. I am resolved that I will so nurture my life in Christ that I will grow in His grace.

REJOICE AND WORSHIP

Dear God, I rejoice in the confidence that You who have begun a good work in my life will see it through to the end. I rejoice in the assurance that You will sanctify me completely and that You will preserve me blameless in spirit, soul, and body at the coming of our Lord Jesus Christ. Amen. (See Philippians 1:6; 1 Thessalonians 5:23.)

DISCIPLESHIP COMMITMENT
My walk of sanctification with God has begun. Therefore I will sanctify myself daily, setting myself apart to God through prayerful consecration and obedience to His Word.

Chapter 20

What Does It Mean to Be Filled With the Spirit?

INTRODUCTION

The Spirit-filled experience is given prominence in the New Testament, especially in the book of Acts. The Bible says, "They were all filled with the Holy Spirit" (Acts 2:4); "Peter, filled with the Holy Spirit, said. . ." (4:8); "They were all filled with the Holy Spirit" (4:31); "'The Lord Jesus . . . has sent me that you may . . . be filled with the Holy Spirit'" (9:17); "Paul, filled with the Holy Spirit" (13:9); "The disciples were filled with joy and with the Holy Spirit" (13:52); and finally, a command: "Be filled with the Spirit" (Ephesians 5:18).

In the early church the Spirit-filled experience was the norm for believers in Christ. The apostle Paul was filled with the Spirit and commanded other believers in Christ to be filled with the Spirit. The biblical command that Christians be filled with the Spirit is still in force. It is no less important for us to be filled with the Spirit than it was for the Christians of the early church.

There are four rules of the Greek language (the language in which the New Testament was written) which lead us to four important truths about the command to be filled with the Spirit recorded in Ephesians 5:18.

First, this statement is in the imperative mood, leaving no question about the fact that this is a command that every Christian be filled with the Holy Spirit.

Second, the tense of the verb is present progressive. A literal translation of the command could be something like this: "Be you always being filled with the Spirit." This means continuous action. Being filled with the Holy Spirit is not a onetime passing experience. It should be a contin-

ual experience for the Christian.

Third, the verb is in the plural number. This means, "All of you be filled with the Spirit." The command to be filled with the Spirit is not directed only to leaders or a few select members of the church. It is God's will for all Christians to be filled with the Spirit.

Fourth, the verb is in the passive voice. This means the subject of the verb is not acting but being acted upon. That is, being filled with the Spirit is not something we can do; it is something only God can do for us. And God will fill us with His Spirit if we will receive the fullness of the Spirit. Through prayer, faith in God and obedience to His Word (Matthew 21:22; Acts 5:32), we can be filled with the Spirit.

The next five sessions will be devoted to explaining what it means to be filled with the Spirit and how to be filled with the Spirit. The five headings for these sessions are

1. Baptism With the Spirit
2. Empowerment to Be Witnesses of Christ
3. Spirit-Controlled Living
4. Fruitful Christian Living
5. How to Be Filled With the Spirit

DISCIPLESHIP GOAL

To understand and appreciate what the Bible teaches about being filled with the Holy Spirit and to be personally filled with the Spirit so as to be a more effective witness and servant of Jesus Christ.

READING ASSIGNMENT
The Living Book, pp. 242 -255

Discipleship

BAPTISM WITH THE SPIRIT

READ AND RESEARCH (John 1:19-34; Acts 1:4-8; 2:1-4)

The doctrine of the Baptism with the Holy Spirit is based on biblical texts which refer to being baptized with the Spirit (Matthew 3:11; Mark 1:8; Luke 3:16; John 1:33). In these parallel passages the Gospels say John the Baptist preached that Jesus Christ would baptize people with the Holy Spirit.

Jesus, before His ascension, told His disciples, "'You shall be baptized with the Holy Spirit not many days from now'" (Acts 1:5). This prophecy of Jesus' was fulfilled when His disciples were filled with the Holy Spirit on the Day of Pentecost (Acts 2:1-4).

Several years after the Day of Pentecost (Acts 2), Gentiles at the house of Cornelius were filled with the Holy Spirit (Acts 10:44-47). Reporting this event to the church at Jerusalem, Peter remembered "the word of the Lord, how He said, 'John indeed baptized with water, but you shall be baptized with the Holy Spirit'" (Acts 11:16).

What was (is) the baptism with the Holy Spirit foretold by John the Baptist and Jesus Christ? It was without question the outpouring of the Holy Spirit on the Day of Pentecost. However, when the Spirit came on the Day of Pentecost, no mention was made of baptism. Instead, the Bible says the disciples of Jesus were "filled with the Holy Spirit" (Acts 2:4). It appears from the book of Acts that the early Christians thought of the baptism with the Spirit as the initial experience of being filled with the Holy Spirit. After this initial infilling with the Spirit, the believer in Christ is under commandment to maintain a Spirit-filled life.

It is important to understand that the baptism with the Spirit is not the same as the indwelling of the Spirit received with the new birth. Every believer in Christ has the indwelling of the Holy Spirit (Romans 8:9; Galatians 4:6). But after the believers at Samaria had already been baptized in water to signify their new birth by faith in Christ, the apostles Peter and John prayed for them to receive the Holy Spirit, "for as yet He had fallen upon none of them" (Acts 8:16).

Speaking with other tongues, as the Holy Spirit gives the utterance, is regarded as the initial evidence of the baptism with the Spirit because this manifestation accompanied the baptism with the Spirit among the early Christians (see Acts 2:4; 10:45, 46; 11:15, 16; 19:6).

REFLECT AND MEDITATE

1. To be a born-again Christian and have the witness of the Spirit in me that I am a child of God is an unspeakable blessing. But even this marvelous experience can be enlarged and enriched by God when I am baptized with the Spirit.

2. To be baptized with the Spirit and then to maintain a Spirit-filled life is not an optional benefit. This is God's will for my life, and therefore it is essential that I be filled with the Spirit.

REACT AND RESPOND

If I have not yet received the gift of the Holy Spirit as Jesus' disciples did on the Day of Pentecost, I will ask the Lord Jesus to baptize me with His Holy Spirit.

If I have already received the baptism with the Spirit, I will pray daily to be filled anew with the Holy Spirit so I can live a Spirit-filled life.

REJOICE AND WORSHIP

Spirit of the living God, fall fresh on me;
Spirit of the living God, fall fresh on me;
Break me, melt me, mold me, fill me.
Spirit of the living God, fall fresh on me.
--Hymns of the Spirit, p. 97

Study 2

EMPOWERMENT TO BE WITNESSES OF CHRIST

READ AND RESEARCH (Luke 24:44-53; Acts 1:1-14)

In the Bible, one clearly stated result of being filled with the Holy Spirit is that we receive spiritual power to be witnesses of Christ (Acts 1:8).

Notice that the word used by Jesus in the passage in Acts 1:8 is *witnesses*--a noun, not a verb. Too often when mention is made of Christians being witnesses of Christ, we immediately begin to think of the verb *witnessing*--something we do. Jesus' emphasis was on what His disciples would be as a result of receiving the gift of the Spirit.

Now to be sure, a witness should be one who witnesses, but an individual becomes a witness by virtue of what he has personally seen, heard or experienced. Any person who is baptized with the Holy Spirit has an overwhelming personal experience of the power of the resurrected Christ. The person who is baptized (filled) with the Spirit is thus empowered to testify and demonstrate in various ways His personal knowledge of Jesus Christ.

Being a witness of Christ definitely means that we should testify verbally of our faith in Him. However, being a witness of Christ also means that our whole life should testify of our faith in Christ.

An example of what it means to be empowered by the Spirit to be witnesses of Christ is given in the passage in Acts 4:31-37. There the Bible says the disciples of Jesus ''were all filled with the Holy Spirit, and they spoke the word of God with boldness'' (v. 31). Then the Bible goes on to say that their lives were distinguished by harmony, goodwill, generosity, compassion, service to others and the obvious grace of Christ. Those they encountered not only heard about the gospel of Jesus, they saw it demonstrated in the lives of the Spirit-filled believers.

REFLECT AND MEDITATE

1. Jesus stressed the importance of being His witness by the empowerment of the Spirit. Am I giving sufficient attention to being filled with the Spirit--so I will be a witness of Christ?

2. Effective witnessing for Christ in the power of the Spirit must involve my whole life. Is my verbal testimony of faith in Christ confirmed by my lifestyle, relationships and service to others?

REACT AND RESPOND

I commit myself to being a Spirit-filled Christian so I will be a more effective witness of Christ. I will endeavor to take advantage of opportunities to give my testimony for Christ. And I will, by God's grace and Spirit, be a witness of Christ by my whole life.

REJOICE AND WORSHIP

Thank You, God my Father, for making available to me in the gift of Your Spirit the power I need to be a witness of Christ. Fill me with Your Spirit so I will speak boldly of my faith in Christ. Fill me with Your Spirit so my life in every way will say to others that I am a witness of Christ. Deliver me from any tendency to desire or use Your divine power for anything other than the glory of Christ. Praise be to the Father, the Son and the Holy Spirit! Amen.

Discipleship

Study 3

SPIRIT-CONTROLLED LIVING

READ AND RESEARCH (Galatians 5:16-26; Ephesians 5:15-21)

One way many people would describe what it means to be filled with the Spirit is to say that a Spirit-filled person lives under the control of the Spirit. Now this does not mean that the Holy Spirit will seize control of an individual's life against his will. But when we are filled with the Spirit, we voluntarily submit to His control.

Many people have surrendered the control of their lives to the works of the flesh (sinful desires and deeds) mentioned in Galatians 5:19-21. The life of an individual controlled by the evils mentioned in this passage is a sharp and tragic contrast to the life of one who is controlled by the Spirit. When we are controlled by the Spirit (living in the Spirit and walking in the Spirit), we will not live according to the desires of the sinful nature.

When a person is filled with the Spirit, yielded to the Spirit's control, that individual is equipped to be of maximum service to God. Of course, this does not mean that every Spirit-filled person will serve Christ in the same capacity. The blessing of being under the control of the Spirit is not that we go beyond our brothers and sisters in Christ but that we go beyond our ordinary selves in service to God.

Biblical examples of Spirit-filled people show that those who are filled with the Spirit, and thus controlled by the Spirit, will have a capacity in their service to Christ and in their work for God such as they have never had before. Under the control of the Spirit, people have exceptional wisdom; amazing love; boundless forgiveness; extraordinary courage, mercy and compassion; and incredible endurance. Submission to the control of the Holy Spirit releases us to be and do and say what we never could without the Spirit.

REFLECT AND MEDITATE

1. The secular humanists say man can do anything he is determined to do on his own-- without God. The Bible says man is mortal, limited, finite and needs the Spirit of God to get beyond himself.

2. Which will it be for me? Will I be locked up within the limits of self, or will I submit to the control of the Holy Spirit? Through submission to the Spirit there are possibilities for my life I cannot even imagine.

REACT AND RESPOND

There is nothing but failure and hopelessness in submitting to the control of the sinful nature and the works of the flesh. But even if I do not stoop to this baser way of living, my best without the Holy Spirit can never be the best. Daily I will ask God to fill me with His Spirit, and I will submit to the Spirit's control to reach my maximum potential for God.

REJOICE AND WORSHIP

Gracious God, I praise You for the promise of a more glorious life beyond the grave for those who believe in Christ. But I also praise You for the wonderful possibilities open to me in this present life as I submit to Your Holy Spirit. God, fill me with Your Spirit. I submit to the control of Your Spirit. Do in me and through me by the power of Your Spirit more than I could ever ask or think. Amen.

Study 4

FRUITFUL CHRISTIAN LIVING

READ AND RESEARCH (Matthew 7:15-20; John 15:1-8; Galatians 5:19-23)

An apple tree produces apples, and a walnut tree produces walnuts. This is the law of nature--a rule so reliable that we can identify trees and other plants by the fruits they bear.

Jesus said the law of fruit-bearing is also a valid indicator of an individual's character. The produce (fruit, harvest) of evil character is evil deeds. The produce of good character transformed by God's Spirit is deeds of righteousness.

Jesus said His disciples would be fruitful in likeness to Him by abiding in Him. To abide in Christ means to maintain a constant relationship with Him as one's Savior and Lord. As Jesus said, He is the vine from whom we derive our spiritual life. And as we have seen in the studies on ''Life in the Spirit,'' Jesus Christ imparts to us the life of the Holy Spirit, making us fruitful in every good word and work.

In Galatians 5:22, 23, nine virtues are listed as being the harvest of the Spirit. Doubtlessly, the apostle Paul did not intend this list to be exhaustive but representative of the good produced in one's life by the Holy Spirit. The virtues which result from the work of the Holy Spirit in our lives are so admirable, noble and intrinsically good that they are universally recognized as being of God. Against these virtues there is no condemning law. To put it another way, the Spirit produces a life that is lawful--in harmony with the good will of God.

The first fruit of the Spirit appears in the life of one who is born again of the Spirit. Sanctification by the Spirit increases an individual's capacity for bearing the fruit of the Spirit. Then it must be that the fruit of the Spirit will be most evident, and more and more evident, in those who are filled with the Spirit. The Holy Spirit will produce love, joy, peace, longsuffering, kindness, goodness, faithfulness, gentleness and self-control in the lives of those who abide in Christ and are filled with the Spirit.

REFLECT AND MEDITATE

1. Only the Holy Spirit in my life can cause me to bear the fruit of the Spirit. All my efforts at goodness without God, however valiant or sincere, can only poorly mimic the graces produced by the Spirit.

2. When it comes to living in the Spirit, the question with highest priority is, Am I bearing the fruit of the Spirit? Do I have Christian character produced in me by the Holy Spirit?

REACT AND RESPOND

I see these graces of the Spirit in my life, but they are not present to the extent I would like to see them. I will yield myself more completely to the influences of the Holy Spirit to see the harvest of the Spirit more and more evident in my life.

REJOICE AND WORSHIP

Deeper, deeper! blessed Holy Spirit,
Take me deeper still,
Till my life is wholly lost in Jesus,
And His perfect will.

Deeper, deeper! tho' it cost hard trials,
Deeper let me go!
Rooted in the holy love of Jesus,
Let me fruitful grow.
--C. P. Jones, *Hymns of the Spirit*, p. 272

Discipleship

HOW TO BE FILLED WITH THE SPIRIT

READ AND RESEARCH (Acts 2:29-39; 5:29-32; 19:1-7)

No one can be filled with the Spirit who is not born of the Spirit and sanctified by the Spirit. But the gift of the Holy Spirit is for every person who is converted to Christ and set apart to God as one redeemed from sin.

A person seeking to be filled with the Holy Spirit should be ''continually . . . praising and blessing God'' (Luke 24:53) and engaged ''in prayer and supplication'' (Acts 1:14) for the gift of the Spirit. And central to these activities of worship should be the recognition that God gives the Holy Spirit '''to those who obey Him''' (Acts 5:32). Obedience to the gospel is the prerequisite to being filled with the Holy Spirit.

When the apostle Peter spoke to the multitude of inquiring Jews on the Day of Pentecost (Acts 2:5, 14, 38), he said to them in effect that they would have to obey the gospel to receive the gift of the Holy Spirit. The disciples of John the Baptist whom Paul encountered at Ephesus were also required to confirm their obedience to the gospel before they could receive the gift of the Spirit.

Obedience to God and the gospel is submission to God's redemptive work through Christ. Complete surrender to Christ is the very heart of how to be filled with the Holy Spirit. For those who obey God, Jesus said it is not difficult to be filled with the Spirit. God has a great desire and willingness to give the Holy Spirit to His obedient people. Jesus said, '''If you then, being evil, know how to give good gifts to your children, how much more will your heavenly Father give the Holy Spirit to those who ask Him!''' (Luke 11:13).

REFLECT AND MEDITATE

1. Do I really want to be filled with the Holy Spirit? That is, am I ready to turn loose of everything in my life that is unlike Christ? Do I want the Spirit more than I want my pride, selfishness, bitterness, wrath and evil thoughts?

2. When it comes to being filled with the Spirit, the real issue is, What will I allow Christ to do in my life? Whatever He asks of me, wherever He leads, I must be willing to say yes to Christ to be filled with His Holy Spirit.

REACT AND RESPOND

All to Jesus I surrender,
Make me, Saviour, wholly Thine;
Let me feel the Holy Spirit,
Truly know that Thou art mine.
All to Jesus I surrender,
Lord, I give myself to Thee;
Fill me with Thy love and power,
Let Thy blessing fall on me.
--J. W. Van Deventer, *Hymns of the Spirit*, p. 275

REJOICE AND WORSHIP

Father in heaven, You are the giver of every good gift. Thank You for the great salvation You have given to us in Jesus Christ. Thank You for the gift of the Holy Spirit. All glory to God, now and forever! Amen.

DISCIPLESHIP COMMITMENT
Daily I will ask God to fill me with the Holy Spirit so I will walk and live in the Spirit, not only in relationship with God but in relation to all people.

CHAPTER 21

What Are the Gifts of the Spirit?

INTRODUCTION

The gifts of the Holy Spirit are not to be confused with innate gifts or acquired gifts. A person may be born with the potential to develop certain skills or abilities because of his genetic makeup. When these "natural" skills or abilities are developed, they are referred to as *innate gifts*, or the gifts with which one is born. In the course of living, a person may acquire by education, practice and experience certain skills and abilities. These are referred to as *acquired gifts*.

The gifts of the Spirit described in the Bible are conferred by God. No person is born with a gift of the Spirit, and no one may obtain a gift of the Spirit by means of education, practice or experience. The gifts of the Spirit are enablings of the Spirit. They are also called *charismata*--enablings of grace. Just as our salvation from sin is an unmerited gift of God's grace, the gifts of the Spirit are also unmerited and bestowed on Christians out of the bounty of God's grace.

The Bible states clearly the purposes of the spiritual gifts bestowed on believers in Christ by the Holy Spirit. These purposes are set forth in the book of Ephesians 4:12-16:

1. For the perfecting of the saints (*KJV*), bringing the people of God to completeness or maturity in grace.

2. For the work of the ministry. Worship is ministry to the Lord. Service is ministry to others. (The gifts are for the perfecting of the saints for the work of the ministry.)

3. To edify the church. Christ builds His church, and it is the purpose of the Holy Spirit to build the church. (*To edify* means "especially to build up spiritually.")

4. To produce unity of faith among believers. This is predicated on the fact that we all have access to the one and only heavenly Father by the Holy Spirit.

5. To increase the knowledge of Christ among believers. This is not mere head knowledge but experiential knowledge of "knowing Him."

6. To bring Christians to maturity in likeness to Christ. To be like Christ is the ideal and ultimate goal for every Christian.

7. To establish believers in the doctrine of Christ so they will not be tossed by every wind of wrong doctrine.

The identification, definition, operation and practical purposes of the gifts of the Spirit will be presented under the following headings:

1. Typical Gifts of the Spirit
2. Ministry Gifts
3. Gifts Implied by Calling
4. Gifts Are for Edification
5. Follow the Way of Love

DISCIPLESHIP GOAL

To understand and appreciate what the Bible says about the gifts of the Spirit and to discover the ways in which I may be gifted of the Spirit for the edification of the church and the work of the ministry

READING ASSIGNMENT
The Living Book, pp. 255 - 267

Discipleship

TYPICAL GIFTS OF THE SPIRIT

READ AND RESEARCH (1 Corinthians 12:1-11)

The nine gifts of the Holy Spirit identified in 1 Corinthians 12:8-11 are not intended to be a complete list of spiritual gifts. These are typical gifts of the Spirit bestowed on believers, but there are other lists of spiritual gifts in the New Testament. It is best not to set a limit on how many gifts of the Spirit there are. Doubtlessly there are as many gifts of the Spirit as the church has need of to fulfill its mission in the world.

However, the nine typical enablings of the Spirit are a good place to start with trying to understand the nature and function of gifts of the Spirit. The nine typical gifts divide naturally into three categories as follows.

Gifts of Revelation:

1. The *word of wisdom* is wisdom imparted directly to the mind by the Holy Spirit--not wisdom obtained by learning and experience.

2. The *word of knowledge* is knowledge obtained by divine revelation and not available through natural means.

3. The *gift of discernment* is divinely given ability to identify and overcome the spiritual forces of evil which oppose Christ.

Gifts of Demonstration:

1. The *gift of faith* is a special bestowal of faith to meet special needs or for unusual accomplishments.

2. The *gifts of healing* are numerous and may be for spiritual, emotional or physical healing. The gifts of healing are for those who need healing.

3. The *gift of miracles* is the divine enabling to perform works of a supernatural nature by the power of the Holy Spirit. Miracles do not occur by the ordinary laws of nature.

Gifts of Utterance:

1. The *gift of prophecy* is manifest in speaking words in response to the inspiration and motivation of the Holy Spirit.

2. The *gift of tongues* is the utterance of a language one has not learned in response to the inspiration and motivation of the Holy Spirit.

3. The *gift of interpretation* is the companion to the gift of tongues. It is the spiritual enabling to tell the meaning of something spoken in tongues.

REFLECT AND MEDITATE

1. As you look back over your life, have you ever been enabled by God with one or more of the nine typical gifts of the Spirit? What specific purposes did these gifts of the Spirit serve for yourself or others?

2. The gifts of utterance (prophesying, tongues and interpretation) are conspicuous among Pentecostals and charismatics. Are these always the most needed gifts of the Spirit? What is the reasoning behind your answer to this question?

REACT AND RESPOND

I would like to be more sensitive to the inspiration and motivation of the Holy Spirit so He can enable me by whatever gift God wills to bestow on me. I will maintain an openness to the Holy Spirit regarding spiritual gifts.

REJOICE AND WORSHIP

Dear God, we acknowledge Your most excellent wisdom in bestowing the gifts of the Spirit on Your people. The challenges of the Christian life and the mission of the church would be overwhelming without the enablings of Your Spirit. Thank You for the gifts of the Spirit. Amen.

Study 2

MINISTRY GIFTS

READ AND RESEARCH (Romans 12:1-8; 1 Corinthians 12:12-31)

In these lists of gifts several of the nine typical gifts of the Spirit are mentioned again. However, there are at least seven additional gifts of the Spirit listed in these passages which many refer to as ministry gifts:

1. Helps--gift for assisting others
2. Governing--gift for leading, guiding
3. Serving--gift for attending to needs of others
4. Teaching--gift for informing, instructing
5. Exhorting--gift for encouraging others
6. Giving--gift for personal generosity
7. Acts of mercy--gift for performing merciful deeds.

It is God's will for every believer in Christ to receive the gift (baptism, fullness) of the Holy Spirit and to be enabled by the Spirit for some ministry. Even if we cannot identify one of the nine typical gifts of the Spirit (1 Corinthians 12:8-11) operating through us, still we are gifted by the Spirit. This fact is clearly stated in these words from the *New English Bible*:

> *For just as in a single human body there are many limbs and organs, all with different functions, so all of us, united with Christ, form one body, serving individually as limbs and organs to one another. The gifts we possess differ as they are allotted to us by God's grace, and must be exercised accordingly* (Romans 12:4-6).

Just as every member of the human body is endowed of the Creator to serve a specific purpose in the body, so every member of the church (the body of Christ) is gifted by God's grace and Spirit to perform some specific ministry. Therefore we are to be good stewards of the manifold grace of God according as we have received the *charisma--*

"gift" of grace (1 Peter 4:10). As stewards of God's gifts of grace, we become ministers one to another and are accountable to God for performing our ministry so as to please Him.

REFLECT AND MEDITATE

1. Examine yourself and ask these questions: In what way is it apparent that God would like to use me to minister to others? Could it be that this is the ministry gift God has bestowed on me by His grace? Am I being a good steward of this gift of grace?

2. Examine yourself and ask this question: Do I recognize and appreciate the ministry gifts God has bestowed on my brothers and sisters in Christ?

REACT AND RESPOND

I will endeavor to be more alert to the enablings of grace and opportunities for ministry God has given to me. There is a work for me to do in the kingdom of God, and I must be a good steward of the gifts of grace I have received. I will also seek to be more understanding and appreciative of the gifts for ministry others have received from God.

REJOICE AND WORSHIP

Wise and holy God, You created the human body to be a most amazing and well-functioning organism. To every part of the body, You gave a special purpose. With that same wisdom You have created the body of Christ, the church. You are to be praised and glorified forever for giving every member of the body of Christ a special purpose. Thank You, God of all grace, for giving our lives meaning and direction by the gifts of Your grace. Amen.

GIFTS IMPLIED BY CALLING

READ AND RESEARCH (Ephesians 4:1-16)

Some gifts of the Spirit are implied by the divine calling one has received. The ministry of apostle was one of the leadership gifts identified by the early church. It was characteristic of the apostle Paul to identify himself as an apostle, and he understood that as an apostle, God had laid claim to his life in a special way. Paul described himself as being "a servant of Jesus Christ, called to be an apostle, separated to the gospel of God" (Romans 1:1).

The passage in Ephesians 4:11-13 identifies four specific callings which imply a divine gift or enabling of grace. One called to be apostle also received an enabling of grace to perform the ministry of an apostle. In the same way, individuals called to be evangelists or pastor-teachers receive an enabling of grace to perform these ministries. In the early church the callings of apostle, prophet, evangelist and pastor-teacher were all leadership roles in the church.

There are spiritual leaders in the church who occupy distinct, specialized positions of leadership in relation to other believers. These individuals are given to the church by Christ for the benefit of the whole church.

In some instances we may identify the ministries of leaders with offices or titles found in the New Testament. In other instances the offices or titles found in the New Testament do not seem to fit, but nevertheless, we recognize in these people divine gifts for spiritual leadership. The purpose of the New Testament is not that we should become preoccupied with offices and titles but that we should recognize and appreciate the fact that God raises up gifted spiritual leaders in the church.

Natural and acquired abilities for leadership are valuable, but these alone will never be sufficient for the ministry of the church. The church, because it is a spiritual organism, the body of Christ, will always need leaders who are divinely gifted by Christ.

REFLECT AND MEDITATE

1. Is God calling me to some specialized role of spiritual leadership in the church? If I have such a calling and gift, in what way am I exercising my leadership role for God's glory?

2. Assuming that God has not laid claim to my life with a special calling to leadership in the church, what is my attitude toward those whom God has called? Do they have the support of my prayers, encouragement and material means to fulfill their calling?

REACT AND RESPOND

I would like to keep always in my mind and heart the truth that Christians are not competitors with each other but laborers together with God. This means that I should be a partner in the gospel with those whom God has called to specialized roles of spiritual leadership in the church.

REJOICE AND WORSHIP

Dear God, I rejoice in the knowledge that the first and highest calling of every Christian is to simply follow Jesus Christ. Rejoicing in my own discipleship, I acknowledge that You have called some to specialized roles of spiritual leadership in the church. They, too, are disciples of Jesus Christ. Help me to follow these leaders as they follow Christ. Amen.

Study 4

GIFTS ARE FOR EDIFICATION

READ AND RESEARCH (1 Corinthians 14:1-26)

The Christians at Corinth placed such a high value on the spiritual gifts of utterance (prophesying, tongues and interpretation) that these gifts had become spiritual status symbols. Viewing the gifts of utterance in this way led to pride, exclusivism and competitiveness on the part of those who judged themselves to possess the coveted gifts of utterance. The instructions in 1 Corinthians 14 were intended to correct the abuses of the gifts at Corinth.

Paul laid down a simple rule to follow in the exercise of any spiritual gift. Every spiritual gift is to be exercised for the purpose of edifying (building up) the church (vv. 12, 26). The gifts of the Spirit can be abused and misused by uninformed, carnal-minded and careless Christians. We are accountable to God and must be responsible for every gift God gives us, including the enablings of His Spirit.

Misuse and abuse of the gifts, especially the gifts of utterance, had led to a general state of disorder and confusion in the worship services of the Corinthian Christians. Under such circumstances they were not helping each other and were also unable to influence unbelievers to come to Christ for salvation.

The fact that God allows us to be used by the Spirit in the exercise of some spiritual gift or the performance of some special ministry should never become a source of pride and seeking of glory for oneself. The manifestation of a spiritual gift through an individual does not mean that person is spiritually superior to other Christians.

By the manifestation of spiritual gifts the Holy Spirit seeks to bring all believers to maturity and completion in Christ. Therefore the spectacular gifts which attract attention and appeal to curiosity are not necessarily the ones most needed by the church. We should earnestly desire to see manifest the gifts that are most needed by the church at any given time. Only God knows what is the best gift (1 Corinthians 12:31) in every situation to bring edification to the church.

REFLECT AND MEDITATE

1. Do you recall some instance where you personally witnessed the misuse or abuse of spiritual gifts in a worship service? What was the result of this misguided activity?

2. Now recall some instances when you have personally witnessed the exercise of spiritual gifts for the edification of the church. What was the result of this wise use of gifts?

REACT AND RESPOND

When God graciously allows me to be enabled by His Spirit to perform some ministry to the church, I will do so in a true spirit of humility toward God and my brothers and sisters in Christ. I will endeavor to live by the rule that all spiritual gifts are to be used to bring edification to the church.

REJOICE AND WORSHIP

Father in heaven, hallowed be Your name. Every good gift comes from You and is for Your glory. The precious gifts of Your Spirit bestowed on us are unmerited gifts of Your grace. I acknowledge that when Your grace is channeled through my life to bless others, it is for your glory and not mine. May it be so in my life, for Yours is the power and glory forever. Amen.

Discipleship

FOLLOW THE WAY OF LOVE

READ AND RESEARCH (1 Corinthians 12:31--13:13)

After appealing to the Corinthian Christians to earnestly desire the spiritual gifts God deems best for the church, Paul appealed to them to follow the more excellent way of love. Proud rivalry and confusion over the gifts of the Spirit had caused the Corinthians to lose sight of the way of love. Yes, they needed the gifts of the Spirit, but they also needed to be restored to following the way of God's love.

Is it possible to speak with tongues, prophesy, have amazing knowledge, exceptional faith and boundless generosity, and even give one's own life and not be motivated by the love of God? The passage in 1 Corinthians 13:1-3 suggests this might be possible, but it would all be in vain because it would be unacceptable to God without love.

The passage in 1 Corinthians 13, inserted as it is in the midst of a discussion of spiritual gifts, is a reminder to us that along with the gifts of the Spirit we also need the fruit of the Spirit (Galatians 5:22, 23). Especially we need that Christian virtue which is listed first as a harvest of the Spirit--love, God's love dispensed into our hearts and then extended to others.

Yes, we need the gifts of the Spirit, and we need balance in our lives between the gifts of the Spirit and the fruit of the Spirit, especially love. This balance will deliver us from arrogance toward others in the body of Christ.

The Corinthian Christians did not lack in their capacity for utterance, knowledge and spiritual gifts (1 Corinthians 1:5-7), but they were in some ways carnal, immature and spiritually ignorant (1 Corinthians 3:1-3; 10:1; 12:1; 14:20, 38). In these things we should not wish to imitate the Corinthians but should desire to follow the way of love. Love will succeed in the kingdom of God when all else fails. Love and all that we do because we are motivated by love will be acceptable to God.

REFLECT AND MEDITATE

1. Jesus placed a lot of emphasis on not only doing the right things but doing right things for the right reasons. This requires me to examine not only my words and deeds but also my motivations.

2. Do I desire to have spiritual gifts manifest through me because I love God and want to bring glory to Him? Do I desire spiritual gifts because I love other people and want to be helpful to them?

REACT AND RESPOND

My first responsibility and privilege as a Christian is to be filled with love for God and then love for my fellowman. The true purpose of all the spiritual enablings God may send to me will be frustrated if I do not obey the commandment to love God and my fellowmen. I will not frustrate the grace of God.

REJOICE AND WORSHIP

I praise the great God of heaven--the Creator of heaven and earth, the Redeemer of man, the Savior of my soul! Oh, how He loved me! Oh, that I might be filled with His love!

DISCIPLESHIP COMMITMENT

I will acknowledge that the gifts of the Spirit are for the church today, and I will earnestly desire the gifts in my own life and in the lives of my fellow Christians for the edification of the church.

CHAPTER 22

What Is an Effective Witness?

INTRODUCTION

When a person becomes a Christian, he not only experiences divine pardon, but he is also called into a totally new way of life. The apostle Paul explained it this way: "Therefore, if anyone is in Christ, he is a new creation; old things have passed away; behold, all things have become new" (2 Corinthians 5:17).

Discipleship is one way of describing this new life. It is a lifestyle reflecting our commitments, our priorities and our values. Discipleship, then, is our total manner of life as reflected in all matters of the heart, the head and the hands. It is a witness to the world, and it involves all that we are and all that we do.

One of the most powerful witnesses to the truth of the gospel will be found, then, in the way we live. It will bring far more lasting impressions than what we say, no matter how knowledgeable or articulate we may be. Make no mistake about it, as Christians we are constantly under the watchful eye of those around us.

For us to be effective witnesses, our lives must be filled with the Holy Spirit and characterized by the fruit of the Spirit--love, joy, peace, long-suffering, kindness, goodness, faithfulness, gentleness and self-control (Galatians 5:22, 23).

Effectively communicating our faith, moreover, requires both words and deeds. The spoken witness is not effective unless it is backed up by the disciplined life. The living deed is ultimately inadequate without the spoken word.

An effective witness, then, is one who consciously and intentionally loves people. He listens personally and privately to their hurts and joys and walks with them toward the cross of Jesus Christ. His entire life is a witness to the fact that he has found the Bread of Life and is compelled to share it with others.

During the next several sessions we will examine the meaning and implications of witnessing. You will be challenged to take a personal look at your own lifestyle to see how it measures up to the claims of biblical discipleship. We will explore the following questions regarding witnessing:

1. What Is an Effective Witness?
2. Who Is to Witness?
3. What Are the Prerequisites for Witnessing?
4. What Is Our Message?
5. What Are the Right Motives for Witnessing?

DISCIPLESHIP GOAL

Your goal should be to recognize and accept your responsibility to be an effective witness and to better understand the meaning, the message and the motive for witnessing.

READING ASSIGNMENT
The Living Book, pp. 267-280

Discipleship

WHAT IS AN EFFECTIVE WITNESS?

READ AND RESEARCH (2 Corinthians 5:11-20)

We are not only called to be disciples, but we are also called to make disciples. We are called to follow Jesus, to be with Him and to carry on His ministry of reconciliation. To be a disciple, then, involves all that we are and all that we do.

The first thing Jesus told His disciples when He called them was, "'Follow me, and I will make you fishers of men'" (Matthew 4:19). The last thing He told them before He left this earth was, "'But you shall receive power when the Holy Spirit has come upon you; and you shall be witnesses to Me'" (Acts 1:8). And He said, "'Go therefore and make disciples of all the nations'" (Matthew 28:19).

If you are like most modern-day Christians, you have a vague idea that you are supposed to be a "witness," but you feel ill-prepared and reluctant to carry out this evangelistic responsibility. Part of the difficulty results from the lack of understanding of what it means to be a witness. Some scholars would take great pains to distinguish between being a witness and being an evangelist. While recognizing that one of the ministry offices is that of evangelist and that not all Christians are called to this office, for our purposes we shall view *witnessing* and *evangelizing* as synonymous.

According to the New Testament, witnessing is sharing the gospel, the evangel, the good news. It is a process of communication in which Christians make themselves mouthpieces for God's message of mercy and hope to sinners. Anyone who faithfully delivers that message, under whatever circumstances--in a large meeting, in a small group, from the pulpit or in a private conversation--is witnessing.

According to the apostle Paul, we are Christ's ambassadors in the ministry of reconciliation. An ambassador is the authorized representative of a government or a sovereign. He speaks not in his own name but on behalf of the government or ruler whose deputy he is, and his whole duty and responsibility is to interpret that ruler's mind faithfully to those to whom he is sent.

Paul said that God has "committed to us the word of reconciliation. Therefore we are ambassadors for Christ, as though God were pleading through us: we implore you on Christ's behalf, be reconciled to God" (2 Corinthians 5:19, 20).

To better understand the true meaning of being a witness, one significant point should be emphasized. An effective witness is not judged by the results. Neither you as an individual nor the church of which you are a member is the agent of redemption. You are a witness to God's redemptive act in Jesus Christ. You are but a channel of the gospel, an instrument of witness. There is great value in understanding that God alone can save a person. It means that you no longer have to be plagued with the fear of failure in your witnessing. Your responsibility is to be obedient to His command. Remember, one plants, another waters, but it is God who gives the increase.

REFLECT AND MEDITATE

What does it mean to be a disciple? What part does witnessing play in being a true disciple?

What are some of the requirements of being an effective ambassador? In your day-to-day living, how are you measuring up as a witness for Christ?

REACT AND RESPOND

Give an example in which you were a witness for Christ during this past week. Think of someone to whom you can witness this week. How will you know if your witnessing has been successful?

REJOICE AND WORSHIP

I am truly humbled when I realize that I am an ambassador for Christ. I rejoice in the fact that God chooses to use me in bringing the good news to others. My prayer is that God will help me to be an effective witness.

Study 2

WHO IS TO WITNESS?

READ AND RESEARCH (Mark 16:15; Acts 8:1)

As a Christian you are under orders to be a witness for Jesus Christ! It is not optional, not something you can take or leave. Every Christian is an evangelist. Any person who has been born into the family of God through faith and trust in Jesus Christ automatically receives the Lord's commission.

Some Christians have the mistaken idea that witnessing is for the minister or for the special layman who is gifted in the art of sharing his faith. Others seem to think that it is a part-time endeavor, one from which they can take extended vacations. But the true disciple of Jesus knows that he must follow the example of the Master, who came to seek and to save the lost.

It has been estimated that 95 percent of our church members have never led anyone to Christ. One factor in this depressing condition is the excuse by laymen that it is the job of the clergy to evangelize. Another equally damaging factor is the lack of understanding on the part of pastors concerning the basic purpose of their ministry. Ephesians 4:11, 12 tells us that Christ has given pastors and teachers to the church for the "equip-ping of the saints for the work of ministry, for the edifying of the body of Christ."

Fortunately, there is a trend in the church today toward greater awareness of the role of laymen in witnessing. It is a recognition that active evangelism is called for, that the Christian witness involves our whole life, and that a primary role of the Church is to train the laity to be effective witnesses.

REFLECT AND MEDITATE

1. Read Acts 8:1, and reflect on the implications of that text for lay witnessing.

2. What might be the results in your church if every Christian recognized his role as a witness?

REACT AND RESPOND

The apostle Paul reminded the Corinthians of their ministry of reconciliation (2 Corinthians 5:19). Write out the advantages and disadvantages of this responsibility.

REJOICE AND WORSHIP

The early church "turned the world upside down" because they understood and accepted their ministry of witnessing. Lord, help me to be obedient to Your command. Lead me to the very ones, this week, with whom You would have me to share the good news. Amen.

Study 3

WHAT ARE THE PREREQUISITES FOR WITNESSING?

READ AND RESEARCH (2 Timothy 2:1-15)

Let us review for a moment what we have said about discipleship and witnessing: (1) Witnessing is sharing the gospel, both in our words and in our whole life; (2) all Christians, both laity and clergy alike, are to be witnesses; (3) in discipleship we are called to follow Jesus, to be with Jesus and to carry on His ministry of reconciliation.

Before you can introduce someone else to the good news, you must be intimately acquainted with the One in whom the gospel is embodied. A desire to help others and a willingness to listen and become involved with others are not enough. You must know your message, and your message is Jesus Christ!

We live in a day when many people in the church might be aptly described as marginal Christians. They operate on the basis of living as much like the world as they can and still remain Christians. We sometimes refer to such individuals as nominal Christians or cultural Christians. Even in evangelical and Pentecostal churches, we find those whose lifestyles and values are very little different from the secular society.

Such anemic Christians, if they are Christians at all, cannot be ambassadors for Christ. Their lives are not characterized by the fruit of the Spirit. If they have accepted Jesus as Savior, they certainly have not accepted Him as Lord. Such people may be "religious" and involved in religious activity, but they are not disciples of Christ and therefore cannot make disciples of others.

You are ready to be an effective witness for Christ, then, when you have accepted Him as your Savior, have an ongoing commitment to the lordship of Christ and have developed the basic disciplines of Christian living and service. Implied in this statement are certain inherent prerequisites for witnessing and making disciples: a basic understanding of your faith, regular devotional time, involvement in good fellowship, instruction in the Word and taking on the yoke of obedience.

REFLECT AND MEDITATE

1. Based on the prerequisites for witnessing and making disciples mentioned in this session, are you ready to share your faith effectively?

2. Have compromise and lukewarmness hindered your effectiveness as a witness?

REACT AND RESPOND

1. Write out your own definition of what it means to be a disciple.

2. What does it mean to you in your personal relationship to be "a worker who does not need to be ashamed"?

REJOICE AND WORSHIP

Lord, mold me and fashion me after Your perfect will. Help me not only to accept You as Savior but also as Lord of my life. Jesus, I submit to Your yoke of service for me, taking courage in Your promise that Your yoke is easy.

Study 4

WHAT IS OUR MESSAGE?

READ AND RESEARCH (John 3:16; Romans 5)

Thus far we have discussed the meaning of witnessing and the fact that all Christians are called to be witnesses. We have also looked at our preparation for witnessing.

But what exactly is it that we are supposed to be communicating to the world? What is our message?

Simply stated, our message is the gospel of Jesus Christ and Him crucified, the message of man's sin and God's grace, of our guilt and His forgiveness, of new birth and new life through the gift of the Holy Spirit.

Dr. J.I. Parker, Trinity College, Bristol, England, identifies four essential ingredients of our message:

1. The gospel we are to share is a message about God. It explains who He is, what His character is like, what His standards are and what He requires of us. Our message, the gospel, starts by teaching us that we, as creatures, are absolutely dependent on God and that He, as Creator, has an absolute claim on us. Only when we have learned this can we see what sin is, and only when we see what sin is can we understand the good news of salvation from sin.

2. Our message is about sin. It tells how we have fallen short of God's standards, how helplessly in sin we are. It tells us we sin because we are sinners by nature and that nothing we can do by or for ourselves can put us back into right relationship with God.

3. The gospel, our message, is a message about Christ--Christ the Son of God, Christ the Lamb of God, dying for our sins. God sent Jesus to earth to rescue us from sin and death. Jesus is both God and perfect man. He died on the cross, taking our penalty upon Himself. Jesus arose from the dead and lives today.

4. Our message is a summons to faith and repentance. All who hear the gospel are commanded to believe and to repent. With these commands go promises of salvation to all who

obey them (Acts 10:43; John 3:16; Revelation 22:17). God's demand is for faith as well as repentance.

REFLECT AND MEDITATE

1. What is the meaning of the gospel?

2. In modern-day living why is the message of the gospel so important?

3. What do we mean when we say that our message is a person?

REACT AND RESPOND

1. Write out our message to someone who does not know about the gospel. Ask an unsaved friend to read it to see if he understands it.

2. Practice telling the good news to a Christian, and ask for his honest feedback.

REJOICE AND WORSHIP

Father God, thank You for revealing Yourself to me through Jesus Christ. Thank You for the good news of eternal life. I rejoice in the fact that my sins have been forgiven and that one day I will see You face-to-face.

Study 5

WHAT ARE THE RIGHT MOTIVES FOR WITNESSING?

READ AND RESEARCH (1 Corinthians 10:31; 1 Corinthians 13)

Some people have the wrong motives for witnessing, and this greatly hinders their effectiveness. The "I am right and you are wrong" attitude is a less than honorable motive. Such people usually think they are commissioned to "straighten out" as many nonbelievers as possible. One way to check yourself here is to take stock of how many of your encounters with others end up in debate or argument.

Then there is the "anti this and anti that" witness who majors in minors. Such an approach seems to be more concerned with sin than with grace.

There are, in fact, two motives that should encourage us to witness. The first is to love God and to glorify Him; the second is love and compassion for mankind.

The first motive is primary and basic. The chief end of man is to glorify God. Paul said in 1 Corinthians 10:31: "Do all to the glory of God." We glorify God by obeying Him. Since witnessing is one of the activities commanded by God and His Son, we glorify God by being obedient to His will.

We glorify Him in this way not only because

witnessing is an act of obedience but also because in sharing the gospel we are telling the world what great things God has done for the salvation of sinners. For you to talk to the nonbeliever about Jesus and His saving power is in itself bringing glory to God.

A second right motive for witnessing is love and compassion for others. Mere proclamation without love means very little. Christ showed us by being a servant and by dying on a cross how much He loved, and if we have felt gratitude for the grace that has saved us from sin, then we should be motivated quite naturally to share our faith with the lost.

While it may be a natural response in view of what Christ has done for us, witnessing is not necessarily easy. It may result in being heartbroken and misunderstood. It may call for sacrifice and humility, but we can do no less and call ourselves Christians.

REFLECT AND MEDITATE

What makes you tick spiritually? Why do you do what you do in the spiritual realm? Do you have insight as to why you speak to another about the Lord?

REACT AND RESPOND

1. In what ways can you show love and compassion to your neighbors this week? _____

_____

Discipleship

2. Write out two wrong motives and two right motives (not mentioned above) for witnessing.

_____

_____

_____

_____

REJOICE AND WORSHIP

Lord, forgive me for the times I have failed to witness for You. Your love and Your compassion as evidenced by Your life and death constrains me to make every opportunity to share Your gospel with others.

CHAPTER 23

How Do We Communicate Our Faith?

INTRODUCTION

Effectively communicating our faith begins with knowing the message. This is, of course, essential; but it is only the beginning. This message must be translated into the individual language of the one to whom we desire to witness.

The fact is that most people do not know how to communicate effectively. The influence of television and other depersonalizing agents have resulted in a generation of people who are lacking in interpersonal and communication skills. But, if are to win the lost and reach out to the hurting, we must recognize the importance of effectively communicating our life-changing message.

Here are some important keys to good communication:

1. Be honest and open.
2. Be positive and encouraging.
3. Be clear so that you are understood.
4. Communicate your feelings.
5. Listen.

David Angusburger, author and counselor, has paraphrased sections of the book of James which speaks of the tongue and symbolizes the whole of human communication.

1. On listening:

"Know this, my beloved brethren. Let every man be quick to listen, slow to speak, slow to anger. For human rage does not achieve the righteous justice which is the will of God . . . . Who is wise and understanding among you? By his good life let him show his works in the meekness of wisdom . . . . The wisdom from above is first genuine, then peaceable, gentle and open to reason, full of mercy and evidence of goodness without uncertainty or insincerity. And right relationships grow from the seeds of peace planted by those who make peace" (James 1:19, 20; 3:13, 17, 18).

2. On speaking:

"We all make many mistakes and the most difficult thing to master is communication. To communicate rightly is to live rightly also. As a small bit can direct a mighty horse, as a small rudder can steer a giant ship, as a small spark can light a terrible forest fire, as a small word can corrupt a person, so it is with evil communication. We can tame all the rest of creation, but we cannot tame the treachery, evil and deception that is always present in human communication. The same words can be heard as either blessing or cursing. The same mouth can speak in appreciation or rejection. As a spring is either fresh or salt, as a tree grows its natural fruit, so must we communicate in clarity, purity and simplicity." (James 3:2-12)

During this week we will be considering the very heart of life as a witness: communicating our faith. The following subjects will be discussed as we seek to learn how to be an effective witness:

1. Your Personal Testimony
2. Lifestyle Evangelism
3. Witnessing to Backsliders
4. Leading Someone to Christ
5. Follow-up: On to Discipleship

DISCIPLESHIP GOAL

To learn the essential elements of communicating the gospel, including the process and the methods of witnessing

READING ASSIGNMENT

The Living Book, pp. 281 -287

Discipleship

Study 1

YOUR PERSONAL TESTIMONY

READ AND RESEARCH (Acts 26; 2 Timothy 1:7-9; 1 Peter 3:15, 16)

What part should your personal testimony play in communicating your faith to others? Since Jesus Christ is our message and should, therefore, be the focus of our witnessing, does this mean that we should not share our personal story about what God has done for us?

The answer to these questions, of course, is that we should use our personal testimony in witnessing. A more pertinent question might be "What part should your testimony play?"

As a new Christian your initial witness is the simple truth about what the Lord has done in your life. Because you know firsthand that your sins are forgiven and you have experienced God's love, joy and peace, it will be virtually impossible not to tell others that He can do the same for them.

Time and time again, the Bible tells of those who met Jesus and went on their way proclaiming the life-changing news they had received.

The wonderful truth is that no one, no matter how skeptical or disbelieving, can explain away or negate what you have personally experienced. In fact, many sinners have been converted to Christ through the hearing of a dynamic testimony.

A word of caution is in order, however, concerning the sharing of your testimony. An insensitive person can get so caught up in himself that he comes across as self-centered and bragging. This should be avoided and the focus kept on what Christ has done in your life.

The apostle Paul provides us with a good pattern to follow in sharing our personal testimony. In his defense before King Agrippa, recorded in Acts 26, Paul gave his testimony in the form of a three-point outline:

1. He spoke first about what his life was like before he met Christ.

2. He told of his encounter with Jesus on the road to Damascus.

3. Paul related what his life had been like since his conversion and his hopes for the future.

While your testimony of conversion may not be as dramatic as the apostle Paul's, it is your story, and it can be told with great conviction and humility. When empowered by the Holy Spirit, it will touch the hearts of those who are open to spiritual matters.

REFLECT AND MEDITATE

1. Can you recall how a personal testimony encouraged you and caused you to better understand the love of God?

2. Why does a personal testimony hold more interest than mere facts?

REACT AND RESPOND

Write out your personal testimony, keeping in mind the three points demonstrated by Paul: (1) life before Christ, (2) encounter with Christ, and (3) life with Christ and hope for the future. Remember to keep it brief and focused on Jesus.

REJOICE AND WORSHIP

Thank you, Lord, that You have personally brought me out of darkness into Your marvelous light. Help me always to be ready to give a reason for the hope that is within me. Amen.

Study 2

LIFESTYLE EVANGELISM

READ AND RESEARCH (1 Corinthians 13; *Lifestyle Evangelism* [available from Church of God Office of Lay Ministries])

The Church of God Office of Lay Ministries has developed a seminar titled "Lifestyle Evangelism--How to Win Your Family and Friends to Christ." The major emphasis of the seminar is that evangelism is a process of lifestyle, not a program or a soulwinning technique. As a process, it takes time and should be a part of everyday life. Much time is spent on just being friends with people, getting to know them and trying to establish points of common ground. Reaping, or encouraging a decision of faith, follows naturally after we become friends with a person and share the gospel with them.

Lifestyle evangelism as a process involves three phases: cultivating, sowing and reaping. In the cultivating phase, the emphasis is on establishing a caring relationship with the lost. The following principles are important in this phase:

1. Let them see Christ in your daily life.

2. Let them know God cares for them.

3. Let them know you care for them.

4. Without overwhelming them, share your personal testimony to let them know how God has changed your life.

5. Let them see your joy as you live for Christ.

6. Develop a servant spirit. Take every opportunity to be ''salt'' and ''light.''

7. Ask God to help you to respond to their needs, not just what you want to see accomplished.

In the sowing phase the emphasis is on proclaiming the truth of God's Word. The communication process is especially important in this phase. Listening with love, valuing the person, answering their questions and telling the truth are all essential principles in the sowing phase.

Phase three in lifestyle evangelism is harvesting. Here the focus is on conversion. If we share God's Word, He promises us it will be productive. His Word says one planted, another watered, but ''God gave the increase'' (1 Corinthians 3:6). We may confidently expect that God will be working in the hearts of men from the time of sowing and cultivating to the time of harvesting.

REFLECT AND MEDITATE

Someone has said, ''What you are speaks so loudly I cannot hear what you say.'' What does this say about lifestyle evangelism?

REACT AND RESPOND

John 4 tells about Jesus' encounter with the woman at the well. Using the three phases of lifestyle evangelism, write down how Jesus went about cultivating, sowing and harvesting.

REJOICE AND WORSHIP

Father, help me that my life will be characterized by the fruit of the Spirit. Enable me to live a life among my friends and family in such a way they will want to know more about You.

Study 3

WITNESSING TO BACKSLIDERS

READ AND RESEARCH (Matthew 13; 2 Peter 2:20-22; *Why Men Go Back* by Charles W. Conn

Unfortunately, there are people who were previously committed to Christ but for one reason or another have not continued to follow Him. We sometimes refer to these people as backsliders.

Backsliders need to be ministered to. God loves them and wants us to love them and help them to turn and find their way back to Christ. The means and methods that will be effective in helping the backslider will vary. Some need encouragement that the Lord will help them overcome the obstacles that turned them aside. For others the key is assurance that God loves them and wants to forgive them for the wrong they have done. Still others need to be warned of the consequences of being out of fellowship with God and to be told in clear language that their way of life must change. Almost all backsliders require personal care and concern to lead them back and to help them be reunited with a body of Christians who will nurture them and hold them accountable.

The Church of God Office of Lay Ministries, in their manual *Lifestyle Evangelism*, offers these observations about backsliders:

1. They can expect chastening. This may take the form of sickness, loss of possessions, and the like (1 Corinthians 11 and Hebrews 12:5-7).

2. Backsliders may die prematurely (1 Corinthians 11:30).

3. They can be fully restored. God wants to forgive them and restore them when they are willing to confess and forsake their sin.

The manual offers three principles you should follow in witnessing to the backslider:

1. Do not ignore him. One factor in his going back may have been the lack of Christian fellowship. It could be, too, that he was mistreated by Christians. The last thing he needs is for you to shy away from him, to ostracize him or to pretend that nothing is wrong.

2. Do not talk about him or his sin. Gossip is clearly forbidden in Scripture and can do great damage even when the person is guilty.

3. Do not condone his sin. In this age of "cheap grace" Christians, there is a tendency to tolerate sin or to pretend that it does not affect the Christian. With love and spiritual sensitivity, the backslider must be confronted with his lost condition.

A backslider, then, is a person who at one time started the Christian life but for one reason or another has turned back or given up on following Christ. He is actually worse off now than he was before coming to Christ. He needs our love and the good news that he can be fully restored.

REFLECT AND MEDITATE

Do you believe that a born-again Christian can backslide and be lost? Defend your answer by citing scriptures.

REACT AND RESPOND

Fill in the blanks:

1. A backslider is _____

_____

2. Three reasons why a person may backslide are: _____

_____

_____

3. Three important principles to remember in witnessing to a backslider are:

_____

_____

_____

.

REJOICE AND WORSHIP

Thank You, Father, that You are the God of the second chance. Help me to be sensitive to my weaker brother who may be tempted to go back. Thank You for being patient and long-suffering toward me.

Study 4

LEADING SOMEONE TO CHRIST

READ AND RESEARCH (Romans 5:12)

Time and time again in our studies, we have emphasized that our life is an essential part of our witness. Further, the power of the Holy Spirit is indispensable in effectively sharing our faith. The third ingredient without which there can be no effective witness is the Word of God. When the seed, which is the Word of God, is planted in a prepared heart, it can bring forth fruit unto everlasting life.

While there is no one right plan or method for leading a person to Christ, there are certain steps that should be helpful. A particular series of steps or phases, sometimes referred to as the "Bridge to Life," has proved to be quite successful in presenting the gospel. This graphic illustration can be used by anyone and requires only a pen and a piece of paper or an index card.

Step one: God's plan

In this initial step of leading someone to Christ (preceded, of course, by the establishment of a relationship), the point is made that God loves man and has made it possible for us to live with Him forever. "For God so loved the world that He gave His only begotten Son, that whoever believes in Him should not perish but have everlasting life" (John 3:16).

Step two: Man's problem--separation

While God has made eternal life possible, it is not automatic. The truth is that all have sinned and fallen short of God's perfect standard. "Therefore, just as through one man sin entered the world, and death through sin, and thus death spread to all men, because all sinned" (Romans 5:12).

Man is separated from God because of sin. Throughout history he has tried to bridge the gap in many different ways. But religion, good works, morality, church membership, philosophy--none of these are successful.

Step three: God's remedy--the Cross

The only way to span the gulf between man and God is through Jesus Christ. When He died on the cross, He paid the penalty for our sin and made it possible for man to be brought in right relationship with God. "For there is one God and one Mediator between God and men, the Man Christ Jesus, who gave Himself a ransom for all" (1 Timothy 2:5, 6).

On the earthly side of the cross, we have man who is sinful, separated and lost. On the eternal side of the cross we have God who loves, forgives and offers eternal life.

Step four: Man's decision

For anyone to become a Christian, he must profess personal faith (commitment) to Jesus Christ. "But as many as received Him, to them He gave the right to become children of God, even to those who believe in His Name" (John 1:12). By faith, man crosses the bridge from death to life eternal through the cross of Jesus Christ.

After you have gone through these steps and if you feel impressed by the Holy Spirit, you should invite the person to accept Christ into his life. Sometimes it is helpful to assist Him in a prayer of commitment. Here is an example of such a prayer: "Dear Lord, I am sorry for my sin and for living apart from You. Thank You for sending Your Son to die on the cross for my sin. I ask You to come into my heart right now. I turn from my sin and receive You as my Savior. Thank You for hearing my prayer. Amen."

After he has prayed, preferably aloud, remind him that he is now born again according to God's Word. Assure him that it matters not how he feels. "He who has the Son has life" (1 John 5:12). Welcome him into the family of God!

REFLECT AND MEDITATE

Do you remember when you were born again?

Do you remember the joy and peace that you had?

Have you personally led someone to Christ?

REACT AND RESPOND

1. List the names of three people you are praying for (or should be) to become Christians.

a. _____

b. _____

c. _____

2. When a person is convinced of his sin and his need of Christ, what should he do?

a. Acts 3:19 _____

_____

b. John 1:12c; John 10:9 _____

_____

REJOICE AND WORSHIP

I will never forget, dear Lord, the day You saved my soul. Thank You for those who prayed for me. Thank You for the Holy Spirit, who convicted and convinced me of my need.

Lord, I want to be a faithful witness for You. Lay some soul upon my heart, and give me the opportunity to share Your gospel with that person. Amen.

Discipleship

FOLLOW-UP: ON TO DISCIPLESHIP

READ AND RESEARCH (1 Thessalonians 2:10-12; 2 Timothy 2:2)

The goal of your witnessing efforts is not only to lead individuals to Christ but also to help them become established Christians and soulwinners.

New Christians need a great deal of follow-up.

Are those we have led to Christ now leading others to Him and teaching them to make disciples like ourselves? Surely we want to win our generation to Christ and to do it now. However, we should never consider our work finished until we have assured its continuation in the lives of those redeemed by Christ.

The test of any work of evangelism, then, is not what is seen at the moment but the effectiveness with which the work continues in the next generation. God wants us to multiply, not just add.

Follow-up is essential if we are to see Christians move toward discipleship. Walter Henrichsen refers to follow-up as "spiritual pediatrics." It has to do with the care and protection of the new babe in Christ. We are shocked when we hear of a baby being left alone without proper attention, but for some reason we seem little concerned when new Christians are neglected. And of course when left alone, many new Christians quickly become carnal; some even die.

Here are some basic guidelines for helping a new Christian grow toward maturity:

1. Take the initiative. Set up a specific date and time to meet with the new convert. A general offer to help is not enough; you must take the responsibility to maintain contact even if you are not asked. Anticipate needs, and make yourself available.

2. Be prepared. Go over with him again the plan of salvation, and offer him encouragement and assurance. One frequently used tactic of the enemy is to make the new Christian think he is not saved or that he cannot live the Christian life. Be prepared to share the basic truths about the Christian life.

3. Pray for him. Intercessory prayer is a powerful force in helping Christians deal with temptation and become mature disciples. Make a list of prayer needs, and ask the Lord to intercede in behalf of your new convert.

4. Be an example. The young Christian needs to see the reality of what you are teaching in your own life. Share with him your victories and your temptations. Let him know the benefits and blessings of walking closely with the Lord.

5. Get him involved in the Word and in the church. Teach him to feed on the Word and thereby increase his faith. See that he becomes a part of a Bible study group. Make sure that he becomes a part of a fellowship of believers where the full gospel is preached and lived. Take him to church with you if at all possible.

REFLECT AND MEDITATE

What do you think about the statement that follow-up is "spiritual pediatrics"? Do you recall who the prominent person was in this stage of your spiritual growth and development?

REACT AND RESPOND

1. On a separate sheet of paper list three hindrances to follow-up with new converts.

2. What do you consider the three greatest needs of a new Christian?

REJOICE AND WORSHIP

Lord, remind me that after I lead a person to Christ, I have the awesome but wonderful responsibility to help him become a mature Christian. Help me not to become so busy that I do not have time to nurture new-born Christians. Amen.

DISCIPLESHIP COMMITMENT

Every "Paul" (mature Christian) needs a "Timothy" (new convert). With the help of the Lord, I am determined not only to lead sinners to Christ but also to nurture them toward spiritual maturity.

CHAPTER 24

What Is My Responsibility for Social Concerns?

INTRODUCTION

In all ages disciples are called to witness to the saving grace of Jesus Christ. This is our first and primary concern. We are not called to present man with a new economic or political society. Rather, we are commissioned to bring people by the power of the Holy Spirit into the kingdom of God through faith in and obedience to Jesus Christ.

But in so doing, the disciple is faced with the responsibility of recognizing that Jesus is Lord over all of life (Psalm 24:1). This demands, then, that we pursue righteousness, justice and equity in all areas of life. We have a definite responsibility for the social concerns of our fellowman.

The true disciple of Jesus Christ will strive with godly fervor for justice for all. This may take many different forms, including providing food, housing and jobs for the poor and homeless; helping to bring about changes in oppressive and unjust laws; striving to tear down prejudice and racism; and speaking out against nuclear war and for peace with honor.

Within the limits set forth in Scripture, the disciple is called on to help change institutions and structures which deny basic human rights. This requires more than exercising the right to vote. It may call for civil disobedience in order to obey a higher law. It certainly will demand that by our lifestyle and our action-oriented love, we become the salt, the light and the leaven in our communities and in our world.

There will not always be agreement within the church as to how the disciple is to fulfill his responsibility for social concerns. It seems wise to avoid the extremes of choosing involvement in social concerns over evangelism, and vice versa. We need to seek a Bible-based balance between social ministry and evangelism. We should embrace both, enthusiastically and wholly, as essential elements of the one gospel of Jesus Christ.

Let us now consider a number of different aspects of social concerns and see how these can be expressions of our life of discipleship:

1. Biblical Basis for Social Concerns
2. Discipleship and the Poor
3. Discipleship and the Sanctity of Life
4. Discipleship and Politics
5. Discipleship and Civil Disobedience

DISCIPLESHIP GOAL

To become knowledgeable about a social concern in your community and make a commitment to become involved in addressing this need

READING ASSIGNMENT
The Living Book, pp. 291-302

Discipleship

BIBLICAL BASIS
FOR SOCIAL CONCERNS

READ AND RESEARCH (Deuteronomy 15:7-11; Luke 4:18, 19)

The biblical basis for the disciple's responsibility for social concerns comes from both the Old and the New Testaments. In Deuteronomy we are commanded to be openhanded toward the poor and needy" (Deuteronomy 15:11). Isaiah tells us to "'learn to do good; seek justice, reprove the oppressor; defend the fatherless, plead for the widow'" (Isaiah 1:17).

It is in the New Testament, however, in the example of Jesus our Lord that we see most clearly our responsibility for social concerns. In Luke's gospel Jesus said, "'The Spirit of the Lord is upon Me, because He has anointed Me to preach the gospel to the poor. He has sent Me to heal the brokenhearted, to preach deliverance to the captives and recovery of sight to the blind, to set at liberty those who are oppressed, to preach the acceptable year of the Lord'" (Luke 4:18, 19).

According to Matthew, Jesus went throughout Galilee, "teaching in their synagogues, preaching the gospel of the kingdom, and healing all kinds of sickness and all kinds of disease among the people" (Matthew 4:23). Here are three distinct ministries: teaching, preaching and healing sick people.

In the book of James we are told that we have a responsibility to reach out to those who are in physical need. "If a brother or sister is naked and destitute of daily food, and one of you says to them, 'Depart in peace, be warmed and filled,' but you do not give them the things which are needed for the body, what does it profit? Thus also faith by itself, if it does not have works, is dead" (James 2:15-17).

Throughout church history, from the day of Pentecost to this present time, those who take seriously the claims of discipleship have been involved in meeting the social needs of hurting people. It was the church that established hospitals, orphanages and shelters for the poor and elderly.

Proclaiming the gospel and applying it to the social concerns of the day went hand in hand. It was understood that responsible involvement in meeting social needs facilitated the ministry of reconciliation. The modern church is experiencing a widespread awakening in regard to social concerns. This is a vital part of spiritual discipleship and is clearly demonstrated in the life of Jesus.

REFLECT AND MEDITATE

How would you respond to a person who says that the church should not be involved with social concerns?

REACT AND RESPOND

Cite examples from the Bible in which Christians demonstrated their responsibility for social concerns.

REJOICE AND WORSHIP

Lord, open my eyes to the needs of those around me. Teach me what it means to give a cup of cold water in Your name. I rejoice in the fact that You are touched with the feelings of my infirmities. Help me to likewise feel for others. Amen.

DISCIPLESHIP AND THE POOR

READ AND RESEARCH (Deuteronomy 15:7-11)

At a time when a "prosperity gospel" is widely preached, some might conclude that to be poor and needy is a consequence of a lack of faith or some other moral flaw. Such people might further conclude that to reach out and help the needy would be to encourage them in their sin.

However, a careful study of Scripture results in a quite different view of the poor. Moses had this to say regarding our attitude toward those in need: "'If there is among you a poor man of your brethren, within any of the gates in your land which the Lord your God is giving you, you shall not harden your heart nor shut your hand from your poor brother, but you shall open your hand wide to him and willingly lend him sufficient for his need....You shall surely give to him, and your heart should not be grieved when you give to him, because for this thing the Lord your God will bless you in all your works and in all to which you put your hand. For the poor will never cease from the land; therefore I command you, saying, "you shall open your hand wide to your brother, to your poor and your needy, in your land"'" (Deuteronomy 15:7, 8, 10, 11).

Throughout the New Testament, concern for the poor is clearly seen as a part of what it means to be a disciple. Direct, personal assistance to the poor was commanded. The love of Christ that impels us to touch the lives of the poor through aid also impels us to touch their lives by advocating changes in public policies that cause poverty.

We sometime think that poverty is a problem only in Third World, underdeveloped countries. While it is true that countries such as Ethiopia and Haiti have extreme poverty, let us not forget that we have hunger and poverty in the United States. The latest Commerce Department statistics show that we have 34 million Americans living in poverty. That means that 13 percent of the population lives at or below the poverty line.

The church, which is supposed to be a community of disciples, can do a great deal to help. In many instances the church is involved in a tangible way--providing a food bank, clothing, housing for the homeless, and job counseling and referrals for the unemployed and the underemployed.

But in addition to these direct-assistance programs, we must speak out and lobby for state and federal programs that will attack the causes of poverty.

REFLECT AND MEDITATE

Why do you think the Bible says so much about helping and showing concern for the poor and needy?

REACT AND RESPOND

Make a list of projects that your church could initiate in behalf of the poor in your community.

REJOICE AND WORSHIP

Lord, I know that Your heart is touched by the needs of the poor. Use me as an instrument of Your love and grace to reach out and help. Thank You for Your blessings to me and my family and for the opportunity to share with those who are less fortunate.

Study 3

DISCIPLESHIP AND THE SANCTITY OF LIFE

READ AND RESEARCH (Genesis 1:26-28; Psalm 139; Matthew 1:18-25)

The late Dr. Francis Schaeffer, in his book *Whatever Happened to the Human Race,* said, "Cultures can be judged in many ways, but eventually every nation in every age must be judged by this test: how did it treat people? . . . The final measure of mankind's humanity is how humanely people treat one another."

Most would agree that human life is sacred, but there is a great deal of disagreement on those issues in which human life is at stake. Issues such as war, abortion and euthanasia evoke strong emotions and differing points of view. Even among Christians there is a great deal of disagreement as to how we are to respond to these crucial issues.

The abortion epidemic in America strikes at the very heart of the sanctity-of-life question. It is estimated that one out of every three children conceived in this country is now aborted. That means that 1.5 million "legal" abortions occurred last year. Washington, D.C., our nation's capital, reports more abortions than live births.

What is the responsibility of the Christian disciple in safeguarding the sanctity of life? The Bible provides some commands and principles that should guide us in fulfilling our responsibilities.

1. The Bible clearly teaches that life begins at conception (Psalm 139).

2. God is the source of all life; life is of infinite worth; children are a gift from God; and conception, pregnancy and birth are in the purpose and providence of God.

3. Abortion is murder (Genesis 9:6; Exodus 23:7).

4. Those guilty of the sin of abortion need forgiveness, and we should be available to minister to them.

What can you as a disciple, or you and your church, do to help in safeguarding the sanctity of life? Here is a list of practical ways you can become actively involved in the abortion alternative movement:

1. Help sponsor or do volunteer work at a crisis pregnancy center. The purpose of a CPC is to help teenagers and others through the problem that leads to abortion. They do pregnancy testing; counsel, with the goal of avoiding abortion; and make referrals for shelter for those in crisis pregnancy.

2. Pray for and support ministries such as Covenant Place, the maternity home operated by the Church of God Department of Benevolences.

3. Encourage your church to take part in the ''Why Wait?'' program sponsored by the Church of God Department of Youth and Christian Education.

4. Encourage your pastor to prepare a series of sermons on the sanctity of life.

5. Help to plan and promote a Sanctity of Life Sunday at your church.

REFLECT AND MEDITATE

In your opinion, is the Christian church community doing enough to promote the sanctity of life? Why or why not?

REACT AND RESPOND

1. List three areas of vital concern involving the sanctity of life.

_____

_____

_____

2. Name four biblical principles related to the abortion issue. _____

_____

_____

_____

_____

REJOICE AND WORSHIP

Lord, I know how Your heart must be broken when every 20 seconds a baby, made in Your image, is aborted. Forgive us, Lord. Help me to do what I can to speak out against this sin. Amen.

Study 4

DISCIPLESHIP AND POLITICS

READ AND RESEARCH (Matthew 5:13-16; 1 Peter 2:11-17)

Webster's Dictionary defines politics as ''the art and science of civil government.'' It comes from the Greek word *polites*, which means ''a citizen.'' Our English word *citizenship* has the same origin.

Christian discipleship demands responsible citizenship. In America we live in a democracy, which by its very nature requires citizen participation in the process of government at all levels.

Throughout the Bible we are encouraged to be good citizens. The apostle Paul, for example, tells us, ''Whatever happens, conduct yourselves in a manner worthy of the gospel of Christ'' (Philippians 1:27, *NIV*). The word *conduct* comes from the same word from which our word *politics* is derived.

Most Christians would agree that Christians should be good citizens and that they should take part in politics. The question is, How are we to participate, and what should be our method of involvement and influence?

Daniel Vestal, a pastor in Midland, Texas, offers the following guidelines and cautions for Christian involvement in politics:

1. Be careful not to engage in politics with the attitude that the end justifies the means. Our methods of influence and our patterns of involvement in politics must always be consistent with the gospel. We must be faithful to our mission and our message. In our zeal to influence government, let us be careful that we never sacrifice character. Our motives should be pure, without judging the motives of others. Let us refrain from rancor or revenge.

2. Be careful not to reduce or identify Christianity with any particular political program. The political agendas of a party or group, however noble, are not identical with the gospel of Jesus Christ.

3. Be careful not to be overconfident in assuming that God is on your side of the issues. We must be careful about making God the champion of our cause, about assuming that we alone understand His ways, about acting as though we alone have discovered Divine Providence.

In summary, we can say that as disciples of Christ we have the responsibility to be good citizens worthy of the gospel. We are to recognize that our primary obedience is to God. We are to obey the law, pray for those in leadership, and work to establish justice and goodwill wherever we can.

REFLECT AND MEDIATE

1. How involved should Christians be in the political arena?

2. Should Christians run for public office?

3. Should Christians vote for non-Christians?

RESPOND AND REACT

Draft a letter to your congressman encouraging him for his stand on a pro-life issue. Let him know you are praying for him.

REJOICE AND WORSHIP

Lord, I thank You that I live in a country that provides the opportunity for me to actively participate in the making of laws and the choosing of those who will govern. Remind me to pray for those in authority, and guide me in my involvement as a good citizen.

Study 5

DISCIPLESHIP AND CIVIL DISOBEDIENCE

READ AND RESEARCH (Romans 13:1-7; 1 Peter 2:11-17; Acts 4:1-31; 5:12-42)

Should Christians take part in civil disobedience? When, if ever, is disobeying government authority or breaking the law an approved way of bringing about change? These questions are being asked more frequently and by more people as Christians become more active in social and moral issues.

Issues such as abortion, pornography and racial prejudice are forcing Christians to take sides on the question of civil disobedience. The question becomes even more complicated in a free society where the laws are passed in a democratic manner and can be changed by the will of the majority. There are several biblical principles, however, which should guide Christian disciples in deciding this issue.

A Christian has the responsibility to submit to and obey governing authorities. The reason for this principle is that government is a divinely ordained institution for the maintenance of order, the punishment of evil and the promotion of good in the world. Dr. Charles Stanley, pastor of the First Baptist Church in Atlanta, says that this premise is supported by these truths: all authority is from God; governing authorities are God's ministers; observing the law is a matter of a positive, public testimony for Christ; observing the law is ordered by God.

While Dr. Stanley concludes that the Bible advocates submission to authority and not civil disobedience as a means of bringing about change, he quickly adds that there is a biblical exception. "It is right to break the law where there is a direct, specific conflict between God's law and man's law because God's law is higher." Examples from Scripture which reflect this exception are seen in the case of Daniel's disobeying the king's decree not to worship anyone but the king and in the case where Peter and John refused to obey the command not to preach the gospel.

In each of these examples there was a direct conflict between God's law and man's law. And in choosing to obey God's higher law, they paid the consequence of that civil disobedience.

Let us not forget that disciples of Christ hold different values from those of a sinful world. These differences will at times bring you into conflict with those whose allegiance is to the enemy of our souls. However, our conflict is not primarily with men but with evil powers and principalities.

REFLECT AND MEDITATE

Do you think the participants in Operation Rescue (blocking entrances to abortion clinics) were justified in their actions? Why or why not?

REACT AND RESPOND

Make a list of social concerns in which there is a present need or a potential need for Christians to become involved in civil disobedience.

REJOICE AND WORSHIP

Remind us, O Lord, that we are aliens and strangers, a colony from heaven, and that our values and beliefs are different from this world system. Lord, as much as possible, help me to live at peace with all men; but let me not forget that I ought to obey God rather than men.

DISCIPLESHIP COMMITMENT

Recognizing my responsibility to be both "salt" and "light" in the world, I am determined to become informed about social concerns and issues and to do what I can to help.

CHAPTER 25

What Is My Responsibility to World Evangelism?

INTRODUCTION

In the Great Commission, Jesus made it abundantly clear exactly what His disciples were to do: they were to go into all the world and proclaim the gospel to all creation. As we have already discussed, believers today are under the same command. We are called to go. This means that we are not saved to sit down and merely enjoy our salvation. Every Christian has the responsibility to be on the move and, in the process, to share the good news of Jesus Christ.

We are called to be world Christians. Warren Webster describes a world Christian as one who "has discovered that his personal commitment to Christ involves him in a worldwide cause. Whether he stays at home or goes abroad, a world Christian accepts personal responsibility for all he can do to help share the message of salvation with the world."

The call to world evangelism is a radical call that cuts through the selfish excuses we offer for not considering missionary work. It is a call to compassion in which we are to reach out to those who suffer and to offer them comfort, care and hope for the future.

While it is true that not all are called to leave their homeland and go into other countries, America has only about 5 percent of the world's population and over a million full-time Christian workers.

It is true that many Christians are called to reach out to the lost here in America. There are needs in our nation's inner cities, on college campuses, in prisons and among special-needs groups. But as disciples of Christ we should be willing and ready to go wherever and whenever He leads and calls. Unless we are called to stay, we are commanded to go!

During this week's lessons we will take a close look at what our responsibilities are to world evangelism. We will examine the following topics:

1. A Radical Call to World Evangelism
2. The Need for World Evangelism
3. Blessings and Rewards
4. Called to Stay, to Pray and to Give
5. Opportunities for World Evangelism

DISCIPLESHIP GOAL

1. To examine, honestly and prayerfully, my call to world evangelism

2. To find out what opportunities my church provides for involvement in world evangelism, in this country and abroad, both short-term and long-term

READING ASSIGNMENT
The Living Book, pp. 303 -315

Discipleship

A RADICAL CALL TO WORLD EVANGELISM

READ AND RESEARCH (Mark 1:16)

In Mark's gospel we read four stories of calls to follow Jesus (Mark 1:16-20; 2:14; 10:17-22). In the first two stories Jesus called Simon Peter, Andrew, James and John. In the third story Levi, the son of Alphaeus, was called. In the last story the name of the man who was called is not mentioned. He is referred to simply as a rich young man.

The first three stories are very similar. They all make this central point: Jesus called, and the men responded. The command was plain and absolute: "'Come after me,'" "'follow me.'" The response is equally absolute: They "followed Him," and they "went after Him."

In the fourth story, Jesus again called someone to become His disciple. We are told that the rich young ruler refused the call because he found the cost of selling his worldly goods too high.

The consequences of answering the call to follow Jesus is apparent. There should be no misunderstanding about the matter. Jesus never tried to deceive anyone or to minimize the cost of following Him. To follow Jesus means leaving everything else behind. Peter and Andrew left their nets and their livelihood; James and John left not only their careers but their hired hands and their families as well.

For these men, answering the call to discipleship meant leaving all behind and starting out on a completely new way of life. They had no idea where following Jesus would lead. In like manner, our choosing to respond to this call, means that we must forsake all without knowing where it may lead.

It is a matter of choice, and it has great and far-reaching consequences. It is radical because it may require you to be snatched out of relative security and comfort and to be thrust into a situation in which questions about your future and well-being are left unanswered. We must be wiling to pay the cost. Apparently the rich young man who declined Jesus' invitation to follow Him was not willing to pay the cost. Jesus took this opportunity to teach us the liabilities of riches and how wealth can be a hindrance to those who would follow Him in radical obedience. Of course it is not the wealth but the love of it and the preoccupation with it that makes it dangerous.

A radical call to world evangelism may mean that you will be called to a foreign mission field. It may mean danger for you and your family. The risk of disease may be greater. These are part of the cost that we need to count when it comes to following Him. But keep this in mind: there is no place of greater blessing than being in the center of God's will. As Jesus has reminded us, "'Whoever desires to come after Me, let him deny himself, and take up his cross, and follow Me. For whoever desires to save his life will lose it, but whoever loses his life for My sake and the gospel's will save it'" (Mark 8:34, 35).

REFLECT AND MEDITATE

Do you consider yourself a world Christian? Are you a disciple of Jesus first and whatever else you may do or be second? Are you willing to go and willing to stay?

REACT AND RESPOND

Make a list of the characteristics you think best describes a missionary. What do you see as the difference between a missionary and a world Christian?

REJOICE AND WORSHIP

Father, help me to be willing to say yes to Your call on my life. Help me to be ready to go or ready to stay according to Your will for my life.

Study 2

THE NEED FOR WORLD EVANGELISM

READ AND RESEARCH (Matthew 9:37, 38)

There are approximately 3 billion people in the world who have never heard the gospel. There are over 7,000 distinct living languages, and over 5,000 of them still do not have Bibles translated in their language. It is estimated that 80,000 unsaved people die every single day. That is approximately 55 people every minute. And if we believe what we say we believe, these people face eternity without God.

Is there any question, then, that there is a need for this gospel to be shared around the world? For the nearly 3 billion people who have not heard the gospel, there are only about 7,000 missionaries worldwide. That calculates to less than one missionary for every 450,000 people.

Keith Green, missionary-singer who died in a plane crash in 1983, had this to say about the need for world evangelism:

"Right now worldwide there are only 85,000 workers on the mission field--working mainly among those who have heard the gospel before. This figure includes missionaries of every nationality from all over the world. When you compare this number with the number of Americans selling Avon or Amway products, the results are staggering. These two companies combined have 14 times more representatives in the United States alone than the church of Jesus Christ has in the whole world outside of America. And what about the Christian representatives we do have in the world? Only 9 percent of the world's population speaks English, and yet 94 percent of all ordained preachers in the whole world minister to the 9 percent who speak English. And 96 percent of all Christian finances are spent in the United States on 6 percent of the world's population. Only 4 percent of all Christian money is spent on missionary efforts to reach the other 94 percent of the world's population. There are over 1 million full-time Christian workers in the United States, while one-half of the world's population (three major groups--Moslem, Hindu and Chinese) have about 2,500 full-time Christian workers."

As you can see from these statistics, there is a great need for us to become involved in world evangelism. We must awake from our lethargy and our limited vision and recognize that there is a whole world out there that needs to hear the gospel. We keep reaching and feeding the same people over and over again.

As someone has aptly put it: "No one has the right to hear the gospel twice while there remains someone who has not heard it once."

REFLECT AND MEDITATE

1. Does it matter to you that half the world has never heard the name of Jesus?

2. Do you think those who never heard the gospel are lost?

REACT AND RESPONSE

1. Find out how many American missionaries and full-time Christian workers the Church of God has ministering outside the United States.

2. How much money did your church give last year for world missions? What percentage of your church's budget was this?

REJOICE AND WORSHIP

Lord, forgive me for my lack of concern for those who have never heard Your gospel. Burden my heart for those people. Show me, Lord, what I can do to respond to the need.

Discipleship

BLESSINGS AND REWARDS

READ AND RESEARCH (Genesis 12:1-3; Mark 10:23-31)

What are the blessings and rewards of obeying Jesus' command to follow Him? If world evangelism often requires sacrifices and hardships on our part, what can we expect in return?

After Jesus had told His disciples how difficult it was to enter the kingdom of God, they were puzzled. They wondered how anybody could be saved, and they questioned if following Jesus was really worth it. Bold and impetuous Peter reminded the Lord that they had left everything to follow Him.

In an attempt to reassure His disciples, Jesus remarked that the reward for following is very great, both now and in the hereafter. Anyone who gives up anything or anybody for the sake of the gospel will receive back a hundred times in this age. The joy of serving the Lord greatly outweighs the loss. And in the age to come, they will receive eternal life and the right to rule and reign with Christ.

The rewards and blessings of following Jesus are certain, but they may not come in the ways we expect. The privilege and blessing of sharing in Christ's suffering may not be what we desire. But talk to those who have suffered for His sake, and you will better understand why they continue in obedience wherever and whenever He calls.

The Bible is filled with examples of the special blessings and rewards God gave to those who left their own people and culture to do God's will.

God commanded Abraham to leave his homeland and his relatives and go to a foreign land. But God also promised that He would bless him and make of him a great nation.

Joseph and Daniel were taken captive to far away places, but they received great rewards and recognition for their obedience. They stood for their faith and shared it with others, and God brought great honor to them. Their experiences were not without persecution, hardship and loneliness, but their rewards greatly overshadowed their sufferings.

No doubt Paul would have preferred to teach and preach among his own people. But the Lord called him to be a missionary to the Gentiles. In Paul's own words, he counted it all joy to be able to serve his Lord.

Special anointing and blessing, salvation and eternal life, joy and glory, all belong to those who are willing to answer God's call to participate in world evangelism.

REFLECT AND MEDITATE

1. Have you experienced any rewards and blessings for answering the call to follow Jesus?

2. Do you think the sufferings and hardships experienced by those who are called to foreign lands are worth it?

REACT AND RESPONSE

The Bible says, "But many who are first will be last, and the last first." What does this imply about the rewards and blessings of following Christ in world evangelism?

REJOICE AND WORSHIP

Thank you, Lord, for choosing to use me in the work of Your kingdom. Help me to reach out and embrace the suffering that comes from serving You faithfully.

Study 4

CALLED TO STAY, TO PRAY AND TO GIVE

READ AND RESEARCH (Philippians 4:10-19; 2 Corinthians 8, 9)

In a very real sense, every born-again believer is to be a missionary. We are to proclaim to the world the good news of Jesus Christ. How this commission is to be fulfilled, however, will vary from person to person.

While it is true that more Christians should be witnessing cross-culturally than are presently doing so, not everyone is called to a foreign mission field. Some are called to be witnesses in their own area and to support world evangelism through intercessory prayer and giving. Many would say that intercessory prayer is more vital than either going or giving.

Missionary work, like all witnessing, involves spiritual warfare. It is oftentimes a life-and-death struggle, with evil forces arrayed against the Christian worker as he attempts to fulfill his mission. In places steeped in primitive religious and occultlike practices, the satanic opposition is especially strong. This is where the ministry of intercessory prayer is so important. Prayer can break down the walls of resistance and bind the powers of evil.

Effective prayer must be specific, persistent and in faith. To pray specifically, you must be well informed about the definite needs of the missionary. To pray persistently, you must keep the vision of world needs ever before you. You must recognize and accept your own responsibility to pray without wavering for the missionary and his work. To pray in faith, you must remember His promises and His faithfulness in fulfilling the promises. Intercessory prayer is not easy. It is spiritual warfare and will require great determination and tenacity.

For those who are called to "stay" rather than "go," there is yet another way to fulfill their responsibility to world evangelism. It is possible to share in missionary work by sacrificial giving.

It has been estimated that Americans spend more than 90 cents of every church dollar on their own personal religious concerns. That means that less than a dime of every church dollar goes for world evangelism. In this country 74 million Protestants give slightly less than 20 cents a week per capita for foreign missions. If each Church of God member in the United States gave an average of a dollar a week for world missions, the outreach in other lands would more than triple overnight.

REFLECT AND MEDITATE

What do you think is the greatest need in meeting the task of world evangelism today? Is it more missionaries, more intercessory prayer or more sacrificial giving of money? Defend your answer.

REFLECT AND RESPOND

1. How could you change your spending habits in order to give more for world missions?

2. Get a list of the names of several missionaries, and pray for them daily. Write them a letter and let them know that you are praying for them. (Names and addresses can be obtained from the Church of God Department of World Missions, Keith at 25th Street, Cleveland, TN 37311.)

REJOICE AND WORSHIP

Lord, I lift up before You those who are laboring for You in other lands and in other cultures. Bless their efforts and give them encouragement and joy in their ministries. Remind me again, Lord, of the joy and privilege of giving sacrificially that Your gospel can be carried throughout the world. Amen.

Discipleship

OPPORTUNITIES FOR WORLD EVANGELISM

READ AND RESEARCH (John 9:4; 1 Corinthians 16:9)

To be sure, there are a number of forces opposing those who would heed the call to world evangelism. Some of the opposition originates right here in America, while some is encountered in other countries. For example, a lack of world vision, prompted by materialism and self-centeredness, will hinder some from answering the call to world evangelism. On the other hand, anti-American feelings, increased nationalism and a revival of militant, non-Christian religions are forces to be contended with outside the United States.

The apostle Paul found a similar climate in his day. He described it like this: "A great and effective door has opened to me, and there are many adversaries" (1 Corinthians 16:9). And Jesus said, "I must work the works of Him who sent Me while it is day; the night is coming when no one can work" (John 9:4).

Many areas of the world that just a few years ago closed to outsiders are now showing signs of opening up for missionary work. There appears to be a new openness in certain Communist countries, which could result in greater opportunities to share the gospel. Government leaders in several African nations are now asking for missionaries, especially those who possess certain skills and qualifications. Laymen such as doctors, nurses, engineers, educators, and other specialists can become modern-day "tentmakers" while sharing the gospel message around the world.

The Church of God offers several opportunities for short-term mission experience through programs such as STEP and WEAC. Through these programs, some will come to know if they are truly called to full-time Christian service in another culture. (Information about STEP and WEAC can be obtained by writing to the Church of God Department of Youth and Christian Education and the Department of World Missions.)

To take advantage of opportunities for world evangelism, the late Keith Green offered the following suggestions:

1. Be available. Be ready and willing to go. If you are burdened down with debts and selfish commitments, you are not in a position to answer such a call.

2. Be informed. Do your homework. Find out what the needs are. Do research on particular areas; talk with missionaries and church leaders. Prepare yourself for the task.

3. Be inspired. Diligently study God's Word on a regular basis. Seek to be filled with the Holy Spirit, and keep on being filled as you walk with the Lord.

4. Expect an open door. Expect an open door by knocking on doors. As you pray and seek direction from the Lord, let the church know of your burden. God is seeking those who will say, "Here am I! Send me!"

REFLECT AND MEDITATE

Have you ever considered the possibility that God wants to use you to share the gospel with people of another culture? How would you know if He has called you?

REACT AND RESPOND

How would you go about finding out what opportunities for world evangelism are available? Write or call the Church of God World Missions Department or the Office of Lay Ministries, and ask for information concerning STEP and WEC.

REJOICE AND WORSHIP

Lord, thank You that You have have set before us our "open door" which no man can shut. Amen.

DISCIPLESHIP COMMITMENT
Use me, Lord, as you wish and in whatever capacity seems pleasing to Your Holy Spirit.

CHAPTER 26

Christian Responsibility

INTRODUCTION

Christians for hundreds of years have sung, "In my hand no price I bring, Simply to Thy cross I cling," in recognition of the deep truth that salvation is based solely on what Christ has done. Yet almost instinctively believers have acknowledged that the redeemed life results in discipleship action addressed to those who are not yet Christians.

Jesus himself said, "He who has My commandments and keeps them, it is he who loves Me" (John 14:21).

Hymnwriter George Matheson captured the essence of the motivation to Christian service when he wrote,

O Love that wilt not let me go,
I rest my weary soul in thee;
I give thee back the life I owe,
That in thine ocean depths its flow
May richer, fuller be.

The Christian life lived to its fullest is one that is regarded as "the life I owe."

Christian responsibility is an acting-out of Christian maturity. It is a demonstration of the truth that "...we are His workmanship, created in Christ Jesus for good works, which God prepared beforehand that we should walk in them" (Ephesians 2:10).

The testimony of the child of God says--without saying anything with the lips--"I'll show you whose I am by what I do."

A man or woman moves through three stages to come ultimately to Christian responsibility. The first of these is the "mine" level. It is analogous to the infant who discovers "my chair," "my bed," "my toy," and so forth, and selfishly guards all the things that are "mine." The second stage is the "yours" level, which recognizes the legitimacy of the claims of others on parts of life's time, possessions and energy. The highest stage, however, is the "Thine" level, which acknowledges God's prior rights to life and all it produces.

The believer who still lives at the "mine" level rightly rejoices at the benefits of his or her Christian experience, for example, *my* salvation, *my* peace, *my* inheritance, but has failed to learn a deeper dimension. It is laudable when the move is made to "yours" and Christian duty is observed. But the apex of Christianity on earth is reached when we can say, "All that I have, all that I am and all I shall ever be belongs to You, Father!"

For the next few lessons we will deal with the implications of Christian responsibility. We will search the Scriptures to investigate our responsibility to evidence discipleship commitment, to manifest holy living, to share Christian witness, to demonstrate Christian caring and to practice Christian concern.

DISCIPLESHIP GOAL

To carry out my responsibility as a model Christian and obedient child of God

READING ASSIGNMENT

The Living Book, pp. 316 - 328

Discipleship

TO EVIDENCE DISCIPLESHIP COMMITMENT

READ AND RESEARCH (1 Thessalonians 5:4-11)

"I'm going to live like a believer!" ought to be the motto of every Christian.

Paul reminded a group of church members on one occasion, "You are our epistle written in our hearts, known and read by all men" (2 Corinthians 3:2). It was his way of telling them that people would know what they believed--what they were committed to--by viewing their lives.

Part of Christian responsibility is to live before unsaved people in a manner that reflects the real Christlife. The passage in 1 Thessalonians is one of many biblical exhortations to live an exemplary life. Others include 2 Peter 3:11, which says, "Therefore, since all these things will be dissolved, what manner of persons ought you to be in holy conduct and godliness?" and Philippians 1:27, "Only let your conduct be worthy of the gospel of Christ." To someone who asks us why, we can give good reasons for living out a discipleship commitment. In one sentence, we can quote Jesus' words, "'By this all will know that you are My disciples, if you have love for one another'" (John 13:35).

What does an exemplary life look like? One Scripture reference for today in 1 Thessalonians is instructive. Basically it says we are to be alert and self-controlled (that is the literal meaning of "watch and be sober"). We are also to encourage each other and build up each other (that is the sense of "comfort . . . and edify").

REFLECT AND MEDITATE

For group discussion:

1. What have you noticed about the lifestyle of one of your fellow Christians (name him) which sets him apart and marks him as a believer? Be specific.

2. Read 1 Thessalonians 5:4-11 and from its verses contrast the actions and outlook of a Christian and a non-Christian.

REACT AND RESPOND

For personal enrichment:

Think of an individual before whom you want to intensify your witness to a discipleship commitment. What one thing can you do or not do tomorrow (action, not words!) which might help him or her see Christ in your life?

REJOICE AND WORSHIP

It brings joy to Jesus when He sees us following in His steps.

TO MANIFEST HOLY LIVING

READ AND RESEARCH (Colossians 3:1-14)

It is a ridiculous idea, and it is surprising that anyone actually believes it, but some people say that a person can be a Christian without living any differently than non-Christians.

This curious claim probably results from a well-meaning desire to deemphasize a works-earned salvation. "We are saved by grace; it is all of grace," they proclaim. Ephesians 2:8, 9 is one of their favorite scriptures. It teaches clearly that believers are saved by grace through faith, not of works lest any man should boast. So far, so good! But often verse 10 seems to be unknown or unacknowledged. It clarifies, "For we are His workmanship, created in Christ Jesus for good works, which God prepared beforehand that we should walk in them."

Holy living does not save anyone, but it reveals that one has been saved.

It is instructive, for example, to read Colossians 3, looking for the commands for Christians to obey. Here is one of many places in the New Testament which emphasizes what we are to do. Elsewhere we find pointed teaching about what

Christ has done for us; here we discover what we are to do in response. The bottom line is *holy living*.

God wants us to manifest holy living because it is the opposite of sinful living. Sin is what brought about the fall of man and produced the heartbreaking scene of Calvary. How ludicrous to suppose that what nailed Christ to the cross could be tolerated in the life of Christ's follower!

God wants us to manifest holy living because it glorifies Him. Part of the Sermon on the Mount (Matthew 5) declares that when men and women let their lights shine, the world sees their good works and glorifies God. A godly saint is a testimony to a darkened world that there is a good and righteous and holy God.

God wants us to manifest holy living because it can be used of the Holy Spirit to attract other men and women to Him. The winsomeness and peace and character of holy living motivates those who see it to desire it for themselves.

What does a holy life look like? Colossians 3 is helpful. Christians are told there are some things they put off and some other things they put on. A key to understanding the commands and expectations of the passage is to realize that these do's and don'ts are built on attitudes which result in these actions. As a consequence, observers can view the lifestyle of an individual and tell almost immediately if it manifests holy living.

Perhaps the most pivotal part of the chapter is the beginning exhortation, "Set your mind on things above, not on things on the earth." Holy living proceeds from a desire to follow Christ, to think His thoughts and do His acts, to please Him.

REFLECT AND MEDITATE

Think of the wooden forms that a carpenter builds before cement is going to be poured. These forms describe the shape which the cement will take. When the cement hardens, they will be thrown away; only the cement will remain. They serve a temporary function, whereas the cement endures. The wooden forms represent the believer's role in sanctification. The believer does not himself work patience, kindness or love into himself. He simple constructs the outward form into which God pours His enduring work of holiness (Larry Christenson, *The Renewed Mind*).

REACT AND RESPOND

Reread Colossians 3. Guided by its instructions, write down one specific thing in your life that you need to put off and one specific thing you need to put on.

REJOICE AND WORSHIP

One of the most poignant and meaningful petitions of the prayer Jesus prayed for us, His disciples, in John 17 asks, "'I do not pray that You should take them out of the world, but that You should keep them from the evil one....Sanctify them by Your truth. Your word is truth'" (vv. 15, 17).

Think of it! Jesus himself prays for you to manifest holy living!

Study 3

TO SHARE CHRISTIAN WITNESS

READ AND RESEARCH (Acts 1:1-8)

"I know the Bible says I am to be a witness and share my faith, but I never feel quite satisfied that I am fulfilling that command" is a comment that many Christians could truthfully make.

Sharing the faith with non-Christians for the purpose of bringing them to faith in Christ and to active participation in the life of the church is part of the exercise of Christian responsibility. So why is it so difficult or so rarely practiced?

One reason may be a misconception of what it means to be a witness. A witness, quite simply, is someone who tells someone else what he has experienced. Obviously some people confuse the term *witness* with the term *apologist*. An apologist is one who can make a logical and skillful argument and defense for a particular point of view. Some approaches to training for evangelism have seemed to attempt to produce apologists, men and women who thoroughly and completely understand and can explain detailed answers to perplexing questions. But--to repeat--a witness is simply someone who shares what he has experienced.

Another misconception, this one in the opposite direction, supposes that a witness is never to say anything; rather, he is merely to establish a presence and be available in case he is ever asked a religious question. One writer suggests that we have reinterpreted Christ's command to be fishers of men and have made it mean that we should don frogmen's suits and join the fish in the water, acting as much like them as possible.

A realistic approach to witnessing lies somewhere between these two extremes of all-knowing theologian and passive bystander. It depends upon a person's having a vital relationship with God and being willing to live it out in daily conduct and to tell others something of what he has experienced, with a view toward persuading them to join him in following Christ.

An informal survey asked a number of active Christians to identify the influences which brought them to faith in Christ. An impressive number explained that the witness of particular individuals--their life and testimony--had been instrumental in moving them toward God. Often the quality of the Christians' lives was mentioned; frequently allusions were made to verbal witness which had been shared after friendship was established.

Let nothing written here discourage any act of evangelism. Testimonies are sometimes shared of an evangelism encounter between absolute strangers which leads a lost person to faith in Christ, particularly when that person is involved in a personal crisis, for example, in the hospital or jail or in a similar situation. But for every cold turkey crisis conversion, there are probably 10 incidences where friendship was first established and, then effective witness resulted in life-changing encounters.

All of this should be an encouragement for you to let your light shine before the people with whom you are in daily contact, constantly seeking situations and opportunities to naturally and easily talk with them. Salt your conversations with personal references to the sufficiency of Christ in your life, taking care to avoid judgmental preachments, praying continually that the Holy Spirit would use your words. Convey to your unsaved friends your personal interest in them as friends, not just as potential trophies in a soulwinning competition. Speak positively to them about church and Christian positions when you have a chance.

A very literal translation of Christ's Great Commission would allow it to say, "As you go everywhere that you are going, make disciples." Sharing Christ can become as natural as breathing ... and that seems to be exactly what Christ wants!

REFLECT AND MEDITATE

The Latin American Mission made a study of the fastest-growing movements and found them to be the Communists, the Jehovah's Witnesses and the Pentecostal churches. Then they analyzed these movements to find their common denominator. Was it their message? Obviously not. Here were an anti-Christian ideology, a heretical cult and a Christian group. Finally they came up with this proposition: "The growth of any movement is in direct proportion to its ability to mobilize its entire membership for continuous evangelistic action" (Leighton Ford, *The Christian Persuader*).

REACT AND RESPOND

Talk with a close Christian friend about the implications of the foregoing discussion of witnessing. Then try to settle on the names of two or three people who are within the sphere of your influence, perhaps neighbors or coworkers, and ask your friend to join with you in ongoing prayer that your Christian witness might be effective with those specific individuals.

REJOICE AND WORSHIP

Out there somewhere are men and women who in the depths their heart are looking from Mount

Nebo into a land that they longingly desire to enter. Whether they enter that land will depend on the effectiveness and success of someone's personal witness, someone who will say, "Look, here is the way! I came this way and found Jesus. Won't you come with me?"

Study 4

TO DEMONSTRATE CHRISTIAN CARING

READ AND RESEARCH (Luke 10:25-37)

To nobody's surprise, Jesus said pointedly, "You have answered correctly," when a young Hebrew scholar observed that God wants essentially two things from His people: that they love God with all their heart, soul, strength and mind and that they love their neighbors as themselves.

Christians have probably been a little better at loving God than at loving neighbors. That might explain the motive for Jesus' telling the story of the Good Samaritan. It gives tangible expression to the meaning of "love your neighbor." It says that we demonstrate Christian caring by practical actions.

Christian responsibility includes a sense of concern for people outside the circle of our immediate family and friends.

C.S. Lewis in his sermon "Weight of Glory" suggested part of the motivation for Christian caring:

The load, or weight, or burden of my neighbour's glory should be laid daily on my back, a load so heavy that only humility can carry it, and the backs of the proud will be broken. It is a serious thing to live in a society of possible gods and goddesses, to remember that the dullest and most uninteresting person you talk to may one day be a creature which, if you saw it now, you would be strongly tempted to worship, or else a horror or corruption such as you now meet, if at all, only in a nightmare. All day long we are, in some degree, helping each other to one or the other of these destinations. It is in the light of these overwhelming possibilities, it is with the awe and the circumspection proper to them, that we should conduct all our dealing with one another, all friendships, all loves, all play, all politics. There are no ordinary people. You have never talked to a mere mortal.

That wounded man lying bleeding in the ditch, the woman who lives in the red-light district, the family of strangers who visited the Sunday worship service, the attendant who takes payment for gas at the service station, the little boy who can't keep up academically with his classmates, the man using food stamps in front of you in the check-out line--these, together with all men and women, are creatures destined to be glorified or damned.

Their needs are as different as their circumstances. Our responses may vary from a friendly smile and handshake to an offer of employment, from speaking a thoughtful word to buying a week's supply of groceries.

Christians care. Real Christians love others as themselves.

It is worthy of notice that in Jesus' Good Samaritan story the very people who ought to have been most sensitive to needs and most ready to help--the clergyman and the lay assistant--opted to remain uninvolved. After asking His hearers who was really neighbor to the Samaritan and getting their correct reply, He said to them what He says to us: "'Go and do thou likewise.'"

REFLECT AND MEDITATE

"If you really fulfill the royal law according to the Scripture, 'You shall love your neighbor as yourself,' you do well" (James 2:8).

REACT AND RESPOND

We are often motivated to neighborly action by the influence of those who have acted in a neighborly way toward us. Have you ever been the recipient of Christian caring? What were the circumstances? Who was the good samaritan? In your consideration of the question, do not equate caring only with benevolent charity. Often it takes other forms. Think about it, then share with someone else a testimony of what someone has done for you or someone close to you. The example may spur someone else to caring action!

REJOICE AND WORSHIP

C.S. Lewis, whose observations are quoted above, put it into crystal-clear perspective when he said that it is immortals whom we joke with, work with, marry, snub and exploit--immortal horrors or everlasting splendors. Remembering the eternal character of men and women, we will thrill to have the opportunity to minister to them.

Study 5

TO PRACTICE CHRISTIAN CONCERN

READ AND RESEARCH (Genesis 1:26-30; Nehemiah 9:6)

Events of recent years have focused the attention of the people of earth, as never before, on consideration of the fragile balance that man maintains with his environment. *Time* magazine in 1988 departed from its long-standing practice of spotlighting a Man of the Year and substituted, in the place of a well-known and significant individual, Planet Earth, its articles chronicling earth's storms, famines, quakes, climatic changes, atmospheric disturbances, disease epidemics and related disastrous events.

Christians who give thought to the matter know that one aspect of their responsibility lies in careful stewardship of the earth and its resources.

"In the beginning God gave man domination over the earth. This does not, however, give us license to pollute our natural environment or to waste the resources of the earth," declares a recently-adopted statement of Practical Commitments of the Church of God. We are finding it necessary to reaffirm a history-long concern for the place which God created for our life and well-being. God has explicit purposes for humankind, and the world itself is instrumental to His intentions.

How can Christians practice responsible concern?

We begin by holding steadfastly to the biblical doctrine of Creation. We do not cop out by unquestioningly accepting glib, pseudoscientific explanations of the universe as a whim of chance. On the contrary, we acknowledge that God created it, hence it has purpose and meaning and direction.

We ought also to educate ourselves to the dangers and choices which confront us and act responsibly, on the level appropriate to our activity, in response to what we learn. For example, if it is determined clearly and undisputedly that fluorocarbons (used in pressure spray cans) damage the atmosphere, wisdom would dictate that we seek a substitute for pressure spray cans. This sort of thing is a small personal decision of a Christian that alone might not signify much, but collectively might mean a great deal. Applied to broader, perhaps most directly applicable issues like hunger, use of land, and so forth, personal decisions could dramatically affect outcomes.

What do environmental issues have to do with the Christian faith? It is surprising to learn how much the Bible addresses itself to creation, and always the testimony is the same: "'You alone are the Lord; You have made heaven, the heaven of heavens, with all their host, the earth and all things on it, the seas and all that is in them, and You preserve them all. The host of heaven worships You'" (Nehemiah 9:6). In the beginning God's ideal was a man and woman living together in a setting of dramatic beauty and peace, in harmony and mutual interdependence with their environment.

All of the implications of ecological sensitivity are far-reaching and significant. It is possible, even with environmental issues, however, to be sentimentally wasteful. Recently the United States, Canada and the Soviet Union invested $6 million, 21 days and countless man-hours to rescue two whales that had been trapped in ice in the Alaskan seas. During the same three-weeks period, whalers from Japan and other nations reportedly slaughtered 53 of the same kind of whales! Christian responsibility does not countenance expending massive resources on tangential issues but insists that wise stewardship of the earth is pleasing to our Creator and Father.

REFLECT AND MEDITATE

About the age of 14, I found one day the nest of a rose-breasted grosbeak just a couple of feet off the path of a familiar trail through the woods. What a sight to see! The mother flew from the nest, rustling leaves and revealing the center of her little world, speckled eggs in a circlet of twigs. All summer I watched the brilliant male and his mate, fully at home in that patch of woods yet so vulnerable to the human community around them.

God still loves gardens, trees, birds. St. Francis was right about that. And God's commission to Adam and Eve in Eden ''to work it and take care of it'' (Genesis 2:15, *NIV*) is not just ancient history or poetry. It is a revelation of the character of the Kingdom and of the King. God still has an inheritance for His people; there is still a Promised Land (Howard A. Snyder, *A Kingdom Manifesto*).

REACT AND RESPOND

Ecological issues vary in intensity and importance. Is there a particular issue in your local area or state which warrants your attention? Talk this over with a friend and frame a plan of action. Would it be appropriate to write a letter to a government official? Sign a petition? Take some personal action? Don't confuse controversial environmental issues with more important biblical/moral issues. Avoid the temptation to get sidetracked and expend energy and time with questionable causes.

REJOICE AND WORSHIP

One of the delightful promises Scripture holds out to us is the prospect of new heavens and a new earth. In His own time God intends to remedy the ills wreaked on the earth by man's sin and thoughtlessness. Rejoice! He makes all things new!

DISCIPLESHIP COMMITMENT

As a result of this week's study, understanding the implications of my responsibilities as a Christian, I will more conscientiously seek to obey God's will for me.

CHAPTER 27

Vocation as Ministry

INTRODUCTION

Pastor Tony Scott produced an interesting television commercial to attract people to the church he leads in Toledo, Ohio. Standing before the camera, Pastor Scott asked the question, "Where is the Cathedral of Praise Church of God?" In rapid-fire sequence the scene shifts, first to a local automobile assembly plant, then to a hospital, next to an insurance office, next to a public school, finally to a residential neighborhood. At each scene change the pastor answers his own question: "It's here!"

We understand what he intends to convey. The church is not a building--it is people. The church is wherever its members live and work.

This unit of discipleship studies investigates the place of work in the life of a believer. It is wrong to view work only as a consequence of the fall of man. From the beginning man was given meaningful vocation by his Creator. "Then the Lord God took the man and put him in the garden of Eden to tend and keep it" (Genesis 2:15). Work was such a natural, expected part of existence that God established His fourth commandment, reminding man that he was to take one day of seven for rest.

The following lessons intend to explore Scripture for the purpose of seeing that labor has dignity and recognizing that our work gives us opportunity to manifest our love and service for God. Two scriptural teachings will be kept in perspective:

"But you are . . . a royal priesthood" (1 Peter 2:9) was written to all believers, not just to so-called clergy; "I . . . beseech you to have a walk worthy of the calling with which you were called" (Ephesians 4:1) has equal application to all men and women, regardless of their secular occupation.

How shall we glorify God with our work? In the next few lessons we will explore

1. Seeking God's Will for Vocation
2. Recognizing Partnership with God
3. Evidencing Diligence in Work
4. Adopting a Servant Lifestyle
5. Demonstrating Dependability.

As a result of these studies, we will understand how our workplace can be a temple in which God is worshiped and served.

DISCIPLESHIP GOAL

To use my vocation (occupation or job) as a field of ministry and service for the kingdom of God

READING ASSIGNMENT

The Living Book, pp. 329 - 341

Study 1

SEEKING GOD'S WILL FOR VOCATION

READ AND RESEARCH (Colossians 3:14-25)

Let's start with this observation: Paul never said God called him to be a tentmaker. He said God called him to be an apostle. Yet none of us would doubt that Paul glorified God both when he was doing apostle-type things and when he was doing tentmaker-type things.

This is a helpful observation, because it enables us to see that the Bible reserves the term *calling* for the spiritual dimension of life. Nowhere in Scripture is it recorded that God called anyone to an earthly profession or trade (even though in certain instances God gave individuals supernatural enablement for certain kinds of secular work). At the same time, it is clear that God intends for us to live out our calling as Christians within the sphere of the workplace. That is precisely the message of Paul, "I, therefore, the prisoner of the Lord, beseech you to have a walk worthy of the calling with which you were called" (Ephesians 4:1). This calling is the summons of the Lord to be His follower and live His lifestyle.

It does seem that God places His hand upon certain ones, equipping them with specific spiritual gifts and burdening them for particular ministries, ordaining them for spiritual leadership and service in the church. We may rightly speak of those individuals as having received sacred callings. What about the rest of us? We pursue secular occupations.

Make sure that you correctly understand that the term *secular* is not the opposite of *sacred*. The Roman Catholic Church has used the terms as opposites, but originally it was not so. The opposite of *sacred* is *profane*. Any occupation or job that would cause you to do anything base, defiled or improper would be profane. But you can glorify God in a secular vocation.

What has God called you to do? He has called you to be a Christian. To what occupation has He called you? Frankly, He seems to leave you with a lot of options at this point. He may be pleased for you to be a plumber, secretary, lawyer, machinist, laborer, politician or one of a thousand other things; but the overarching call is to glorify God in your work and in your workplace.

"Therefore, whether you eat or drink, or whatever you do, do all to the glory of God," Paul exhorted in 1 Corinthians 10:31. He echoed the same sentiment again in Colossians 3:17, "And whatever you do in word or deed, do all in the name of the Lord Jesus," and repeated it in verse 23, "And whatever you do, do it heartily, as to the Lord and not to men."

Would it make any difference how you worked--wherever you work--if it were Jesus Christ himself in the flesh who served as your administrator, supervisor, foreman or boss?

You might not particularly say, "God has called me to be an electrician" (some individuals do sense that certainty of vocation); but if you are an electrician, it is altogether fitting for you to say, "God has called me to be a Christian electrician."

Whatever your job, glorify God in it.

REFLECT AND MEDITATE

In the New Testament we discover that a man's work means something other than daily toil. A man's real work is not really his work at all but God's. His work, insofar as it is good at all, is strictly the effect of God's working within him. He cooperates with God and thus becomes a fellow worker with God (William J. Keech, *The Life I Owe*).

REACT AND RESPOND

Write a simple statement of how you think you can glorify God in the place where you work. Sign your name. Share your statement with someone else who is participating in this discipleship study.

REJOICE AND WORSHIP

"Father, where shall I work today?"
And my love flowed warm and free.
Then He pointed me out a tiny spot,
And said, "Tend that for me."

Discipleship

I answered quickly, ''Oh, no, not that.
Why, no one would ever see,
No matter how well my work was done.
Not that little place for me!''
And the word He spoke, it was not stern,
He answered me tenderly,

''Ah, little one, search that heart of thine;
Art thou working for them or me?
Nazareth was a little place,
And so was Galilee.''
--Author Unknown

Study 2

RECOGNIZING PARTNERSHIP WITH GOD

READ AND RESEARCH (John 15:1-8)

God is at work in the world.

The method of His work is sometimes obvious to us; but probably more often, unknown. He has made no secret, however, of the truth that He frequently chooses to work His will through men. The most delightful sense of fulfillment in life comes when we realize we are in partnership with God and that He is doing His will through our lives.

Partnership with God is beautifully represented in the John 15 imagery of the vine and its branches. Jesus identifies Himself as the vine and us as the branches. Through this living connection with Him, He assures us, ensures fruitfulness. The vital relationship, constant communion resulting in nourishment and strength, makes it possible for fruit to be produced and to mature.

God desires the kind of partnership that has us working with Him to do His will. Paul explored this truth when he reflected on the contributions of various workers to the development of the church at Corinth. One had planted, he explained, another had watered, and God gave the increase. Summarizing, he emphasized that all who were part of the process had been laborers together with God (1 Corinthians 3:9).

A key condition to the vine-branches, fellow-workers relationship is voiced by the ancient prophet Amos, who asked discerningly, ''Can two walk together, unless they are agreed?'' (Amos 3:3). You want to be in partnership with God? Well, then, Amos implied, make sure you are going in the same direction He is going.

Francis Schaeffer in *True Spirituality* underscores the ultimate importance of remaining in partnership with Christ when he writes, ''As an illustration, imagine a married couple of one race, both of the one color of skin. Suddenly the wife brings forth a child clearly of another race. All the world would know that she has been unfaithful to her proper mate.''

The true disciple seeks to conform his own will and desires to the plan of the Father. That makes him available to God, ready to do His work. If we have that kind of relationship with Him, it will be possible for the world to say of us, as it said of the first disciples, ''They went out and preached everywhere, *the Lord working with them* [italics for emphasis] and confirming the word through the accompanying signs. Amen'' (Mark 16:20).

REFLECT AND MEDITATE

Perhaps the Old Testament personality most dramatically identified as a fellow worker with God was Moses, the man said to have actually seen God and lived to tell about it. To Moses' reluctant excuses of not being able or eloquent, God answered simply, ''I will be with you.'' Despite our own protestations of inability, once we have accepted God's invitation to join in partnership with Him, nothing will be impossible that He wishes to do through us.

REACT AND RESPOND

Try to think of biblical examples of individuals who were said to be in partnership with God. Mention the name of one such person, and tell what that person accomplished as he or she was used in God's service.

REJOICE AND WORSHIP

God and I together form a majority!

Study 3

EVIDENCING DILIGENCE IN WORK

READ AND RESEARCH (2 Peter 3:10-14)

"Whatever your hand finds to do, do it with your might" (Ecclesiastes 9:10) is good advice for the man or woman who wishes to glorify God in the workplace.

David in his formative years is a model of diligence for today's disciple. When Samuel arrived at Jesse's house, led there by God to anoint the future king of Israel, David was not present in the house because he was dutifully keeping his father's sheep.

During his years as a shepherd on the hills of Bethlehem, the boy not only faithfully tended the flocks, he used his time to practice on the harp until he earned a reputation for being a quite good musician, so good, in fact that he was summoned to play at the royal court to calm the soul-troubled King Saul.

The young shepherd of Bethlehem further demonstrated diligence by fearlessly fighting off the lion and bear which threatened the flock. He lived out that dictum of biblical wisdom, "Whatever your hand finds to do, do it with your might."

We live in a day when diligence is a rare quality, so unusual as to attract interest and attention when it is observed. It is easier to perform shoddy work and just get by than to put forth sustained, faithful attention to detail. A builder recently complained about the carpentry work that was being done on an apartment building he was constructing. "There aren't any craftsmen anymore," he lamented.

Diligence carries with it the companion virtues of honesty, industry and integrity. It is valued not only by good men but also by God. Jesus talked about his personal approach to His own work and left this record: "'My food is to do the will of Him who sent Me, and to finish His work'" (John 4:34). Paul reflected to the leaders of the Ephesian congregation, "'But none of these things move me; nor do I count my life dear to myself, so that I may finish my race with joy, and the ministry which I received from the Lord Jesus'" (Acts 20:24). For David and Jesus and Paul it was not enough to begin work entrusted to them and perform it halfheartedly; it must be done well and completed.

It is worth noting that faithful performance of duty deserves reward and that God keeps good accounts (Matthew 25, parable of the talents).

Being diligent in the workplace is a testimony before the world of whose we are and whom we serve.

REFLECT AND MEDITATE

One of the greatest defeats in the modern training of youth is that accomplishment is not stressed sufficiently. Our lads and lassies study after a fashion, know some arithmetic but not the multiplication tables, play an instrument only passably, read occasionally and write indifferently, work passively without inquisitiveness into what they are doing or imagination as to how they could be more effective. They can do most things "just a little," but nothing "well." The world is looking for the man or woman who can do at least one thing, and be a master of it (V. Raymond Edman, *The Disciplines of Life*).

REACT AND RESPOND

Some of us have had our lives blessed by coming into contact with a true *master*, whether he or she was an artist, craftsman, mechanic or whatever. Think of such a master you have known and write a short paragraph describing the person. What is there about the quality of that individual's life that you can translate into your own experience to enhance your performance?

REJOICE AND WORSHIP

Holy Father, thank You for putting into our hearts to seek to please You by being diligent in work. Give us always the Spirit of your Son, whose motivating watchword was "I must be about My Father's business." In Jesus' name. Amen.

Discipleship

ADOPTING A SERVANT LIFESTYLE

READ AND RESEARCH (John 13:1-17)

Servant is a quaint word, little heard in modern parlance, usually relegated in our thinking to an earlier, simpler time. No one nowadays has servants. Nobody in our time is a servant.

Nobody but a Christian.

Remember what Jesus said: "'As the Father has sent Me, I also send you'" (John 20:21). We are sent into the world not only with the same mission for which Jesus was sent, but also we are sent in the same spirit in which Jesus was sent. He came as a servant. "'For even the Son of Man did not come to be served, but to serve, and to give His life a ransom for many'" (Mark 10:45).

Not only is a servant lifestyle Christlike, it is a demonstration of our love for Him. When Simon Peter ardently proclaimed his love for the Lord (John 21), Jesus responded by giving him a servant task, as if to say, "You may now show me the depth of your love by the faithfulness of your service."

Adopting a servant lifestyle will make it possible for us to lighten the burden of life for others, because a true servant carries others' loads. In return, however, the servant's own life is ennobled, for Jesus teaches that the person who is the servant of all in reality is the greatest of all.

Human nature resists servanthood. Our natural tendency is to desire that others serve us, not that we serve them. This battle with our nature can be won, however, if we acknowledge whose servant we are called to be. We are God's servants. Often our service to God may take the form of duties done for other people, but the servanthood to which we are called is first and foremost to God.

The Lord concluded the powerful action lesson of foot washing with a brief teaching session. Here is what He said to His disciples: "'Most assuredly, I say to you, a servant is not greater than his master; nor is he who is sent greater than he who sent him. If you know these things, happy are you if you do them'" (John 13:16, 17).

REFLECT AND MEDITATE

By nature we are selfish, so when someone performs an act of loving service like this [Christ's act of foot washing], it speaks volumes for Christ, even though the person doing it may not say a single word.

We can perform "foot washing" jobs in our homes by washing up, cleaning the house, putting the children to bed, getting the tea ready, saying sorry, being ready to forgive. In a world characterized by selfishness, sensitivity to the needs of others and love shown in service for others can transform the atmosphere in our homes.

Being a "foot washer" at work involves being punctual, honest, reliable, positive in our comments about others and refusing to fiddle the accounts or take any part in petty pilfering.

In church, we might never be teachers or evangelists, but we might have other gifts to offer-- helping, giving hospitality, administering, typing, printing, plumbing or contributing to the worship (British pastor David Watson, *Grow and Flourish).*

REACT AND RESPOND

How is your SQ, your servant quotient? Just for your own benefit, make a brief list of acts of service you have performed for God or others in the past week. To show that you understand the concept of servanthood, tell two ways you have benefited from the service of others (above their usual level of normal duties) recently.

REJOICE AND WORSHIP

Using the previous exercise as a "thanksgiving guide," ask God's blessings on individuals in whom you have witnessed a servant spirit. Ask God to give that same spirit to you!

Study 5

DEMONSTRATING DEPENDABILITY

READ AND RESEARCH (Romans 12:9-21)

"Consistency, thou art a jewel!" Shakespeare's evaluation of that bright virtue, echoes the sentiments of Scripture, which affirms, "But let your 'Yes,' be 'Yes,' and your 'No,' 'No,' lest you fall into judgment" (James 5:12). God seems to highly value integrity.

One of the best ways Christian men and women can translate their faith into powerful witness is by living consistently good and faithful lives in the workplace. It is altogether proper for the community to be shocked when a so-called Christian does something unworthy of the name on the job.

Tucked away in an obscure Old Testament passage recounting the remodeling of the temple under King Jehoash is a remarkable compliment paid to the accountants and paymasters involved in the project. Money that had been donated by the people was entrusted to these men, and as the record has it, "Moreover they did not require an account from the men into whose hand they delivered the money to be paid to workmen, for they dealt faithfully" (2 Kings 12:15). What confidence they had in these men of God! That is the way it ought to be.

Integrity means wholeness, completeness. It comes from the root word which also gives us *integer*, a whole number as opposed to a fraction. A word which contrasts with integrity in Scripture is *hypocrisy*. A hypocrite is not whole or complete; he is a mask wearer, representing himself outwardly to be something that he is not inwardly. True Christianity, the Romans text instructs us, is without hypocrisy.

Do you want to express integrity in your life and work?

Gene Rice once declared his intent to write a book about how to quit smoking. The cover would announce in bold type *HOW TO QUIT SMOKING*, he explained. Then all the inside pages would be blank, except for the first one,

which would scream in boxcar letters, "QUIT!" That's the way someone quits smoking.

The way you demonstrate integrity is to *be consistent!* Live out what is right on a daily, regular, unvarying basis. Believe the truth, and show it by example. Never make a moral exception. Keep the faith.

"Then those who feared the Lord spoke to one another, and the Lord listened and heard them; so a book of remembrance was written before Him for those who fear the Lord and who meditate on His name. 'They shall be Mine,' says the Lord of hosts, 'On the day that I make them My jewels. And I will spare them as a man spares his own son who serves him.' Then you shall again discern between the righteous and the wicked, between one who serves God and one who does not serve Him" (Malachi 3:16-18).

REFLECT AND MEDITATE

I take a long walk on Saturdays when I am home, both for the physical exercise as well as the chance to clear my mind. Last winter I came around a sharp bend in the road up in the Hollywood hills and found a little boy resting and looking out across the valley. It was a cloudy day and had been raining. It looked as if it might begin again most any moment. I stopped to visit with him and found him a most interesting youngster. Finally, I said to him, "Son, do you think it's going to rain?" He looked around and replied, "I don't know, but if it does, I 'spect I can find some shelter." As I have thought about that reply, it seems to me that it is one of the best illustrations of faith I ever encountered.

He was saying in effect that he could not tell what the future was. Neither can we. It might be raining or sunny; it might be difficult or easy; it might be pleasant or unpleasant. No one, as the prayer has it, knows what a day may bring forth. That boy was saying that whatever happened, someone would provide him with "shelter from the stormy blast" and he would trust that and go on his way (Bishop Gerald Kennedy, *For Laymen and Other Martyrs*).

Discipleship

REACT AND RESPOND

Most of us probably recognize particular areas in our lives where we are prone to have difficulty in translating what we know to be right into consistent daily practice. Make a list of three such areas and ask God to help you get a handle on them, living out your testimony before fellow workers without exception.

REJOICE AND WORSHIP

The Malachi quotation gives us great delight and encouragement as we are reminded that the Lord knows those who are His. Thank Him for His complete understanding and His faithful remembering.

DISCIPLESHIP COMMITMENT

As a result of this week's study, reminded of how God wants me to use my job as a place of ministry, I will look for opportunitites to speak and act for Him.

CHAPTER 28

Christian Stewardship

INTRODUCTION

Of one particular young man who had an encounter with Christ, the Scripture says explicitly, "Jesus, looking at him, loved him" (Mark 10:21). Who was this individual who elicited an affirmation of compassionate caring from the Lord of love, and what came of this dramatic meeting?

Mark 10:17-31 tells the sad story. It is repeated in Matthew 19:16-30 and Luke 18:18-30. Marks did not identify him, but Matthew noted that he was young, and Luke called him a "ruler," a member of a regal court or an official council.

His approach to Jesus seems to have been rightly motivated. He expressed to the Lord his desire to obtain eternal life. He voiced a question that interests all of us: What can I do to go to heaven? Theologians speculate about the appropriateness of his phrasing of the query, for it was asked, seemingly, with the expectation of some reply that would instruct him how he might earn salvation. But we know that salvation cannot be earned; it is a gift.

At any rate, Jesus shortly zeroed in on the key issue, which was the barrier that kept the young man from following Him as His disciple--his attitude toward his personal possessions. "'Go your way, sell whatever you have and give to the poor . . . and follow Me,'" Jesus demanded. Mark recorded the youth's doleful and wordless response: "But he was sad at this word, and went away grieved, for he had great possessions."

Men make a mistake when they read this account and suppose that Jesus demands poverty as a universal condition of discipleship; there is no indication that this is a word for all men. It was directed specifically to this rich young ruler. But let it be noted, Jesus' words and actions throughout His ministry let us know unequivocally that a man's attitude toward his possessions dramatically affects the quality of his life as a disciple.

The thrust of the next five lessons is upon Christian stewardship. We will answer the question, How can a disciple manage his time, his abilities and his resources in such a way that will advance the kingdom of God, bring glory to Him, and permit a full exercise of Christian discipleship?

The sessions are
1. Believing Kingdom Claims
2. Adopting Kingdom Values
3. Setting Kingdom Priorities
4. Obeying Kingdom Commandments
5. Acknowledging Kingdom Accountability.

DISCIPLESHIP GOAL

To discover why I should, as well as how to, dedicate my time, my talent and my treasure to God and His service

READING ASSIGNMENT

The Living Book, pp. 342 - 355

Discipleship

Study 1

BELIEVING KINGDOM CLAIMS

READ AND RESEARCH (Matthew 13:24-52)

Jesus taught more about one particular subject than He did about anything else: the kingdom of God. It is called variously kingdom of God, kingdom of Heaven or kingdom of Christ, all meaning the same thing.

The kingdom of God includes essentially three interrelated truths: (1) It is the rule or reign of God; (2) it is the realm in which men experience the benefits and blessings of His rule; and (3) it is the age to come, when everything opposed to God will be destroyed and He will reign supreme everywhere.

A twisted, unbiblical form of Kingdom teaching has spread in recent years, causing some Christians to avoid using the term. We should not surrender a good, biblical term to heretics, however, but we should continue to teach and preach what the Bible says about the kingdom of God. No one suggests that we should avoid the word *Jehovah* just because an aberrant cult has misrepresented Him, and no one has ceased using "saints" because Mormons employ the word as part of their denominational identi- fication. The term kingdom of God is a biblical possession of the people of God, and we should keep it in our vocabulary.

Consider the claims of the Kingdom.

The Matthew 13 parables teach us vital lessons about the kingdom of God. Among several key truths, one keeps emerging in the parables. It is this: The kingdom of God is the most important thing in the world. The parable of the hidden treasure (Matthew 13:44) and the parable of the pearl of great price (45, 46) are twin affirmations of its inestimable value.

If it is true, then, that the kingdom of God is of ultimate importance, doesn't it follow that we should learn all we can about it and make it important in our own personal lives?

Paul picked up this theme in a discussion with the Corinthian Christians. "Let a man so consider us, as servants of Christ and stewards of the mysteries of God. Moreover it is required in stewards that one be found faithful" (1 Corinthians 4:1, 2).

The things of God have been entrusted by Him to us men, Paul was saying. Using the imagery of a steward--familiar to his readers--Paul underlined our tremendous responsibility. The word *steward*, from which we derive *stewardship*, identified the trusted senior member of the household staff of a wealthy family to whom was given the task of management. He guarded the keys to all the rooms, and he had authority over household financial accounts. He was expected to exercise all necessary initiative to keep the household ordered, prosperous and progressive. And he answered only to the master of the house.

The kingdom of God does not exist in a vacuum; it lives in the hearts and lives of men and women. In a mysterious sense we are its stewards, responsible under God for its faithful management and expansion in our world.

It is a serious claim and one we must take seriously.

REFLECT AND MEDITATE

The kingdom of God is His kingship, His rule, His authority. When this is once realized, we can go through the New Testament and find passage after passage where this meaning is evident, where the Kingdom is not a realm or a people but God's reign. Jesus said that we must "'receive the kingdom of God as a little child'" (Mark 10:15). What is received? The church? Heaven? What is received is God's rule. In order to enter the future realm of the Kingdom, one must submit himself in perfect trust to God's rule here and now (George Eldon Ladd, *The Gospel of the Kingdom*).

REACT AND RESPOND

How can you fulfill a steward's kind of responsibilities as you think they might relate to the kingdom of God? That is, when you are told that you are entrusted with the stewardship of the Kingdom, what does that mean to you, and how do you see yourself fulfilling the responsibilities? Discuss this with a fellow student.

REJOICE AND WORSHIP

The Jewish people misunderstood the Old Testament prophecies of Messiah. They expected a Davidic king or a superhuman being from heaven. Their rabbis drew two circles next to each other and labeled one "this present world" and the other "the world to come," believing that a great cataclysm would terminate the first and initiate the second. Christians know that, in reality, the circles overlap. We still live in this world, but since Jesus spoke His kingdom into being, we can say we live also in the world to come. One theologian said that we live in the "already" and the "not yet." God's kingdom has begun, but it will reach its climax when Jesus comes again and all things are made new.

Lord, hasten that day!

Study 2

ADOPTING KINGDOM VALUES

READ AND RESEARCH (Matthew 6:19-34)

A right attitude about stewardship of our time, talent and treasure will be built only on a foundation of Kingdom values.

What is ultimate, what is finally important, according to the Kingdom way of looking at things? Jesus in the Sermon on the Mount addressed the common issues of life, like food, clothing and shelter, and concluded, "'But seek first the kingdom of God and His righteousness, and all these things shall be added to you'" (Matthew 6:33).

He made the Kingdom a life and death choice when He declared that you cannot serve God and riches. One of them will be your master, He explained, and you just can't serve two master (Matthew 6:24).

Adopting Kingdom values means seeing things the way Jesus sees them. Some people who have a hard time living right or ordering their priorities confess rightly that the basic problem is one of ultimate loyalties. Who or what occupies first importance in your life? The Christian can have but one answer to that question.

Living life based on Kingdom values leads to stewardship that puts God and others above self. Jesus repeatedly taught and exemplified this truth, and His apostles caught it from Him. Peter would later write, "As each one has received a gift, minister it to one another, as good stewards of the manifold grace of God" (1 Peter 4:10). When you begin to recognize God as the ultimate owner and master of any possessions in your charge, it becomes easier to know how to manage them.

Do you have 168 hours in the week? Whose hours are they, really?

Do you have the ability to perform certain skills for which you receive money? Where did they come from, actually?

Do you receive a weekly or monthly paycheck for your work? Whose money is it, ultimately?

The Christian steward has the sort of outlook on life that causes him to acknowledge that God is the giver of time, the source of skills and the provider of money. Because he recognizes this is true, it becomes simpler to know how to use these gifts in God's service. The kingdom of God is the realm in which he lives and moves and has his being.

In short, we can say Christian stewardship is putting all areas of life under its rightful Lord.

REFLECT AND MEDITATE

Thine is the loom, the forge, the mart,
The wealth of land and sea;
The worlds of science and of art,
Revealed and ruled by Thee.
Then let us prove our heavenly birth
In all we do and know:
And claim the kingdom of the earth
For Thee, and not Thy foe.
--John Ellerton

Discipleship

REACT AND RESPOND

Write out a bill-of-sale type document, giving God the right to all your time, talent and treasure. List God as the receiver and you as the seller. Indicate the price that He paid for all rights to you: "For goods and services received."

REJOICE AND WORSHIP

"'The kingdoms of this world have become the kingdoms of our Lord and of His Christ, and He shall reign forever and ever!'" (Revelation 11:15)

Study 3

SETTING KINGDOM PRIORITIES

READ AND RESEARCH (Matthew 6:5-13)

Three men engaged in a building project were each asked the same question by a passerby, "What are you doing?"

The first replied, "I am laying blocks." The second responded, "I am earning $96 a day." The third answered, "I am building a cathedral."

All of them were performing exactly the same task, but one had an infinitely more meaningful sense of involvement in it than the other two. Viewing life from the perspective of a Christian steward makes it infinitely more meaningful.

Christian stewardship rightly practiced will require us to set priorities in line with Kingdom realities. Where does the process start? No better starting place may be found than in the words of Christ's model prayer: "Your kingdom come. Your will be done on earth as it is in heaven" (Matthew 6:10).

Not only must we pray this prayer, but we must also translate it into appropriate actions in our life. John gave concrete shape to this suggestion in his first epistle: "But whoever has this world's goods, and sees his brother in need, and shuts up his heart from him, how does the love of God abide in him? My little children, let us not love in word or in tongue, but in deed and in truth" (3:17, 18). He was echoing a theme expressed by Paul to the Galatians: "Therefore, as we have opportunity, let us do good to all, especially to those who are of the household of faith" (6:10).

If we try to make a list of priorities of the Kingdom, what does it look like? It would certainly include at least some of the following items:

1. Acknowledging the lordship of Christ by worshiping and and serving Him

2. Participating in the expansion of the kingdom of God by sharing our witness with nonbelievers

3. Ministering to the needs of fellow members of the household of faith

4. Offering help to those who are the victims of sin.

Your list might be longer or different, but we must agree that our God has expressed His will concerning certain actions and attitudes that assume importance from His perspective. These should form our priorities.

Have you adopted Kingdom priorities for your life?

REFLECT AND MEDITATE

There is no surer test of the character of our faith in God than how we deal with what we consider belongs to us. To believe in God as our Creator and in Jesus Christ as our Lord and to yield ourselves to the rule of God as He comes to possess us in His Spirit is to acknowledge that we are not our own, nor is there anything that is primarily ours; we belong to God, entirely and unconditionally. The world about us must be approached with respect because it is God's; it is not ours to exploit as we will. Our nation is under a higher rule than president, Congress and Supreme Court; Jesus Christ is its hidden king whether it knows it or not, and our first loyalty as Christian citizens is to Him. My family, my children belong to God before they belong to me, and I sin not just against them but against God if I deal with them as though I owned them. Even my body is not my own to do with it what I will, for God has chosen it for the dwelling place of His Spirit. And my possessions, though I have earned them all by my own labour, are not mine. If for a moment I delude myself into thinking they are mine I hear a voice saying, ''Thou fool, this night thy soul shall be required of thee: then whose shall those things be, which thou hast provided?'' (James Smart, *The Theological Groundwork for Christian Stewardship Education*).

REACT AND RESPOND

Read over again the list of priorities suggested in the ''Read and Research'' section. Make your own list. What else will you wish to add? How would you rearrange the items to indicate top priority? Show your list to someone else who is studying this discipleship course, and ask to see his or hers.

REJOICE AND WORSHIP

''Well done, good and faithful servant'' will be spoken by the Lord Jesus Christ to those who have correctly set their priorities.

Study 4

OBEYING KINGDOM COMMANDMENTS

READ AND RESEARCH (John 14:15-24)

Disciples grow and mature and become effective as they become more like the Master. That process involves a relationship of love. Jesus laid it on the line to His followers when He told them, ''He who has My commandments and keeps them, it is he who loves Me'' (John 14:21). You don't affirm your love to Christ just by talking about it; you prove your love by keeping His commandments.

Whole books have been written about obeying Kingdom commands, and it would be impossible in a few paragraphs to treat the subject adequately. In the context of a discussion about Christian stewardship, however, certain key issues come to light. We can show our love to Christ by following His instructions relating to stewardship.

He told us that we should assume the attitude of a servant, happily demonstrating willingness to put others before ourselves.

He let us know that we evidence our faith in Him by trusting Him for our daily, routine needs. Our utilization of what we own will show where we place priorities. Many people are surprised when they learn that Jesus addressed one-sixth of His teaching and discourses to the subject of money and related issues--more than to any other single subject.

In a scathing condemnation of the Pharisees, who meticulously tithed everything they possessed-- even garden herbs and cooking spices--Jesus scored them for neglecting weighty ethical and faith issues, but commended their faithfulness in tithing (Matthew 23:23). '''For where your treasure is,''' He taught, '''there your heart will be also''' (Matthew 6:21). Obeying Christ's commands will involve serious consideration of how we use money.

He commanded us to go into all the world and make disciples. So profoundly did His missionary mandate impact His followers that all of the Gospels record it. No serious disciple will neglect involvement in some dimension of world missions. Remember, we prove our love by our obedience to His commandments.

He made it clear that all of our works and deeds go unnoticed and unrecorded unless they are built on a foundation of love for God and others. The first commandment, He clarified, is to love God with all we have and all we are; and the second commandment is to love others.

A biographer of England's famous Duke of Wellington said that his most useful resource in writing his posthumous account of the general's life was his lifetime record of check stubs. You learn where a man's values and priorities really lie when you study his checkbook, the researcher explained.

Do you want a report card measuring your love for Christ? Just examine the extent of your faithfulness in keeping His commandments, and you will know where you stand.

REFLECT AND MEDITATE

I do not believe one can settle how much we ought to give. I am afraid the only safe rule is to give more than we can spare. In other words, if our expenditure on comforts, luxuries, amusements, and so forth, is up to the standard common among those with the same income as our own, we are probably giving away too little. If our charities do not at all pinch or hamper us, I should say they are too small. There ought to be things we should like to do and cannot do because our charitable expenditure excludes them. For many of us the great obstacle to charity lies not in our luxurious living or desire for more money but in our fear--fear of insecurity. This must often be recognized as a temptation. Sometimes our pride also hinders our charity; we are tempted to spend more than we ought on the showy forms of generosity (tipping, hospitality) and less than we ought on those who really need our help.

REACT AND RESPOND

Christians frequently enjoy going together to a restaurant or snack shop following church services, and they sometimes spend large amounts of money doing it. Discuss with a trusted friend this issue: Does the fellowship which results from these eating encounters warrant the expenditure or not? Would there be some other alternative? What are some of the ways that we hinder ourselves from fulfilling obedience to Christ's commandments?

REJOICE AND WORSHIP

In one sense, no person can ever claim that he has a right to stand in the presence of God. In another sense, however, we recognize that He has given us that right. How pleasant it is to come before Him with an awareness that--to the best of our ability--we are keeping His commandments. Read Psalm 15, and worship the Lord!

Study 5

ACKNOWLEDGING KINGDOM ACCOUNTABILITY

READ AND RESEARCH (Matthew 25:14-30)

A thread which runs throughout the New Testament, woven into the teachings of Jesus and the apostolic writers, is that believers will give an account of themselves to God. "So then each of us shall give account of himself to God" (Romans 14:12).

Jesus' story of the talents in Matthew 25 instructs disciples about accountability and its consequences. The key ideas of the parable seem to be that God imparts greater gifts to those who are faithful and he requires each individual to explain his stewardship of what has been entrusted to him. From other scriptural passages, we understand that accountability extends to time, abilities and possessions--what we have called in these lessons time, talent and treasure.

The consequences of accountability are reckoned both in the world to come and in this present world. To those who have exercised faithful stewardship, the Master says, "'Enter into the joy of your lord.'" About the unfaithful servant who fails to use his talent, the Master says, "'Take the talent from him, and give it to him who has ten talents.'" Faithfulness, then, is rewarded in the future world ("'enter into the joy'") and in the present ("'take the talent from him'").

A graphic illustration of God's judgment on the use of time, talent and treasure is recorded in 1 Corinthians 3. The works of Christians are depicted as construction elements of a building, classified either as gold, silver and precious stones or as wood, hay and straw. The building is erected of these disparate materials, then subjected to fire. The flames naturally consume the wood, hay and straw. The value of the work is determined by what remains after the fire has passed through-- the gold, silver and precious stones. Paul's commentary follows the explanation of the judgment: "If anyone's work which he has built on it endures, he will receive a reward" (1 Corinthians 3:14).

Jesus clearly expects His followers to be good

for goodness' sake. Rewards *will* be given to the faithful, however. But the opposite is true also: ''You are the salt of the earth; but if the salt loses its flavor, how shall it be seasoned? It is then good for nothing but to be thrown out and trampled under foot by men'' (Matthew 5:13). Disciples ought to be good for *something*, not good-for-nothing!

Knowing that we are doing our best with time, talent and treasure, it is a delight to look forward to standing in the presence of the King and hearing His ''Well done, good and faithful servant.''

REFLECT AND MEDITATE

Time is one of the greatest assets God has given you. When you were born, you were given a bag of gold coins, one for each day of your life. These coins are time, and they disappear one by one from the day of your birth.

How will you use your coins? For eternity, I hope! God wants each of us to use part of each day's time for work, for play, for study, for family, for friends, for Him. In the past you haven't given much thought to using your time for God. It's easy to spend time (or sometimes waste it) on the affairs of this earth. Suddenly your priorities are all changed because you have placed yourself firmly into the ways of God.

Just as your money all belongs to God, so does your time. How does He want you to use it? If you take 10 percent--a tithe of your day--that means 10 percent of the 15 hours you are awake each day; that is, one and a half hours for God. Prayer, Bible reading and study time are an important part of your time tithe. What are some other ways to give God your time? (Kenneth Taylor, *How to Grow*).

REACT AND RESPOND

Taking a cue from the preceding quote by Kenneth Taylor, make a list of ways you can invest your time as a tithe to God. Remember this guideline: It should not be dedicated primarily only to your own welfare but to God. Share your list with a friend.

REJOICE AND WORSHIP

Some of the most beautiful scenes of worship in the Bible relate to the giving of gifts. Those who contributed to the construction of the tabernacle, and later the temple, worshiped as they gave. The wise men in Matthew 2 worshiped with their gifts of gold, frankincense and myrrh as they bowed in the presence of the King. Worship the Lord with the tithe of your time, talent and treasure!

DISCIPLESHIP COMMITMENT

As a result of this week's stewardship study, I commit my time, my talent and my treasure to my Lord.

CHAPTER 29

Christian Citizenship

INTRODUCTION

The Christian life is lived in relationships.

As a Christian, I relate first and foremost to God the Father. I know Jesus Christ as Savior and also as Elder Brother. I experience the companionship, comfort and guidance of the Holy Spirit.

But the relationship with the Trinity is only part of the story. I relate also to my family, my friends, my neighbors, my co-workers, my church, my community and my nation. *How* do I relate? Thankfully, the Bible does not leave us in the dark about how we live out our faith among many different publics. The thrust of this week's study is on the Christian's relationship to those outside the church.

It is difficult to reconcile the truth that we are citizens of heaven at the same time that we live on earth. Yet our lives on earth are so vital and important for God that a second-century writer, unknown except as the originator of a letter called ''The Epistle to Diognetus,'' could write, ''The Christians are the soul of the world; they hold the world together.''

We will explore the salt and light functions of Christians. There is some sense in which the world should not be the same if Christ's followers live in it. At times we come to the decision that we would be unfit to bear the name of Christ if we refused to cry out against injustice and wrong. How do we determine if an issue merits our efforts and attention, as oppposed to one which would just sap our energies and resources in unimportant causes? We will try to decide in this week's lesson.

One of the key issues we will examine is prayer. Prayer really does change things, sometimes starting by changing us. Those who engage in meaningful prayer soon discover that it draws us closer to the One to whom we pray, the one for whom we pray, and the one with whom we pray.

The final focus of the week concentrates on what it means to become a world Christian--not a worldly Christian but a world Christian. Seeing the globe as God sees it, teaming together to accomplish what He desires, dedicating ourselves to a cause which transcends personal interests and cultural boundaries--this is world missions. How do we fit?

Here are the five themes:
1. Recognizing Dual Citizenship
2. Working for Change
3. Confronting Problems
4. Praying for Leaders
5. Becoming a World Christian

The faithful and obedient disciple of Christ will fulfill his citizenship in two worlds.

DISCIPLESHIP GOAL

To better understand what it means to be a citizen of two worlds

READING ASSIGNMENT
The Living Book, pp. 355 - 369

Study 1

RECOGNIZING DUAL CITIZENSHP

READ AND RESEARCH (Romans 13:1-7)

International law acknowledges the dual citizenship of babies of aliens born in foreign countries. A couple who are U.S. citizens may experience the birth of a child while visiting in Brazil. The infant will be considered a citizen of both the United States and Brazil and will have until the age of 18 to opt for permanent citizenship in one or the other country.

Christians, too, claim dual citizenship. We are enrolled in the kingdom of God, but at the same time we are citizens of an earthly kingdom. We owe dual allegiance.

Living in two worlds is sometimes problematic. The claims of the one sometimes seem to infringe on the demands of the other.

Romans 13, written to Christians living in the capital of the world, reminded them--as it does us--that God is the ultimate sovereign of both worlds. In ways and for reasons that are not completely clear to us, He has not chosen at this time to exercise the power of His sovereignty. He expects us to recognize and be subservient to the powers that are in authority in civil rule.

The Bible is explicit about our duties to the earthly kingdom. The authorities that exist are ordained of God, the passage affirms. Giving obeisance, paying taxes, obeying laws-- these are expected of Christians. Comparing Romans 13 with Acts 5 and other relevant scriptures lets us know, to be sure, that we owe supreme allegiance to God; and when human law contravenes His law, we ought to obey God rather than men. But under normal conditions, loyalty to the state and participation in its activities are not counterproductive to the Christian faith.

The Jews tried to trick Jesus with a question about the lawfulness of paying taxes to Rome, but Jesus used the opportunity to instruct them to "'Render . . . to Caesar the things that are Caesar's'" (Matthew 22:21). Earthly government has its place. The Christian is not exempt from human government nor above its demands.

In certain circumstances, great glory can come to God from the faithful service of a citizen to his nation.

REFLECT AND MEDITATE

Prayer is political action. Prayer is social energy. Prayer is public good. Far more of our nation's life is shaped by prayer than is formed by legislation. That we have not collapsed into anarchy is due more to prayer than to the police. Prayer is a sustained and intricate act of patriotism in the largest sense of that word--far more precise and loving and preserving than any patriotism served up in slogans. That society continues to be livable and that hope continues to be resurgent are attributable to prayer far more than to business prosperity or a flourishing of the arts. The single most important action contributing to whatever health and strength there is in our land is prayer. Not the only thing, of course, for God uses all things to effect His sovereign will, and the "all things" most certainly includes police and artists, senators and professors, therapists and steelworkers. But prayer is, all the same, the source action (Eugene H. Peterson, *Earth and Altar*).

REACT AND RESPOND

What are some of the demands of the civil government that Christians tend to resent or refuse? Make a list of two or three. Are Christians correct in their attitude? Why or why not? Compare your answer with the response of someone else.

REJOICE AND WORSHIP

American Christians are sometimes accused of "civil religion" because of their attempts to identify the hand of God in the history and progress of the nation. Israel, in its moments of highest good, recognized God was working in and through the nation. Read Psalm 87, and thank God for the way He uses the nation to bring people to Him.

Discipleship

WORKING FOR CHANGE

READ AND RESEARCH (Ephesians 6:10-18.)

We start with two basic premises. First, we recognize that Christ's word to us to be salt and light means that we should project our influence and standards (really, His standards) into our contemporary society. If Christ did not intend to convey that, what did He mean? Second, we acknowledge that demonic influences often stand behind secular governments. Ephesians 6:12 identifies our opponents as something other than flesh and blood. Although our battles may be fought in a secular arena, they have a distinctly spiritual character.

Christians sometimes need to try to bring about change. The issues vary with the years, but today's subjects which should be addressed by the followers of Christ include abortion, sexual immorality, substance abuse, divorce, euthanasia and others.

We should start with the realization that the nation is not the church and the church is not the nation. The nation belongs to the world order; the church belongs to the Kingdom order. However, we cannot abandon the nation to its own devices (or to Satan's), because we live in it, too.

The church itself can do some things as a church. It can offer prayer and fasting for specific situations. It can raise its voice publicly against moral wrongs. Its pulpits can remind the world of God's way and can thunder judgment when necessary. Its institutional lifestyle can reflect proper values.

But individual Christians may make the greatest difference. We begin by rekindling the essential missionary and evangelistic character of the church. God changes the world by changing individuals. We share the good news with the aim of bringing men and women to faith in Christ and into the fellowship of the church.

We can participate in parachurch organizations set up for particular focused purposes, such as opposing abortion or caring for unwanted children. We can participate in the political arena, actively supporting men and women who advocate Christian positions, realizing at the same time that a total alliance of the church with political parties is unwise and may be counterproductive. We can take our viewpoints with us on the job and in the marketplace and not hesitate to make them known. We can do all of this from a posture that although His standards may suffer temporary setbacks, God will ultimately triumph.

REFLECT AND MEDITATE

Christian humanists believe the church is called to act as "salt" and "light," to witness to its hope, and to restrain evil, but secular humanists believe the church stands in the way of freedom. If the church is to be Christ to the world, it has a task. Ministering to the world and caring for the world in the name of Christ implies an active engagement in every area of human life and vocation. The ideal is for the Christian to permeate all of life, sharing in its failures, experiences, and successes (Robert E. Webber, *Secular Humanism: Threat and Challenge*).

REACT AND RESPOND

Imagine that you are in a debate. Your opponent makes this statement: "Our Constitution guarantees us certain rights, and you Christians wish to impose your views on us instead of giving us our rights." How would you answer? Make a few notes to state your position, and share them with someone else studying these discipleship materials. (This is very much like the situation in which Christians often find themselves!)

REJOICE AND WORSHIP

Read Revelation 21:1-5, and praise God for the coming day when He will reign in righteousness and power.

Study 3

CONFRONTING PROBLEMS

READ AND RESEARCH (1 Peter 2:13-17)

The Christian who lives in today's world confronts problems as he attempts to relate to God and the state. What are the problems, and how can they be resolved?

If people are going to live together, they must have a system of laws and controls. The state is man's answer to those needs. (It might be ventured that if man had originally obeyed God's laws and will, no external structure would be necessary; however, we do not live in a world that has made that choice.) ''The authorities that exist are appointed by God'' (Romans 13:1) indicates that the state is ultimately in the hands of God.

States have expressed their purposes in differing formulas. The United States government exists, according to its Constitution, ''in order to form a more perfect Union, establish justice, insure domestic tranquillity, provide for the common defense, promote the general welfare, and secure the blessings of liberty to ourselves and our posterity.''

Problems arise when there is conflict between what Christians conceive to be the will of God and what the state believes to be proper. Often these issues take the form of questions of conscience. A vivid example of this problem is typified in Acts 5, where the duly-constituted authorities reminded Peter, ''We gave you strict orders not to teach in . . . [Jesus'] name'' (v. 28, *NIV*) and Peter answered, ''We ought to obey God rather than men.'' This kind of conflict underlies issues like the propriety of Christians distributing gospel tracts in public places.

A similar problem emerges when the issue of religious freedom is discussed. If Christians in the United States are free to worship and propagate our faith, do Buddhists and Hindus have the same right? If tax monies support denominationally chosen military chaplains, should there also be Islamic chaplains for the Moslem soldiers in the U.S. military? How do Christians respond to this issue?

Moral questions also become problematic. Christians understand that the Bible condemns homosexuality, but certain city and state ordinances are giving it legal protection.

None of these matters are easily dismissed or answered to the satisfaction of all concerned. Despite tensions and conflicts, however, the institutions of the state and church complement one another in our kind of world. If the state provides a setting in which the church can function and if the church furnishes law-abiding citizens who influence the conscience of the state, the two can contribute to each other and both can do well.

REFLECT AND MEDITATE

Men, by nature, are sinful and selfish. Some external authority to restrain the evil is necessary if men are to have a society with fairness and justice for all. This does not mean that constituted authority is the result of sin. It does mean that since men have sinned and come short of the glory of God, some kind of government is necessary.

God is the ultimate source of government among men. The state is a part of God's plan for man. Just as the home was instituted by God and the church was founded by Christ, so ''the authorities that exist are appointed by God'' (Romans 13:1).

REACT AND RESPOND

What, in your estimation, is the most difficult present problem which confronts Christians in their relationship to the state? Would the issue be different in another country? Write down your opinion, and be prepared to discuss it with a friend.

REJOICE AND WORSHIP

Our fathers' God to thee, Author of liberty,
To thee we sing;
Long may our land be bright
With freedom's holy light;
Protect us by Thy might,
Great God, our King.

Discipleship

PRAYING FOR LEADERS

READ AND RESEARCH (1 Timothy 2:1-4)

It is doubtless true: We talk a lot more about governmental authorities than we pray for them.

The Scripture admonishes us, however, to pray for leaders. "Therefore I exhort first of all that supplications, prayers, intercessions, and giving of thanks be made for all men, for kings and all who are in authority," Paul instructed Timothy. He explained why: "That we may lead a quiet and peaceable life."

Christian disciples ought to pray for their national and state leaders, regardless of whether they agree with their politics. Those who use a prayer list to guide their prayer time should include the names of the president and the governor, among others.

In Old Testament times God's people were given directions to pray for the city to which they were taken in captivity, "And seek the peace of the city where I have caused you to be carried away captive, and pray to the Lord for it; for in its peace you will have peace" (Jeremiah 29:7).

Prayer works. It produces results. How pitiful we sometimes sound when we admit our helplessness and confess, "Well, all we can do is pray." Prayer is more important than action, for when we act, we get what we can do; but when we pray, we get what God can do.

It is correct, in a sense, to say that we can touch people through prayer, even political leaders. Our prayers can take us into the Oval Office, into cabinet meetings, Senate deliberations, governor's conferences. We have been commissioned to be royal priests before God, and part of the ministry of the priest is to offer intercession for the people. It is not mindless fanaticism or empty boasting to claim that we can actually reach up to the throne of God in behalf of others.

Pray for leaders. It helps them. It helps the nation. It helps us. Prayer for authorities, according to the will of God, is a blessing.

REFLECT AND MEDITATE

Our nation needs a great spiritual awakening to sweep across our land. Our people have largely forgotten God. Sin, violence and crime are destroying the potential of our civilization. Our literature, our language and our media have been polluted. Our youth are growing up with very little awareness or knowledge of God. For at least a generation or two, many families have been almost godless. While thousands of us call ourselves born-again evangelicals, we are making far too little impact on our educational system, our government and our society. We as a people need to return to God. When will God send new reformation, new spiritual awakening and such a movement of God's Spirit that multitudes turn to God? When? Only when we prepare the way of the Lord.

Given these conditions, how is the church to advance across our world, reaching our generation for God? How are the unreached peoples of the world to hear the gospel when necessary visas for Christian workers and missionaries are so difficult to obtain? How are small groups of believers to be established in hostile environments? There is only one answer to all these questions. There must an adequate team of prayer warriors preparing the way (Wesley L. Duewel, *Touch the World Through Prayer*).

REACT AND RESPOND

Upon completion of this study, make a prayer list for your use in praying for those in authority. Include, as a minimum, the president, the governor and the highest local authority where you live. Write their position titles and their names. Use the list when you pray.

REJOICE AND WORSHIP

Thank the Lord for the freedom to worship Him. Pray that our nation will afford that freedom until He comes.

Study 5

BECOMING A WORLD CHRISTIAN

READ AND RESEARCH (Matthew 28:16-20)

Looking at the first-century situation of Christ and His disciples, sequestered as they were in a small, out-of-the-way, cultural backwater of the Roman Empire, it is absolutely amazing that they envisioned their movement as a world-embracing cause. Within a generation, however, His followers had begun to move out from the boundaries of Judea and Galilee; before a hundred years had passed, followers of Christ were found in every nation under heaven.

From the divine perspective we can say that God's will was being carried out. From the human vantage point, we can explain it by saying that the Christians had become ''world Christians.''

A world Christian is a man or woman who sees the faith in global terms. It is as the Bible proclaims: ''God so loved the world.'' If He loved it and gave Himself for it, we must love it, too.

One of the tests of a true disciple is his commitment to involvement with the Great Commission of Christ. Christian citizenship, the subject that has occupied our attention for the past few lessons, is incomplete if it focuses only upon the state in which we live. The Christian is truly a citizen of the world. His concerns bridge the gaps of culture, class, language, race and geography.

Jesus told His first followers that they should go into the world and make disciples of all peoples. A literal translation of the Matthew account of the Great Commission helps us understand its import. Four principal verbs are contained in the passage. As they were originally recorded in Greek, three of them are participles: *going, baptizing, teaching*. (The word *go* of the King James Version, which sounds like an imperative, is rendered, literally, ''going,'' its sense being ''as you go . . . wherever it is you are going.'') The single imperative is the second verb; the command form says, ''Make disciples.'' That is the primary task of the church. We are sent, not after decisions, but after disciples. Corollary to the disciple-making task is baptizing and teaching, both of which are part of the process. But the imperative--the command or commission--is simply ''Make disciples among all people groups.''

These are the missionary marching orders of the church. The litmus test of any so-called disciple of Christ today is the question ''Are you involved in the discipling of the nations?'' One who fails to answer yes has not yet discovered an important aspect of his faith.

Jesus Christ came into the world to save sinners. Only those who hear about what He has done for them can respond to it. His plan calls for some to go and for others to send them (Romans 10). All of us, someone has said, are either missionaries or a mission field.

Have you become a world Christian?

REFLECT AND MEDITATE

The full commitment of millions of Germans, prior to and during the Great War, was to Adolf Hitler and his cause. Other millions are today committed to Marxism. Christians have no monopoly on commitment; they simply have a different object. A Christian is a person who confesses that amidst the manifold and confusing voices heard in the world, there is one voice which supremely wins his full assent, uniting all his powers, intellectual and emotional, into a single pattern of self-giving. That voice is Jesus Christ . . . he believes in Him with all his heart and strength and mind. Christ appears to the Christian as the one stable point or fulcrum in all the relativities of history. Once the Christian has made this primary commitment, he still has perplexities, but he begins to know the joy of being used for a mighty purpose by which his little life is dignified (Elton Trueblood, *Company of the Committed*).

REACT AND RESPOND

Suppose someone asks you, ''Tell me why the claim is made that Christians should be 'world

Christians.''' What would you answer? Make a list of several reasons why. Be prepared to share your list with a friend.

REJOICE AND WORSHIP

The kingdoms of this world have become the kingdoms of our Lord and of His Christ!

CHAPTER 30

Is There a Personal End?

INTRODUCTION

One of the issues most contemplated is the end of life. Numerous proposals have been offered by a variety of people about death. Some suggest that death is simply the end of consciousness. Others say that the soul continues to exist after physical death to be reincarnated in another body or life form. Still others have resigned themselves to uncertainty, arguing that it is useless to speculate about death and its consequences.

Is it possible to know what takes place at death? Is there any reliable information from which we may draw? Fortunately, as Christians we can look to the Bible for answers to such questions.

In this chapter we will study various aspects of human death. Particularly, why did God allow death to take place initially, and what is death's purpose today? What is the extent of death (do all die)? And what about believers who have already died, where are they now, and what is their state?

While the subject of death is an uncomfortable and painful topic for many to discuss, it is imperative, nonetheless, for Christians to understand the biblical view of death. Such knowledge will enable the believer to discern unfounded speculation which often distorts the truth. It also will bring encouragement and comfort to know that God himself is in control of human history, even death itself.

During the next few lessons we will deal with the following dimensions of the question "Is there a personal end?"

1. Sin's Entrance
2. Sin and Death
3. None Is Righteous
4. Everyone Will Die
5. The Intermediate State

DISCIPLESHIP GOAL

To understand the origin, purpose and nature of death

READING ASSIGNMENT

The Living Book, pp. 370 -380

Discipleship

SIN'S ENTRANCE

READ AND RESEARCH (Genesis 3:1-24)

In the beginning, when God created the world, there was no sin. All things were perfect. Such a state meant that God's communion with human beings was not disturbed (disrupted) by sin.

As part of this perfect creation, God placed Adam in the position of caretaker, for he was to have dominion over the world. He even named all the animals.

Only one restriction was placed on Adam and Eve. They were not to eat the fruit from the tree of good and evil. God warned them that they would die if they disobeyed.

Genesis 3:1-24 describes the way sin entered into the world. This event is commonly referred to as the fall of humanity.

The main characters in this story are the serpent, Eve, Adam and God. One day the serpent, apparently speaking on Satan's behalf, encountered Eve and challenged the validity of God's command concerning the tree. The serpent's challenge took three forms. First, he questioned whether God really did prohibit eating from the tree. Second, the serpent denied the truthfulness of God's warning that death would be the consequence of disobedience. Third, he promised Eve she would be like God if she ate the fruit. In effect, the serpent implied God was a liar and that the human beings could control their own destinies.

The serpent's promise proved to be so powerful that Eve took the fruit and ate it. Adam, following her lead, ate also. Their disobedience resulted in an immediate change in their moral understanding and the loss of their innocence.

Later, when God confronted them, they were in hiding. As He questioned them, they began to accuse and blame others for their disobedience.

The consequence of Adam and Eve's disobedience was a threefold curse. First, for his part in such an evil act, the serpent was doomed to crawl on his belly and to experience hostility with humans.

Second, Eve would experience great pain in childbearing and a change in her relationship with Adam. Third, instead of having a natural dominion over the earth, Adam would have to contend or battle with the ground to derive a livelihood. Eventually, Adam would return to the soil.

Although God provided clothing for Adam and Eve, their disobedience resulted in expulsion from the Garden of Eden.

Not only did they lose their home and innocence, but sin had made its entrance into the world.

REFLECT AND MEDITATE

1. Notice the techniques which the serpent used to challenge God's commands. Does Satan use these same tools in tempting God's people today?

2. How did Adam and Eve respond to God after they had disobeyed? Why did they respond in this fashion?

REACT AND RESPOND

Identify the time when Satan tempted you to sin, using these same techniques. In your study guide, write how you should respond to such temptation in the future.

REJOICE AND WORSHIP

In your prayer time, make a confession of those times when you have believed Satan instead of God. Ask God for strength to follow His commands.

Study 2

SIN AND DEATH

READ AND RESEARCH (Romans 5:12-21)

Sin did not enter the world without severe consequences. Although the relationship between sin and death is mentioned in other passages, Paul gave us one of the most informative discussions on this topic.

After explaining the way in which God brings salvation to those who believe, Paul contrasted the consequences of sin with the blessings of grace.

Clearly, the apostle attributed sin's entrance to Adam. Equally clear is Paul's understanding that Adam's sin brought death to all people.

Paul argued that through Adam all men and women sinned and that all will die. Apparently, the Jews' idea of solidarity was in Paul's mind at this point. That is to say, most Jews held that the actions of one's ancestors could have enormous effect upon an individual. An example of this is evidenced by the way in which Achan and his entire family were put to death for his disobedience to God (Joshua 7:1-26).

Paul stated that just as children inherit certain physical and emotional traits from their parents, so all humanity has inherited sin from the first human. In other words, sin is part of one's life from the very beginning. There is no way to escape this condition.

If all people inherit sin, then everyone reaps the consequence of sin, which is death. This is true because death is sin's wages (Romans 6:23). James wrote that death is the unavoidable result of sin (1:15).

Death follows sin so naturally because sin causes separation from God. Such separation leads to the complete destruction of one's relationship with God. Since God is the God of the living and life itself comes from Him, it is rather obvious that those separated from God should experience death.

The Bible does not describe death as being independent from God. Rather, death is seen as being under God's own control. This view is true even though death can be described as the last enemy.

The biblical view of death is that it originated with sin. In fact, death is the final stage or natural consequence of sin. Death is a sign that demonstrates the presence of sin.

REFLECT AND MEDITATE

1. Compare the biblical explanation for death's origin with views proposed by unbelievers.

2. Describe the way you feel about the way original sin has been transmitted from Adam to us all.

REACT AND RESPOND

The next time the subject of death comes up (whether in conversation with family, friends or others) attempt to bring out the biblical teaching about the origin of death and its connection with sin.

REJOICE AND WORSHIP

"The wages of sin is death, but the gift of God is eternal life" (Romans 6:23).

Discipleship

Study 3

NONE IS RIGHTEOUS

READ AND RESEARCH (Romans 3:9-20)

The effects of Adam's sin have been so powerful that absolutely no one has escaped them. The scope of sin is universal. No one has gone unscathed.

The Bible affirms humanity's sinfulness in a variety of places, but in one powerful passage Paul made the sinfulness of all people very clear.

Romans 3:9-20 is the culmination of Paul's argument that no one can stand before the Lord God as righteous. Both Gentile and Jew come up short when measured against God's own holiness and purity.

In these verses Paul was addressing the Jews, a very religious group of people. His charge was that they were no better than the Gentiles when it came to standing before God. This accusation is true despite the giving of the Law to the Jews.

To prove his point, Paul utilized a collection of biblical passages from the Old Testament. The care with which these passages have been arranged is immediately evident.

Verses 10-12 emphasize the main point that one may search in vain for a righteous person. Apart from God's grace there is no understanding, searching or desire for God and a relationship with Him.

Verses 13 and 14 stress that even the words spoken testify against the speaker. The death, deceit, lying, cursing and bitterness that come forth from fallen human beings is valid witness of the sinful status of humanity. This evidence is particularly important because that which comes out of individuals defiles them.

Verses 15-18 highlight the fact that the acts or deeds of sinful people reveal their unrighteous position. Their actions contradict the characteristics of a life led by the Holy Spirit. Instead of loving, they hate; rather than encouraging, they cause misery; and instead of being peacemakers, they could not even find the way to peace.

Perhaps the most damning judgment is verse 18, which indicates that the fear of the Lord is not part of their vision. They are utterly oblivious to God and His concerns. These verses make clear that no area of human existence is without the marks of sin.

Paul went on to observe that God used the Law to make clear the sinfulness of humanity. Using the Law as a standard of measurement, Paul showed that no one has a claim to righteousness on his own merits.

Since all are sinful, all are in need of righteousness. A recognition of humanity's sinful nature helps us see our need for salvation.

REFLECT AND MEDITATE

1. Does the biblical teaching about the extent of sin help explain the actions of people around you?

2. Explain how one can be religious without being righteous.

REACT AND RESPOND

When you meet with the discipleship group, describe the tendency Christians have to rely on their own good works instead of the righteousness of Christ. Make a covenant with the group to rely on Christ's righteousness every day.

REJOICE AND WORSHIP

Give thanks to God for His marvelous grace.

Study 4

EVERYONE WILL DIE

READ AND RESEARCH (Hebrews 9:16-28)

In the past three studies we have read about the way sin entered the world, the way sin introduced death into human existence and that no one has escaped the curse of sin. In light of these studies the words of Hebrews 9:27 come as no surprise.

While describing the way Christ died, the necessity and the effects of His death, the author of Hebrews compared and contrasted Jesus' death with that of every person. Here, in no uncertain terms, we are told that every person born is destined to die. There are no exceptions. God has ordained that everyone will die. Obviously, each person dies because each is part of this sinful and fallen race. Regardless of social, economic or political status, everyone will die. No one is too great or too lowly--all will taste death.

Notice how closely judgment is aligned with death in Hebrews 9:27. Death is a sign that the human being will be judged by God. This reinforces the point that death itself is within God's jurisdiction.

There is no escaping death or judgment. People may choose to ignore death by not talking about it. Or they may seek to explain it simply as a part of life itself. However, sooner or later every living person will die and stand before the living God.

Death reminds us that we do not control our own destiny. Life is a gracious gift God bestows through His goodness. We can make no claim upon it, for He controls it. In fact, Jesus said the one who seeks to save or cling to life would lose it. It is like having your hands filled with grains of sand. The more tightly you hold it, the quicker it slips through your fingers.

Death also reminds us that we bear responsibility for our own actions. Because life does not continue on endlessly nor repeat itself in cycles, we are faced with the reality that what we do at any moment in time can never be undone. There is a permanence to our actions. Death tells us that we

are going *somewhere*. There will be a day of reckoning.

In facing death the Christian is brought face-to-face with the reality that he still lives in a fallen world. The effects of sin continue to be present. Death has not yet been destroyed.

And yet, there is hope. For the Christian knows that one day even death itself will be no more.

REFLECT AND MEDITATE

1. What three things come to mind when you think about death?

2. Explain why it is necessary that all people should die?

REACT AND RESPOND

In response to this study of Scripture, how should you live your life? What changes need to be made?

REJOICE AND WORSHIP

Encourage a brother or sister with a word of testimony concerning God's lordship over death itself.

Discipleship

THE INTERMEDIATE STATE

READ AND RESEARCH (2 Corinthians 5:1-10; Philippians 1:19-26)

Throughout this chapter we have been examining sin and its consequence. We have observed that all people are destined to die. Before leaving this topic, one more issue must be addressed. What is the state of those believers who die before the Lord's return? Do they sleep or are they already present with the Lord? Both 2 Corinthians 5:1-10 and Philippians 1:19-26 supply information with which we may answer these questions.

In 2 Corinthians 4 Paul described the frailty of the body, likening it to a clay jar. In chapter 5 he continued this thought by encouraging us not to despair when this body is destroyed. The reason for his encouragement is that God has prepared a dwelling in heaven.

Yet Paul indicated there will be a lapse of time between death (the destroying of the earthly tent) and resurrection (being clothed with our heavenly dwelling). This time is unnatural in a sense. Paul described this state as being naked. By this description, Paul wanted to underscore the fact that God has created us whole, which includes having a body. Therefore, to be away from the body can only be temporary.

But such an assessment of the intermediate state is not all that Paul says about this time. Despite the temporary nature of the Christian's existence between death and resurrection, we are still assured that absence from this body means we are present with the Lord. Even such a naked existence is to be preferred to earthly existence, for it will be with Jesus.

A similar idea is expressed in Philippians 1:19-26. In this passage Paul recounted his own struggles concerning life and death. Each alternative is viewed as an opportunity to serve and glorify God. His presence in the flesh meant labor in Christ's vineyard. His absence from the body is described as gain.

Paul struggled with these options because he desired to depart from this life and be with the Lord. His rationale for such a motive is simply that being with the Lord is better than earthly existence. Yet for the sake of the Philippians, Paul was willing to continue in the flesh.

It is clear from these passages that upon death the believer goes into the presence of the Lord. There seems to be no room here for the idea that believers sleep from the time of their death until the resurrection. Immediate and complete communion awaits those who depart from this body.

There is no need to worry about any moment of existence. God has made provisions for the believer in life and in death. Communion with our Lord is always possible.

REFLECT AND MEDITATE

1. Do you ever think about life after death? How have these passages affected your thoughts?

2. What comfort is there for you in knowing that God will never forsake you?

REACT AND RESPOND

Perhaps you know someone who is facing death and/or is concerned about it. Use the next opportunity the Lord gives you to bring words of comfort and consolation about the Lord's loving care.

REJOICE AND WORSHIP

In your discipleship group meeting, testify of the strength and courage there is in knowing of God's faithfulness, even in death.

DISCIPLESHIP COMMITMENT

I commit to live a life of discipleship in which death confronts me with my responsibility in life but does not paralyze me with fear. For God has made provision for me in life and in death.

CHAPTER 31

The Resurrection

INTRODUCTION

In last week's studies we saw how sin and death are related. Among other things, we noted that all human beings are considered to be sinful and as a result will die. Such a study could be discouraging due to the desperate condition of humanity. However, that is not the whole story.

Fortunately, God has intervened on our behalf. He raised Jesus from the dead and has promised us a similar destiny.

In this section we will study the Old Testament prophecies concerning the resurrection, Jesus' resurrection, the promise of our own resurrection and the manner of existence in the resurrection.

This subject is the most important in all of salvation, for without Jesus' resurrection there would be no salvation. Without a knowledge of the resurrection, our Christian faith is defective. We might even say that faith in Jesus is faith in the resurrection.

Due to the threats of sin and death, it is essential for the believer to be rooted and grounded in the knowledge of the resurrection. With this firm foundation as our assurance, life is not so threatening and the believer is confident of God's providential care.

When we believe in Jesus' resurrection and are sure of our own future share in it, we can face the uncertainties of life with more security. For we know that our future is in the hands of God himself.

During the next few lessons we will deal with the following aspects of the Resurrection:

1. Old Testament Teaching
2. Jesus' Resurrection
3. Jesus' Resurrection (cont.)
4. The Believers' Resurrection
5. The Resurrection Existence

DISCIPLESHIP GOAL

To understand the biblical teaching about the nature and purpose of the resurrection

READING ASSIGNMENT
The Living Book, pp. 381 -395

Discipleship

THE OLD TESTAMENT TEACHING

READ AND RESEARCH (Isaiah 26:1-21; Daniel 12:1-4)

A number of biblical teachings emerge rather gradually in the pages of Scripture. It seems that God has chosen to allow His revelation to unfold over a long period of time. Therefore, human beings have not always understood fully a given teaching because they were born at a particular point in history. But as God's plan of salvation continued to unfold, godly men and women were able to understand more fully different aspects of salvation.

Generally, God would reveal small portions of information from time to time as His people were able to handle such knowledge properly. Therefore, not all believers have had access to equal portions of salvation history.

Such is precisely the case with the teaching about the resurrection of the dead. In fact, the Old Testament describes thousands of years of history before there is a mention of this teaching. Although the evidence is rather slim, there are a couple of places where the Old Testament discusses the resurrection. We will begin our study there because it is important to see the process God used to reveal His truth.

The first discussion of the resurrection is found in Isaiah 26:1-21. In this prophetic song, Isaiah extolled the marvelous abilities of God. He provided peace and security for Judah. While others might rejoice at the apparent victories of other gods, Isaiah rejoiced in the fact that Judah's enemies all lay in the grave. God had destroyed them and taken their very life.

Isaiah saw the people of God as a remnant who struggled to bring salvation. In fact, many had died in the attempt to serve God. But Isaiah made it clear in verse 19 that even death is no obstacle for the God of Israel. For those who lie in the dust will rise again. Their bodies will rise; the dead will live. In other words, God will vindicate His name even by reclaiming those faithful ones who have died before the day of victory.

What Isaiah began to reveal, Daniel made even clearer (12:1-4). At the end of his book, Daniel gave attention to the battles that will take place at the end of time. During this period a great distress will come upon the earth. The distress will be worse than anything that has preceded it.

At this time, deliverance will come. All the righteous (those whose name are written in the book) will wake up. Just as Isaiah said, those in the dust will rise. This sleep will be interrupted, and the righteous will inherit eternal life. Clearly, the believer will never taste death again.

It is important to notice what additional information Daniel included. Unlike Isaiah, Daniel recorded the fate of those who do not believe. Some people will be called to shame and everlasting contempt. This means there will be a general calling forth of all people from death.

Although the Old Testament does not contain an exhaustive description of the resurrection, both Isaiah and Daniel introducethe essential elements of what the New Testament makes clear. There will be a day when God calls forth His saints to eternal life. God will surely vindicate His name.

REFLECT AND MEDITATE

1. Pay attention to the fact that both passages which speak about the resurrection do so in the context of God's vindicating His name. How do you think God's name is glorified by a resurrection of the dead?

2. Notice how God's care extends even to those who have died. What emotions does such wonderful concern call forth from you?

REACT AND RESPOND

Describe in your study guide how you feel about the promise that not even death is an obstacle for God in accomplishing His purpose.

REJOICE AND WORSHIP

Offer a song to the Lord for His marvelous provision and care.

Study 2

JESUS' RESURRECTION

READ AND RESEARCH (1 Corinthians 15:1-11)

The central claim of Christianity is that Jesus, who was crucified, rose from the dead. In fact, it is fair to say that if the resurrection of Jesus had not taken place, there would be no basis for the Christian faith. Therefore, it is important to establish the facts of the Resurrection.

The earliest information on this topic is recited in 1 Corinthians 15:1-11. In this passage, Paul made clear the resurrection of Jesus is the most important part of his message. He equated the gospel with the preaching about Jesus' resurrection.

Verses 3-7 contain materials which were passed on to Paul from those who were believers before him. We know this from the way he used the words "received" and "passed on" (*NIV*). These were technical terms the rabbis used to describe the transmission of material which they deemed to be important, even sacred. Paul's use of these terms in verse 3 draws our attention to the fact that the Resurrection was a well-documented event in the early church. It may even be that verses 3-7 were recited in early Christian worship services.

It is important to pay close attention to the contents of this passage. Verses 3 and 4 lay out the fact that Jesus actually died (for our sins) and was buried. These words counter any suggestion that Jesus was not really dead. The reality of His death, Paul said, is beyond dispute. But despite His death and burial, God raised Him from the grave. Notice that both the death and resurrection of Jesus occurred in accordance with the Scriptures. In other words, these events did not just happen, they were part of the eternal plan of God.

Special attention should also be given to the list of those mentioned as witnesses to the Resurrection. Surprisingly, Paul began with Peter. The reason for this may be to demonstrate that despite Peter's threefold denial of our Lord, Jesus made one of His first Resurrection appearances to him. It is interesting that Paul next mentioned the Twelve. This reference to the apostles as the Twelve is made in spite of the fact that there were then only 11 apostles (Judas was dead).

Not only did Jesus appear to His circle of apostles, He appeared to more than 500 brothers at one time. There were so many of these witnesses that a number of them were still alive. With this notation, Paul seems to have been saying, "If you need proof of the Resurrection, call these witnesses. There are plenty of them."

Paul also made special mention of James, the brother of the Lord. According to John 7:5, Jesus' brothers did not believe in Him before the Resurrection. This appearance seems to have been convincing proof to James about Jesus' identity. Later, James became the leader of the church in Jerusalem (Acts 15).

Finally, the Lord appeared to Paul. This appearance took place after the ascension of Jesus to heaven. It also seems to have had a visionary quality to it. But despite these differences from the other Resurrection appearances, Paul claimed the same experience as the other apostles and distinguishes it from other visionary experiences.

The point for Paul was very clear. The evidence for the resurrection of Jesus is beyond dispute. Jesus really did rise from the dead!

REFLECT AND MEDITATE

1. What two things in 1 Corinthians 15:1-11 make the most significant impression on you?

2. How important was Jesus' resurrection to Paul?

REACT AND RESPOND

In light of the impressive list of witnesses to Jesus' resurrection, prayerfully consider how you might utilize this truth in witnessing to others.

REJOICE AND WORSHIP

As a part of your family devotions, discuss this passage and render thanks to God for such firm testimony to this most important event.

Discipleship

JESUS' RESURRECTION (CONT.)

READ AND RESEARCH (Matthew 28:1-11; Luke 24:1-12)

In addition to Paul's discussion of the Resurrection, each of the Gospels also discusses the resurrection of Jesus. Two of those accounts form the basis of our study in this session.

Matthew 28:1-11 and Luke 24:1-12 preserve a number of important points. It is very interesting that in neither account is the Resurrection itself described. Nor is there any attention devoted to a description of Jesus' physical appearance. We are told that early on the first day of the week (Sunday), several women went to the tomb to anoint the body of Jesus. When Jesus was taken down from the cross to be buried, there has been little time for anointing.

Before they arrived, the Lord had sent an earthquake with an angel to remove the stone. The brilliant appearance of the angel frightened the guards to the point that they seem to have gone into shock.

The stone had not been removed so that Jesus could get out of the tomb (He was able to pass through barriers according to John 20:19) but for others to enter into the tomb. Much to the women's surprise, the body of Jesus was not there.

One of the angels spoke the Resurrection message to the women. Their living Messiah was not to be found among the dead. In fact, these women were reminded of Jesus' words concerning this very event.

After receiving the promise of further Resurrection appearances and instructions to inform the disciples and others, the women hurried off. On their way they met Jesus, who comforted them by demonstrating that He was alive. There were many other Resurrection appearances of Jesus, many of which Paul recorded.

There are several issues in these two passages which deserve special comment. First, it is important to observe that emphasis is placed on the empty tomb. Both the women and, later, the disciples entered into the tomb and saw for themselves that the body of Jesus was not there. This situation meant that either the body had been stolen or that Jesus was alive. Since there was no corpse, the resurrection of Jesus must be understood to mean that it was a bodily resurrection. In other words, His resurrection was not a matter of spirit only but also of the body. There is little room for the idea of only a spiritual resurrection.

Second, it is extraordinarily significant that Jesus appeared to the women first, for the testimony of women was not admissible in a Jewish court of law.

Third, it is clear that the Resurrection demonstrates the victory Jesus won over death. His resurrection vindicated His claims to be the Son of God, to have authority to forgive sins and to be Lord of the Sabbath. It proved that He was who He claimed to be. Through this very act Jesus conquered sin, death, hell and the grave.

Finally, take special note of the fact that in these Resurrection appearances, Jesus (and the angels) instructed the disciples to proclaim this message.

REFLECT AND MEDITATE

1. Why do you suppose Jesus appeared first to women after His resurrection?

2. How important is the Resurrection to the Christian faith? Why is this true?

REACT AND RESPOND

Since Jesus instructed the women to tell His disciples about the Resurrection, perhaps it would be in order for us to tell those who may have failed the Lord in some way that Jesus still cares. Together with another believer, prayerfully seek out one who is in need of reconciliation and take this message to them.

REJOICE AND WORSHIP

In a time of consecration with the discipleship group, rededicate yourself to the task of taking the Resurrection message to others.

Study 4

THE BELIEVERS' RESURRECTION

READ AND RESEARCH (1 Corinthians 15:12-34; 1 Thessalonians 4:13-18)

In previous sessions we have studied about sin and its effects. We learned that according to Scripture all people will eventually die, due to sin. It is the resurrection of Jesus that looses the bonds of sin and death. However, the raising of Jesus from the dead is not an isolated event but is closely connected with our own deliverance from sin and death. To be very specific, the New Testament states that all believers will be raised from the dead because of Jesus' own death and resurrection. We will examine two passages that discuss this issue.

The passage in 1 Corinthians 15:12-34 is one of the most important discussions about the relationship between the resurrection of Jesus and the believers' future resurrection. There were those in the church at Corinth who denied the resurrection of the dead. Paul emphatically opposed such false teaching by arguing that either the dead will rise or Christ did not rise from the grave.

In other words, for Paul, all of salvation depends upon Jesus' resurrection and our own resurrection. Paul did not simply desire a release from the body at death, He longed for the redemption of the body.

Paul used an analogy from the world of agriculture. He likened Jesus to the firstfruits of the harvest. Farmers know that when they see these first crops, the whole harvest cannot be far behind. Therefore, since Jesus has been raised from the dead, it is absolutely certain that believers who have died will be raised also. The resurrection signifies the completion of our salvation. For after this event, Jesus will deliver the Kingdom to God our Father.

In 1 Thessalonians 4:13-18 we find some other details about this event. Apparently, the believers at Thessalonica were discouraged by the fact that some of their brothers and sisters had died. Did this mean they would not participate in the resurrection or that they would be at some disadvantage because of their state?

Paul responded to their anxious thoughts with words of encouragement and instruction. Not only did the apostle affirm belief in the Lord's own resurrection, but he emphasized that Jesus will return for His own. Those who sleep (have died) will be at no disadvantage at His return, for they will rise first from the grave. Then those Christians who are alive will be transformed and called to meet the Lord in the air.

Jesus' return will be accompanied by the Lord's own call, the archangel's voice and the blast of the trumpet. All these actions will signal the Christian to readiness. The promise of the Lord's return and our subsequent uninterrupted life with Him is a message with which believer's should comfort one another.

REFLECT AND MEDITATE

1. Describe the connection between Jesus' resurrection and our own resurrection.

2. In 1 Thessalonians 4, what distinguishes the believer's view about death from the view of others?

3. What will announce the resurrection of the dead?

REACT AND RESPOND

Pinpoint one or more ways by which you can encourage another believer with the message about the resurrection.

REJOICE AND WORSHIP

Those of us who have the assurance of our Lord's return and our own resurrection can live unencumbered by the fear of death. From time to time each day, thank the Lord for such a liberating revelation.

Discipleship

THE RESURRECTION EXISTENCE

READ AND RESEARCH (1 Corinthians 15:35-58; 1 John 3:2)

Quite naturally, there is a great deal of interest in the manner of existence the Christian will have after the resurrection. In this area, speculation can often run wild. While a complete understanding of the resurrection existence is not within our grasp, Scripture does furnish us with some information.

Perhaps the best place to begin is with the cautious and yet very promising words found in 1 John 3:2. John openly acknowledged that he did not know what we shall be when Jesus returns. His reserve is remarkable considering his close association with the resurrected Lord. But despite this reserve, John said that we shall be like Him. This statement means that although the details of the resurrection existence are not given to us, we can rest assured in the knowledge that Jesus' resurrection existence is the model for what our own will be.

In 1 Corinthians 15:35-58, Paul discussed this issue in greater depth. What kind of body will the resurrected ones possess? Paul made clear that there is continuity between our present earthly bodies and our future heavenly bodies. For on the one hand, these present bodies are the very ones which the Lord will transform. On the other hand, these present bodies are in need of transformation.

Paul did not suggest for one minute that the present body is unimportant. Nor was he thinking in terms of a ''spiritual'' resurrection unrelated to our present body. No, these bodies will be changed.

The need for transformation exists because the resurrection body is designed for heavenly existence. These bodies of sin and death are perishable, dishonorable and weak and must be changed in order to accommodate the new manner of existence prepared for us.

The resurrected body will be imperishable, glorious and powerful. It will resemble that of the Man from heaven (verse 49), just as John said.

Therefore, these bodies of sin and death will be transformed into bodies designed for the purpose of giving ultimate praise to the Lord.

This mysterious occurrence will take place when the Lord returns for His people. At that moment, death loses its sting for the Christian forever, for the resurrection body will never die.

REFLECT AND MEDITATE

1. What emotions are aroused when you think about the fact that your body will be like that of Jesus' resurrected body?

2. Describe the ways in which our resurrected bodies will differ from our present bodies. 3. Why does death lose its sting for the Christian, and when does this occur?

REACT AND RESPOND

Call one of your discipleship partners, and share the feelings which this lesson stirs up within you.

REJOICE AND WORSHIP

'''Where, O death, is your victory? Where, O death, is your sting?''' (1 Corinthians 15:55, *NIV*).

DISCIPLESHIP COMMITMENT

I commit to live a life of discipleship which exhibits my belief that Jesus will transform my body into a spiritual body. This commitment means that I will not fear death nor consider this world my final home. Jesus has defeated death so that I might live eternally.

CHAPTER 32

The Second Coming

INTRODUCTION

Without question, one of the most fascinating topics of discussions within Christian circles is the return of Jesus. Will He really return to earth? When will His return take place? These questions have been raised by a variety of Christians since Jesus ascended into heaven.

There are always those who claim to be *the* authority concerning end-time prophecy. There are even those who claim to know the exact time of Christ's return. With so much genuine interest in the topic, there is an enormous amount of material available on this subject. Unfortunately, much of this information is worth very little, for often the biblical material is made to fit contemporary events rather than allowing the Scripture to be heard on its own terms.

In this section of our study, we will examine several important dimensions of Jesus' return. This investigation begins with the confession that much in Scripture is too lofty for us to comprehend fully and that humility is a necessity when approaching this topic. Of one thing we can be sure: whoever claims to have all the answers concerning biblical prophecy is almost certainly wrong.

One of the best ways to be kept from false teaching and outrageous ideas concerning the end time is to have a firm grounding in biblical knowl-edge. This foundation can only be laid through careful study and prayerful reflection.

While there is much that remains unclear concerning biblical prophecy, a number of issues can be addressed with some degree of certainty. Each part of this lesson centers on an important aspect of our Lord's return.

It is important to remember that the return of Jesus marks one of the most significant events in history. Jesus will return for His own, do battle with the powers of evil and deliver individuals to their final home. The Christian can rejoice in the confident knowledge that Jesus will return for His people and bring final salvation.

During the next five lessons we will study the following aspects of the Second Coming:

1. Promises and Signs of the Second Coming
2. The Great Tribulation
3. The Millennial Reign
4. The Final Judgment
5. Life in Heaven

DISCIPLESHIP GOAL

To understand the biblical teaching about the nature and purpose of the return of Jesus

READING ASSIGNMENT
The Living Book, pp. 399 - 406

Study 1

PROMISES AND SIGNS OF THE SECOND COMING

READ AND RESEARCH (Luke 17:20-37; 2 Thessalonians 2:1-12)

A number of New Testament passages make clear that Jesus promised the disciples He would return one day for them. In most cases these sayings are in the context of Jesus responding to questions raised by the disciples or His opponents.

One reason Jesus spent so much time on this teaching is that first-century Judaism had a variety of views about the end of time. Jesus seems to have taken great pains to warn His disciples about false teaching and to direct them to His own words.

Luke 17:20-37 records the words of Jesus on one occasion when He was asked when the kingdom of God would come. Jesus' response included a statement about the presence of the Kingdom within, but He made unmistakable the fact that the Kingdom would also come in a spectacular way in the future.

First, Jesus warned the disciples not to be confused or swayed by those who claim to have seen the returned Lord. The Lord's coming will be sudden.

Second, Jesus noted that people will be caught up in the daily routine of life. Just as Noah and Lot were ignored by their neighbors, so there will be those who pay no attention to the Son of Man.

Third, there is a note of certainty in Jesus' words that He will come for those who are looking for Him and attending to His affairs. Such will be "taken" at His return. Just being close to a believer is not good enough. Each must be ready.

When Paul wrote 2 Thessalonians, the church was torn with worries about the Lord's return. Some had report His secret return.

Paul consoled the Christians at Thessalonica, charging them not to be deceived by anyone about the Lord's return. He pointed to one sign which must be manifest before the Lord returns--the man of lawlessness, or the lawless one, must be revealed. This individual, called the Antichrist in other parts of the New Testament, will oppose God and seek to put himself in God's place.

The Thessalonians were not to be disturbed by claims that Jesus had returned, for the man of lawlessness had not yet been revealed. In verse 6 Paul said something restrains him ("you know what is restraining"), and in verse 7 he noted that a person ("He who") restrains this man. Obviously, the Thessalonians knew what Paul meant. We do not have access to the same information. For that reason, many guesses have been made about the restraining agent's identity. These suggestions range from the church to the Holy Spirit to the Roman Empire. Perhaps God's law and order ("what") and divinely appointed governmental leaders ("He who") are those that restrain this evil one. If that is the case, when law and order are removed, it is natural that the man of lawlessness will be revealed.

At any rate, the Christian is instructed by Paul that the man of lawlessness must be revealed before the Lord returns. This lawless one will perform miracles, signs and wonders and will deceive many. But the believer has been warned about what is to come.

REFLECT AND MEDITATE

1. In light of these passages, how should Christians respond to claims that Jesus will return at a specific time or that He has already returned?

2. How entrenched are we in everyday life? Is it possible for us to miss the coming of the Son of Man?

REACT AND RESPOND

What steps can you take to avoid being so caught up in daily life that you might miss the coming of the Son of Man? Write your thoughts down in your manual.

REJOICE AND WORSHIP

As an act of worship, greet a brother or sister with the words "The Lord is coming!"

Study 2

THE GREAT TRIBULATION

READ AND RESEARCH (Matthew 24:15-31; Revelation 16:1-21)

Before the Second Coming, the Scriptures tell us, there will be a time of unparalleled tribulation.

The two passages you read for today's study deal with this time. From these chapters we get a glimpse of the severity of the suffering and the cosmic events which will transpire.

In Matthew 24 Jesus warned the disciples about the fall of Jerusalem and foretold His own return. It is not always easy to discern when He was speaking of which event. There appears to be some intentional overlap. In any case, Jesus informed the disciples that a period of great tribulation would precede His return. After this time the Lord will send His angels with a trumpet to gather together His "elect."

Revelation 16 gives a graphic description of the judgments of God that are to fall upon the earth during the great and final tribulation. The first three bowls of wrath will poured out on the earth (people), the seas and other sources of water. The second three bowls will affect the sun, the throne of the beast and the Euphrates River.

Despite all the judgments, unrepentant humanity will still refuse to confess their sinfulness. Just as Pharaoh encountered God but would not believe, so these individuals will not believe in the Lord.

The seventh, and final, bowl of wrath will bring utter destruction. Cosmic signs and destruction are its result. The end of the world will have come. The return of Jesus will be then!

Christians have differing interpretations of where the church will be during the Tribulation. There are three primary views.

Many Christians believe that sometime before the Tribulation begins, the Lord will return for His church. Although He will not come to the earth, His appearing will be in midair to summon all believers unto Himself. Those who hold this view believe that God would never require the church to endure His wrath. Therefore, it is necessary for Jesus to rapture the church. Those who maintain this view that the Lord will return before the Tribulation believe that this period of time will span seven years.

A second view is that Christ will return for the church in the middle of the Tribulation, that is, after three and a half years. Advocates of this position point out that the Antichrist must be revealed before the church is caught up (2 Thessalonians 2:1-12). They believe, however, that before the intense suffering begins, the Lord will return secretly for His church.

Another Christian perspective is that the Lord will return after the Tribulation. Those with this view believe that the church will suffer persecution from the hand of the Antichrist, but will be spared from God's wrath as the Israelites were spared from the plagues God sent to Egypt.

Each of these views are held by godly men and women who seek to interpret Scripture accurately. To differ in opinion about this issue should not disrupt fellowship between believers. All are looking for the Lord's return.

In any event, the Great Tribulation will be a time when God pours out His wrath on all the earth. Biblical prophecies concerning the Tribulation underscore the fact that punishment is coming. God will judge the world.

REFLECT AND MEDITATE

1. Describe the effects of the Great Tribulation upon the earth.

2. Reflect on the nature of this period. What makes it worse than any other time?

REACT AND RESPOND

Considering that this terrible day is approaching, how can you prepare your heart for the Lord's return?

REJOICE AND WORSHIP

Sing unto the Lord a song of praise that describes the promise of His return.

Discipleship

THE MILLENNIAL REIGN

READ AND RESEARCH (Revelation 20:1-6)

A number of important events will take place after the return of Jesus, some of which affect Jesus' enemies and others which affect the believers.

Just after Christ's return and victorious battle with the Beast and the armies of the world (Revelation 19:11-21), an angel will come down out of heaven, having a key to the "bottomless pit." This unnamed angel will seize Satan and bind him for a thousand years. Various names for Satan are used in this passage, which emphasizes the breadth of his evil work.

It is noteworthy that after causing all the trouble that he has, Satan will not be arrested by God the Father, Jesus or even an archangel. An unnamed angel is sufficient for the task of binding Satan.

After being thrown into the bottomless pit, completely outside the realm of humanity, Satan will be securely locked up. Not only will he be locked up, but a seal will be placed on the door to ensure his confinement. If Satan should escape, the seal would be broken. This device would alert those given charge over him. The length of his sentence is a thousand years.

In verses 4-6 we learn that those who are redeemed by Christ, including those who are killed for the sake of the gospel, will be given authority to judge and will reign on earth for a thousand years. All of those who have been resurrected will reign with Christ. This thousand-year reign is called the Millennium.

Christians have often disagreed over the precise nature of the Millennium. Some have taken the thousand-year period to be symbolic of the availability of God's power which began in the ministry of Jesus and will continue till the return of Christ. This interpretation is called the amillennial view.

Others believe that the thousand years will precede the return of Christ. This view (postmillennialism) holds that the church will establish the Millennium here on earth before the return of Christ.

The Church of God, along with many evangelical Christians, believes that Jesus will come back before the Millennium. This view appears to fit these passages in Revelation better than the other two interpretations. This view is called premillennialism.

But exactly what is the purpose of the Millennium? From the Old Testament we know that God desires to establish His kingdom on the earth in a literal way. The Millennium is the time when God will allow His people to enjoy life on this earth as it was intended to be. As the people of God, we will rule, reign and judge with Christ for this thousand-year period.

This existence will be similar to the way of life in the Garden of Eden. As things were in the beginning, so shall they be at the end.

During this time the devil will not be present to tempt the nations. This period will be a time of peace and harmony. God will rule His people, and He will be our God.

REFLECT AND MEDITATE

1. What can we conclude about Satan's power, in light of the fact that a single angel is able to bind him and cast him into the bottomless pit?

2. Some who reign in the Millennium will be there because of their faithfulness to Christ to the point of death. What reactions does that willingness to suffer for the sake of Christ call forth from you?

REACT AND RESPOND

After reflecting on this passage, how would you describe your own devotion to the Lord? What hardships are you willing to endure? Discuss your thoughts with a family member.

REJOICE AND WORSHIP

With gratitude for God's wondrous provisions, ask the Lord to strengthen your faith and devotion to Him. After asking Him for strength, wait before the Lord.

Study 4

THE FINAL JUDGMENT

READ AND RESEARCH (John 5:16-30; Revelation 20:11-15)

The Bible makes clear that God is holy. He loves righteousness and hates evil. Many passages describe God as sending judgment upon the world and on particular human beings. Yet, God's work as judge is not confined to individual situations. One day He will judge all people.

The two passages we have read for today's study tell us about this event. John 5:16-30 emphasizes the unity of the Father and the Son. Jesus does those things which the Father does because the Father reveals them to the Son. Part of Jesus' authority is to arouse the dead from their sleep. It is His voice that will quicken them to life. But this awakening will not be restricted to believers. Jesus said that even those who have been evil will be raised to judgment.

Revelation 20:11-15 picks up where John 5:16-30 stops and describes what takes place at the Great White Throne Judgment. The event is awesome, for on that day His holiness and glory will cause everything else to draw back. No one will be able to utter an excuse or offer an argument in His holy presence.

All humanity, regardless of social, economic, educational or political status, will be summoned to the judgment.

No corner of the world can hold back their dead. Even the sea and hell must offer them up. Everyone will be judged. Among the books used in this judgment is the Book of Life. In this book are written all the names of the saints. Many other biblical passages discuss the Book of Life. The other books used contain a record of what each person has done. Many ancient kings had books in which they wrote their subjects' names and their actions.

The basic criterion for judgment is the Book of Life. If one's name is there, eternal fellowship with God will be the reward. Therefore, regardless of what the other books contain, if one's name is in the Book of Life, eternal salvation is assured.

However, if one does not belong to the Lamb of God, his/her name will not be recorded. Those individuals are to be thrown into the lake of fire, a place of eternal torment prepared for Satan and his followers.

These passages are graphic reminders that a day of reckoning is on the way. While it may appear that the wicked prosper and the righteous suffer, God promises that one day all wrongs will be made right. No one will escape this divine judgment.

Yet the Christian does not need to fear this or any other judgment, because of the Lord Jesus. He has forgiven our sins, He makes intercession on our behalf, and He acknowledges us to the Father. Although it is true that all human beings are sinners, Jesus has offered a wonderful escape.

All history is moving toward this day when some will be cast into the lake of fire, while others will hear our God say, ''Well done.''

REFLECT AND MEDITATE

1. What is the first thing you think of when reading about the Great White Throne Judgment?

2. According to the passage in Revelation 20:12-15, identify the ways by which God ensures the completeness of this judgment.

REACT AND RESPOND

Make a list of things you need to attend to in your life in order to be prepared for the Judgment.

REJOICE AND WORSHIP

In a time of prayer, ask the Lord to prepare you for this final judgment.

Discipleship

LIFE IN HEAVEN

READ AND RESEARCH (Revelation 21:1-22:5)

In the last several studies we have considered issues concerning the end of life and the end of time. All these topics have been moving toward today's study.

Every Christian looks forward to the day when fellowship with the Lord will be complete and unending. This state is the one for which we were created and redeemed.

Revelation 21:1--22:5 describes our future life with God. John described this life as he saw it in his vision in the context of the new heaven and new earth. Eternal life is designed to be lived out in the New Jerusalem, which will come down to earth from heaven. No existing city is equipped to function as this new city will, for this city is designed as the dwelling place of God himself.

The New Jerusalem, unlike any other city, will be a place of peace, joy and love. Only those whose names are written in the Book of Life can enter. All others will be excluded. Verse 8 lists those who cannot enter but will be assigned a place in eternal torment, the lake of fire. Such a fate is what has earlier been called the second death (20:6).

The believer will dwell in a place the construction of which baffles the mind. Precious stones, streets of gold, gates of pearl are part of this majestic scene. The names of the 12 tribes of Israel on the gates and the names of the 12 apostles of Jesus on the foundations demonstrate the unity of God's redemptive history. All God's people from every age will be present.

The city is a picture of perfection itself. Its dimensions are that of a cube, equal on all sides, just as was the holy of holies in the ancient temple (1 Kings 6:20).

Most importantly, the Lord God and the Lamb are there. Their presence makes other needs obsolete. No temple is needed for communion with God; no light is needed by which to see. The Lord is all-sufficient. His presence fills the city. The Lamb is the light.

All the provisions needed for salvation and life are there: a river of life flowing from God's throne and the tree of life, with leaves that provide healing. All these things ensure salvation. In that perfect world, the curse of sin will be no more. All the effects of sin will be reversed in that new city.

Finally, believers will fulfill the longing of their hearts, for they will look into the face of God. His name will be upon their foreheads, indicating that they are His possessions.

Here they will reign forever and ever. Salvation will be complete.

REFLECT AND MEDITATE

1. Compare this heavenly city with an earthly city. What are the differences?

2. When you read that all suffering, mourning and pain will be removed, what do you think of first in your own life that will be resolved?

REACT AND RESPOND

Knowing of the joy and reward that lies ahead, can you handle present suffering and disappointment better? What specific steps can you take?

REJOICE AND WORSHIP

''And I heard a loud voice from the throne saying, 'Now the dwelling of God is with men, and he will live with them. They will be his people, and God himself will be with them and be their God. He will wipe every tear from their eyes. There will be no more death or mourning or crying or pain, for the old order of things has passed away''' (Revelation 21:3, *NIV*).

Come quickly, Lord Jesus!

DISCIPLESHIP COMMITMENT

In view of God's control of history and the direction in which He is taking it, I commit to live a life of discipleship that exhibits an unreserved trust in God and an understanding of the transitory nature of my earthly existence.

CHAPTER 33

How Should We Live?

INTRODUCTION

For the past several months you and other believers have been studying various aspects of the Christian life. You have encountered new ideas and come to more accurate interpretations of vital biblical teachings. This course has involved reflection upon the biblical text. Additionally, you have been putting into practice much of what was studied and including the results of all this effort in your praise and worship. Last but not least, the entire endeavor has been accomplished within a community setting, where dialogue with brothers and sisters help to confirm and correct each member's role.

The knowledge acquired through study, dialogue and experience should have resulted in a deeper walk with the Lord, richer fellowship within the body, and a stronger direction and sense of calling from the Lord.

One of the most important dimensions of this process is to see how Scripture relates to contemporary life and directs our Christian walk.

Your discipleship manual has been a guide throughout the year and now contains many personal notes and observations. Do not discard this book, but preserve it so that you may consult it in the future. This discipleship training course is not the end but a beginning in your life with the Lord.

In this final week of study, we will seek to answer the question "How shall we live?" This series of studies not only serves as a fitting conclusion to the entire study but is particularly important as it concludes this segment of our study of life in the future and the return of the Lord.

Too often, people who spend a lot of energy studying the end of time become so caught up with what will be that they exhibit little concern about the present. It is as if they cop out of the responsibilities of the here and now.

But such attitudes and actions are clearly in violation of the Scriptures. Instead of advocating laziness, unconcern and sloth, the Bible calls the church and Christians to specific action.

This week we will study five such commands:
1. Watch
2. Purify
3. Occupy
4. Proclaim the Gospel
5. Rejoice

DISCIPLESHIP GOAL

To understand the biblical reasons for godly living in light of the Second Coming

READING ASSIGNMENT

Review *The Living Book.*

Discipleship

WATCH

READ AND RESEARCH (Luke 12:35-48)

If Jesus is going to return to earth one day, what characteristics should His people exhibit? One of the most helpful passages is found in Luke 12:35-48. Here we find several verses devoted to the idea of being ready and watching for the Lord's return.

In verses 35-40 Jesus instructed the disciples to be ready for the return just as a servant who stands by patiently with lamp in hand for service. Jesus uses the analogy of servants waiting for their master's return from a wedding banquet. Although the servants are unsure as to the exact moment of the return, they are certain it will take place.

Most people during the time of Jesus wore long, flowing robes. While such dress was comfortable, it was extremely impractical for running or hard work. Therefore, the individual would tie the loose-fitting clothes together at the waist in order to work more effectively. Jesus admonished the disciples that they should always dress for work.

When the Master arrives and knocks on the door, there will be no time for preparation. Preparation must be made in advance, for the Son of Man will come suddenly and unexpectedly. It could be late in the night, when only the most faithful servants are on watch; or it could be when least expected, as when a burglar breaks into a home.

Watching for the Lord will ensure that the Master will get a proper reception, which will in turn be to the advantage of the servants (verse 37).

In response to Peter's question (v. 41), Jesus turned His attention to leaders within the church, by using an analogy of the servant whom the master places in charge of feeding the other servants. This servant, or steward, has a special responsibility. If he is found to be responsible and reliable by his lord, he will be placed in charge of everything the master possesses.

Unfortunately, not all servants are faithful. The absence of the master will lull some of them into sleep, thinking that the master will not return. This belief results in mistreatment of others and self-indulgence. Such actions are the direct result of not being ready for the master's return. For this servant, and for those like him, the master's return will mean most severe punishment.

All are held accountable. Those who know more, will be punished more severely for their disobedience. The more the lord invests, the more the lord expects.

These verses emphasize the absolute importance of being ready for Jesus' return. They also make clear that His return should motivate the believer to proper action. This is especially true for the Christian leader. When the focus of attention is diverted from the Lord's return to one's own situation, improper action results. When leaders become oppressive in their rule, they will be punished. The Lord makes it painfully clear that the more one is entrusted with, the more accountable such a person becomes. It emphasizes that leaders must be servants and not lords.

Therefore, watch and be ready.

REFLECT AND MEDITATE

1. Describe the kind of watchfulness required in verses 35-40. Evaluate the way in which you are watchful.

2. Using verses 41-48 as a basis, compare and contrast your own actions and treatment of others with the various servants described.

REACT AND RESPOND

After your reflection upon this passage, what kind of servant do you want to be? What specific steps do you need to take to effect the appropriate changes? (Write them down in your manual.)

REJOICE AND WORSHIP

Share with the group any changes in your own watchfulness for the Lord's return and what this means to you.

Study 2

PURIFY

READ AND RESEARCH (1 John 2:28--3:3)

In addition to watchfulness, the believer is called to a life of purity. John wrote his first epistle to combat false teaching which had sprung up in some of the churches. Part of this teaching concerned sin and its practice. Apparently, there were those in the community who claimed sin was not an issue for the believer, that they need not be concerned about it, for it had no effect on them.

However, John made very clear that such an understanding is not accurate. Rather, all are guilty of sin, and only through the work of Jesus, our advocate, are we able to maintain our status before God.

Related to this teaching is the return of the Lord. The passage we read for today, 1 John 2:28--3:3, makes this connection clear. John urged the believer to abide in Jesus continually so as not to be ashamed when the Lord appears. The implication of verse 28 is that when the Lord appears, judgment will soon follow. Those who are not "in the vine" will be cut off. This warning is given to Christians.

The way to avoid such shame is to be like Jesus. Verse 29 tells us that He is righteous, or just. Those who abide in Him, who gain their strength from the Lord, will bear a resemblance to Jesus in their actions. Those born of God will manifest that birth by a life of righteousness. All of this is possible because God has lavished His love upon us.

The other side of resembling Jesus is that the world does not know or recognize the Christian because it did not know or recognize Him. But we can take solace in the knowledge that even in persecution we are like Him.

But the similarity between Lord and disciple does not end there. Even though John did not have knowledge of the resurrection condition or state, he asserted that we shall be like Jesus. In other words, the similarity will extend into the resurrec-tion life itself. All children of God will be like the Son of God.

By implication, John urged Christians to engage in self-examination (v.3). This examination is to be carried out against the backdrop of the return of Jesus. Whoever possesses hope of the return of Christ should purify himself. The standard or basis of purity with which comparison should be made is the Lord himself. When John advocated purity, he was calling for lives free from sin and the bonds of Satan.

It is clear from this passage that John viewed the Second Coming as motivation for purity in life. Because Jesus himself is that standard, the Christian cannot help but be impressed with the seriousness of the command.

When we consider our Lord's return and His own holiness and purity, we do not need anyone to tell us about our sin. It becomes quite obvious. We are also confronted with the essential nature of our task. There are no options. The people of God must be pure. In such times of reflection we are faced with the utter hopelessness of our condition aside from His extraordinary love. But Jesus can cleanse us from all unrighteousness.

If we have the hope of His appearing, let us purify ourselves just as He himself is pure.

REFLECT AND MEDITATE

1. Describe the similarities which should exist between Jesus and His followers.

2. What do you think it means to be ashamed at the appearance of Jesus?

REACT AND RESPOND

Using Jesus' purity as the measuring rod, what areas of your life do you need to purge in order to be prepared for His appearing? What actions do you feel compelled to take on the basis of 1 John 3:3?

REJOICE AND WORSHIP

In your time of prayer, confess your sins to the Lord, and allow the Spirit to transform your life in preparation for His appearance.

Discipleship

OCCUPY

READ AND RESEARCH (2 Thessalonians 3:6-15)

Unfortunately, there are numerous examples of people who have taken the promise of the Lord's return as an encouragement for idleness. This attitude was present very early in the church's existence. It is also clear that such action and thought are clearly condemned in the New Testament churches.

Paul's ministry in Thessalonica was quite profitable, but it seems to have been troubled constantly because of misunderstandings concerning the Lord's return. In earlier studies we discovered believers' concerns as to whether the dead had forfeited their part in the resurrection, as well as claims that the Lord had already returned secretly. In both places (1 Thessalonians 4:13-18 and 2 Thessalonians 2:1-12) Paul responded to such concerns and cleared up the problems.

In 2 Thessalonians 3:6-15 we find still another problem with the Thessalonian view of the Second Coming. This time the difficulty did not involve false teaching so much as it involved faulty reasoning. It appears that several in Thessalonica thought that since the Lord's return was expected soon, there was no need to work or become involved in the affairs of this world. In fact, not only had their reasoning caused them to become idle, they were living off the generosity of other believers.

Paul's advice to the Thessalonians is consistent with his other writings. There is no room in the Christian community for idleness. Such behavior violated the teaching Paul had earlier delivered to them when he ministered there. Not only did that attitude violate Christian teaching, it was also contrary to the example of Paul and his fellow workers. While Paul believed that a minister had the right to financial support (1 Corinthians 9), he was very reluctant to accept this support himself, preferring to earn his own way.

The point is that Paul and his fellow laborers were conscientious about serving as models. The idle Thessalonians were not following their example and were violating the rule "If anyone will not work, neither shall he eat."

Not only had they ceased to work in the Lord's vineyard through their idleness, but they were hurting the cause of the Kingdom. Paul's instruction was to settle down and earn your own bread. Notice that in verse 13 Paul encouraged the believers to continue to do what is right. Most likely, Paul wanted to encourage the Christians to continue to care for the poor, despite the fact that some were attempting to live off the community.

Paul's final words in this section speak of discipline. The believers were to avoid association with those offenders in order to bring them to their senses. The idle ones were regarded as brothers in need of discipline.

This passage contains much that is relevant to us. Sadly, there are Christians who interpret the nearness of the Lord's return as a license to idleness. This conclusion could not be further from the truth. As we have seen in earlier studies, the Lord's return should spur us on to productive lives of service to Jesus.

REFLECT AND MEDITATE

1. How do you suppose the Thessalonians were justifying their idleness to those in the community?

2. What value does this passage place upon the nature of work?

REACT AND RESPOND

In considering this passage and your own life, are there areas in which you have become idle and lax because of the nearness of the Lord's return? (These areas may include ministry as well as vocation.)

REJOICE AND WORSHIP

In a time of fellowship with the discipleship group, confess those areas of negligence and testify of what God is calling you to do.

Study 4

PROCLAIM THE GOSPEL

READ AND RESEARCH (2 Timothy 4:1-8)

In the last study, we saw that Paul encouraged the Thessalonians to keep busy and avoid idleness. Today's study picks up on the idea of working until the Lord's return.

This second epistle to Timothy was one of the last letters that Paul wrote. In it he marked out a number of important issues to which Timothy should give attention. Of particular interest are Paul's words about the conditions which will be present in the last days (3:1-9).

Of equal importance are the words contained in the text for today. In this passage Paul gave Timothy instructions concerning his future activities. Specifically, he gave his younger disciple a charge, or command, to ministry.

Paul began these remarks by reminding Timothy of the Second Coming and the judgment of God that awaits all humanity. Through Paul's opening words we understand that Timothy's charge to ministry was to be motivated by the soon return of the Lord.

The primary task with which Timothy was to be concerned was the proclamation of the gospel. In view of the sinfulness of the world, primacy must be given to preaching. For without the proclamation of the gospel, salvation will not come to sinners. Timothy was charged to stand ready to minister at any and all times.

But Paul identified other reasons for such a readiness to preach. In addition to evangelism, the proclamation of the gospel serves to correct, rebuke and encourage the Body. These dimensions of preaching are terribly important and must be carried out with sensitivity and care. Such preaching must preserve the church from the difficult times that lie ahead.

The time will come, Paul said, when sound doctrine will not get a hearing. Those who give careful attention to sound doctrine do so because they desire to learn how they should live and what they should believe from the Scripture. But a time will come when people will not desire to be informed by the Bible but will be interested in supporting and justifying their own lusts and desires.

Such people will acquire teachers to do no more than entertain them. Their ears will be tickled. Their intentions are to prop up their own desires and lifestyles. Such self-centered and trivial pursuits will be manifested in their inability to discern between truth and myth. These people have cut themselves off from the truth for so long they wind up completely helpless.

Even so, Timothy was charged to keep his wits about him always, endure hardship, evangelize and perform all the tasks of ministry.

Paul encouraged Timothy that all those who long for the Lord's return and serve Him faithfully will be rewarded for their devotion with a crown worthy of the righteous.

These clear words remind us all of the importance of proclaiming God's Word because His return is so near and certain.

REFLECT AND MEDITATE

1. Describe the close connection between Paul's instructions and the certainty of the Lord's return.

2. Identify the parallels between verses 3 and 4 and our own time.

REACT AND RESPOND

Prayerfully prepare yourself to share the gospel message the next time the Lord opens the door. Make a commitment to the group that you will be ready "in season and out of season."

REJOICE AND WORSHIP

"How, then, can they call on the one they have not believed in? And how can they believe in the one of whom they have not heard? And how can they hear without someone preaching to them? And how can they preach unless they are sent? As it is written, 'How beautiful are the feet of those who bring good news!'" (Romans 10:14-15, NIV).

Discipleship

REJOICE

READ AND RESEARCH (Philippians 4:4-9)

Over the past few months, we have been exploring various dimensions of the Christian life of discipleship. This session completes the weekly studies. This week's studies have not only brought our study of life in the future to a close, they have also served as the finale of the entire program.

It is fitting that the exhortations to watch, purify, occupy and proclaim are examined during the last week, for all these commands ought to be constantly before the Christian. Armed with the knowledge of the previous weeks of study, these lessons focus in a practical way upon the character of daily life.

This final study is also devoted to Paul's instructions. Again, we find his words are delivered in view of the soon return of the Lord. In a word, his final command is to rejoice.

Philippians is perhaps the most personal of all Paul's letters. The epistle contains some biographical information about the apostle that is included in no other source. It also exhibits that Paul and the Philippian believers were very close. Both he and they had endured many hardships but, in spite of their difficulties, were leading examples of Christianity.

Paul ended this epistle with encouraging and challenging words. The passage we read for today's study, Philippians 4:4-9, records last-minute instructions.

In verse 4 the believers were told to rejoice in the Lord. Such an exhortation is not mere talk, but is rooted and grounded in the apostle's very life. Two things testify to the seriousness of Paul's words. First, he repeated the command. Second, this rejoicing is to be done always. It is significant that Paul, who had suffered much, was writing to a church that had also suffered greatly. This fact underscores the point that rejoicing in the Lord should not be determined by circumstances.

The believer is to rejoice and be gentle, for the Lord is near. Anxiety must give way to confidence in the Lord. The Christian, with thanksgiving in his heart, can petition God for intervention. Through prayer God's peace is manifest to such a degree that it stands guard over heart and mind.

Instead of accentuating negative issues and failures, Paul highlighted those things worthy of Christian consideration. Only those things which glorify God deserve Christian reflection. Such qualities are not transcendent ideals but may be found in Paul's own life. Paul was confident that not only through words but through his very actions he had modeled the right walk. If they followed Paul, they would not go wrong.

All Christians are admonished in these words to the Philippians. The joy of our salvation is to be nurtured and cherished as a prized possession, for despite the uncertainties of life, God is faithful. His love and care are the basis of our joy.

The Lord is coming soon. Let us watch, purify, occupy, proclaim and rejoice because of His soon return. Such an event calls for action. Let us prepare ourselves for Jesus' return.

REFLECT AND MEDITATE

1. Explain the rationale behind Paul's instructions to rejoice in the Lord always.

2. Describe the relationship between prayer and the manifestation of God's peace.

REACT AND RESPOND

Identify those things which cause you great anxiety and are obstacles to a life of rejoicing. Confess them to the Lord, and leave them with Him.

REJOICE AND WORSHIP

In your family devotions, discuss the richness and fullness of God's salvation. Lead in worship.

DISCIPLESHIP COMMITMENT

In view of the soon return of our Lord, I pledge myself to watching, purifying, occupying, proclaiming and rejoicing.
